AF675614

74 Structure and Bonding

Editors:
M. J. Clarke, Chestnut Hill
J. B. Goodenough, Oxford · J. A. Ibers, Evanston
C. K. Jørgensen, Genève · D. M. P. Mingos, Oxford
J. B. Neilands, Berkeley · G. A. Palmer, Houston
D. Reinen, Marburg · P. J. Sadler, London
R. Weiss, Strasbourg · R. J. P. Williams, Oxford

Metal Complexes with Tetrapyrrole Ligands II

Editor: J. W. Buchler

With contributions by
L. A. Andersson, J. H. Dawson, M. Hanack,
H. Lehmann, M. Rein, H. Schultz

With 51 Figures and 27 Tabels

Springer-Verlag
Berlin Heidelberg NewYork London
Paris Tokyo Hong Kong Barcelona

Editorial Board

Professor *Michael J. Clarke*, Boston College, Department of Chemistry, Chestnut Hill, Massachusetts 02167, U.S.A.

Professor *John B. Goodenough*, Inorganic Chemistry Laboratory, University of Oxford, South Parks Road, Oxford OX1 3QR, Great Britain

Professor *James A. Ibers*, Department of Chemistry, Northwestern University, Evanston, Illinois 60201, U.S.A.

Professor *Christian K. Jørgensen*, Dépt. de Chimie Minérale de l'Université, 30 quai Ernest Ansermet, CH-1211 Genève 4

Professor *David Michael P. Mingos*, University of Oxford, Inorganic Chemistry Laboratory, South Parks Road, Oxford OX1 3QR, Great Britain

Professor *Joe B. Neilands*, Biochemistry Department, University of California, Berkeley, California 94720, U.S.A.

Professor *Graham A. Palmer*, Rice University, Department of Biochemistry, Wiess School of Natural Sciences, P.O. Box 1892, Houston, Texas 77251, U.S.A.

Professor *Dirk Reinen*, Fachbereich Chemie der Philipps-Universität Marburg, Hans-Meerwein-Straße, D-3550 Marburg

Professor *Peter J. Sadler*, Birkbeck College, Department of Chemistry, University of London, London WC1E 7HX, Great Britain

Professor *Raymond Weiss*, Institut Le Bel, Laboratoire de Cristallochimie et de Chimie Structurale, 4, rue Blaise Pascal, F-67070 Strasbourg Cedex

Professor *Robert Joseph P. Williams*, Wadham College, Inorganic Chemistry Laboratory, Oxford OX1 3QR, Great Britain

ISBN 3-540-52899-7 Springer-Verlag Berlin Heidelberg New York
ISBN 0-387-52899-7 Springer-Verlag New York Berlin Heidelberg

Library of Congress Cataloging-in-Publication Data
(Revised for vol. 2) Metal complexes with tetrapyrrole ligands I.
(Structure and bonding; 64-) Includes bibliographies and index.
1. Tetrapyrroles. 2. Porphyrin and porphyrin compounds. 3. Organometallic compounds. I. Buchler, J. W. (Johann Walter), 1935-. II. Dolphin, David. III. Series: Structure and bonding; 64, etc.
QD461.S92 vol. 64, etc. [QD441] 541.2'2 s 87-9591
ISBN 0-387-17531-8 (U.S.: v. 1) 547.593

This work is subject to copyright. All rights are reserved, whether the whole or part of the material is concerned, specifically the rights of translation, reprinting, re-use of illustrations, recitation, broad-casting, reproduction on microfilms or in other ways, and storage in data banks. Duplication of this publication or parts thereof is only permitted under the provisions of the German Copyright Law of September 9, 1965, in its current version, and a copyright fee must always be paid.

© Springer-Verlag Berlin Heidelberg 1991
Printed in Germany

The use of general descriptive names, trade marks, etc. in this publication, even if the former are not especially identified, is not to be taken as a sign that such names, as understood by the Trade Marks and Merchandise Marks Act, may accordingly be used freely by anyone.

Typesetting: Macmillan India Ltd, Bangalore-25; Printing: Colordruck, Berlin; Bookbinding: Lüderitz & Bauer, Berlin
2151/3020-5 4 3 2 1 0 Printed on acid-free paper

Preface

The second issue of Structure and Bonding carrying the subtitle "Metal Complexes with Tetrapyrrole Ligands" is being issued with two contributions:

1. "Extended X-ray Absorption Fine Structure Spectroscopy of Heme-Containing Oxygenases and Peroxidases"
   (L. A. Anderson and J. H. Dawson)
2. "Porphyrinatometal and Phthalocyaninatometal Complexes with Special Electrical and Optical Properties"
   (H. Schultz, H. Lehmann, M. Rein, M. Hanack)

The first article describes the technique of EXAFS spectroscopy and then turns to specific applications in the field of those heme proteins in which the central iron adopts an elevated oxidation state during the catalytic cycle. Experience in EXAFS spectroscopy is thus extended to oxoiron(IV) porphyrins or oxoiron(IV) porphyrin radicals in which the porphyrin ring is oxidized as well; previous studies had dealt with the oxygen-carrying or electron transporting heme proteins. The EXAFS data of the native species cytochrome P-450, chloroperoxidase, peroxidases in general, and catalases as well as their protein-free model compounds are presented and discussed in view of the complete catalytic cycles. Evidence concerning oxoiron(IV) porphyrins or oxoiron(IV) porphyrin radicals is compared with results from other physical measurements. The state of the art in the understanding of the function of these oxygenases and peroxidases is, therefore, described as well. Professor Dawson is also an expert in magnetic circular dichroism studies of metal porphyrins and heme proteins.

The second article is devoted to metal tetrapyrroles which might in some near future serve as materials in special electronic or optoelectronic devices. The various reaction paths leading to the required synthetic phthalocyanines and porphyrins, their metal derivatives, and finally their structural alignment as polyassociated, polymeric or polycondensated stacks is described. Not only work on solids, but also on liquid crystals and Langmuir-Blodgett films is presented. Photoconductors, photovoltaic cells, and gas detectors may be constructed starting with metallotetrapyrrole materials. Professor Hanack is well known in his field and was president of a recent International Conference of Science and Technology of Synthetic Metals (ICSM '90, Tübingen, Sept. 2–7, 1990).

The two articles thus document the wide area between bioinorganic chemistry and materials research which is open to researchers who are actively investigating metal complexes with tetrapyrrole ligands. The editor is very grateful to the authors that they have postponed some urgent research in favour of preparing these manuscripts.

The contents of the first volume (Struct. Bonding Vol. 64) which appeared in 1987 is repeated in the Table of Contents. A third volume is planned.

Darmstadt, September 7, 1990 Johann W. Buchler

Table of Contents

Structure and Bonding, Vol. 64
Metal Complexes with Tetrapyrrole Ligands I

EXAFS Spectroscopy of Heme-Containing Oxygenases and Peroxidases

Laura A. Andersson[1, 2] and John H. Dawson[3]

[1] Department of Chemical and Biological Sciences, Oregon Graduate Institute, Beaverton, OR 97006-1999, USA
[2] Present address: Department of Biochemistry, Kansas State University, Manhattan, KS 66506, USA
[3] Department of Chemistry, University of South Carolina, Columbia, SC 29208, USA

The application of extended X-ray absorption fine structure (EXAFS) spectroscopy to the structural characterization of the active sites of heme-containing oxygenases and peroxidases is reviewed. Metal–ligand bond distances for first shell atoms can be established to an accuracy of ± 0.02 Å and coordination number to $\pm 25\%$. EXAFS spectroscopy is particularly well suited for establishing the presence of a sulfur donor axial ligand to the heme iron, as is shown to be the case for cytochrome P-450 and chloroperoxidase. In addition, the technique has been used to demonstrate that very short Fe=O bonds (~ 1.65 Å) are consistently present in high-valent oxo-iron intermediates, such as those in the reaction cycle of horseradish peroxidase. Structural information derived from the use of EXAFS spectroscopy, especially of unstable intermediates for which crystallographic analysis is difficult, provides the foundation for a more thorough understanding of the mechanisms of dioxygen and peroxide activation by heme enzymes.

Structure and Bonding 74
© Springer-Verlag Berlin Heidelberg 1990

1 Introduction

1.1 Scope

Over the past fifteen years, extended X-ray absorption fine structure (EXAFS) spectroscopy has developed from a controversial new technique to become a powerful method for structural analysis. In fact, the proven ability of EXAFS spectroscopy to determine metal–ligand (*M–L*) bond distances to a high level of accuracy has led to increasingly frequent applications of the method to the study of metalloproteins. This development has been aided both by the relative rapidity with which an EXAFS spectral study may be performed and by the lack of a necessity for crystalline samples. The latter is, obviously, a key advantage. Indeed, for investigating the active site of a metalloprotein, EXAFS spectroscopy may actually be preferred over single crystal X-ray crystallography in that the method leads to more precise metal–ligand distances. It is possible to determine bond lengths to a precision of 1% (± 0.02 Å) with EXAFS spectroscopy. Furthermore, it is not necessary to solve the entire protein structure to gain useful information. This, in turn, makes it possible to consider the mechanistic implications of relatively subtle differences in the active site structures of similarly ligated metalloproteins.

There have been a number of recent review articles on the application of EXAFS spectroscopy to the study of metalloproteins [1–8]. The theory of EXAFS spectroscopy and the historical development of the field have also been extensively discussed [1–5, 7–19]. Here we will briefly cover the practical aspects of data analysis for biological heme (iron porphyrin) systems and the appropriate model complexes. We will then focus on the EXAFS of two types of biological heme system: (a) thiolate-ligated heme enzymes; and (b) oxo-ferryl [oxo-iron (IV), $Fe^{IV}{=}O$] states of heme enzymes. All of the enzymes discussed herein have in common the iron protoporphyrin IX ("heme") as the prosthetic group, Fig. 1.

The choice of topics derives from our ongoing interest in the structural and chemical properties of Fe–S(thiolate) and $Fe^{IV}{=}O$ heme systems. It also arises because the EXAFS spectral properties of such systems are quite distinctive. As will be seen, EXAFS spectroscopy is particularly well suited for the study of heme

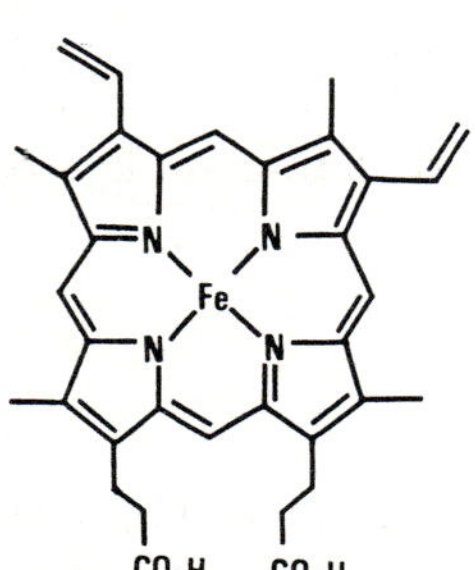

Fig. 1. Iron protoporphyrin IX, Fe(PPIX), the most common biological heme. Axial ligands are not shown

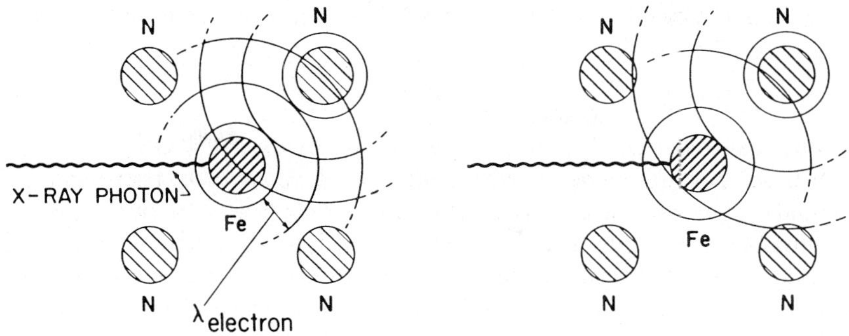

Fig. 2. The mechanism leading to EXAFS for the first ligand shell of an iron porphyrin. (**Left**) Constructive interference of the outgoing and backscattered waves leads to an increase in absorption. (**Right**) Destructive interference leads to a decrease in absorption. Reproduced with permission from Ref. [13]

proteins. This is because the porphyrin macrocycle, a relatively symmetric ring structure, produces strong EXAFS signals characteristic of the four nitrogen ligands (backscatterers) to the central iron atom (absorber); Fig. 2; see Section 2 for a more detailed description of the EXAFS experiment. Thus, it is relatively easy to identify a single sulfur donor ligand to a central iron in the presence of the four fixed porphyrin nitrogens, as in the cases of cytochrome P-450 and chloroperoxidase. The defined background pattern from the porphyrin macrocycle facilitates analysis of the EXAFS spectra, so that the short Fe=O bonds of the oxo-ferryl states of the peroxidases may be studied even though it is considered to be more difficult to analyze short (< 1.7 Å) bond lengths.

EXAFS studies on porphyrin complexes containing metals other than iron are briefly reviewed in Sect. 5.

1.2 Background

1.2.1 Thiolate-Ligated Heme Systems

Cytochrome P-450 and chloroperoxidase have catalytic and spectral properties that differ significantly from those of other heme systems. As the current state of knowledge of these two proteins has been extensively reviewed [20–29], we focus here on the structural origin of their unique spectral properties and the correlation of these properties with the novel catalytic activities of the enzymes. As will be shown, both enzymes are now well established to be thiolate-ligated heme systems.

1.2.1.1 Cytochrome P-450

The ubiquitous cytochromes P-450, found in plants, animals, yeast, and bacteria [20–29], are mono-oxygenase enzymes. They catalyze the oxygenation of substrates by insertion of one atom of dioxygen while the other atom is reduced to water, Eq. (1).

$$R\text{–}H + O_2 + 2H^+ + 2e^- \rightarrow R\text{–}OH + H_2O \quad (1)$$

Substrates for the P-450 enzymes are quite diverse, ranging from alkanes and alkenes, to arenes and sulfides. The enzymatic transformations are equally diverse, including production of alcohols, epoxides, phenols, and sulfoxides, respectively. Because it is water soluble and can be obtained in large quantity, the P-450 from camphor-grown *Pseudomonas putida* (P-450-CAM) has been the most extensively studied with physical methods. This enzyme was discovered by Gunsalus [30]. Secondary amine mono-oxygenase from *Pseudomonas aminovorans* [31–35] is the only other known example of a heme-containing monooxygenase.

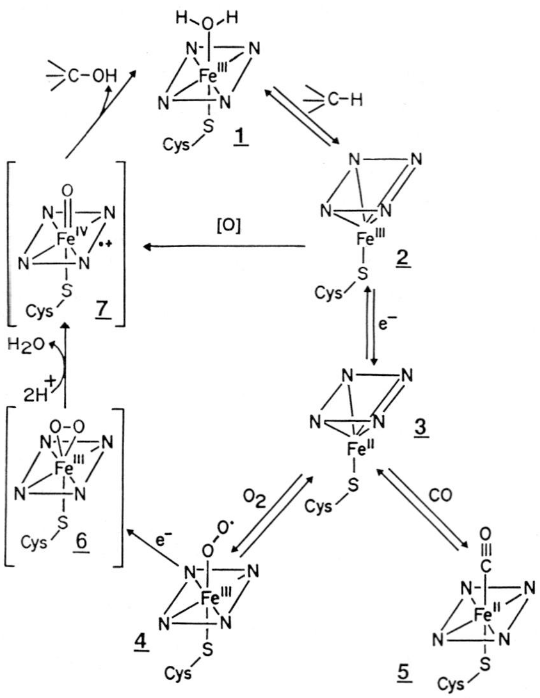

Fig. 3. Catalytic cycle of cytochrome P-450 and the postulated partial structures of the intermediates. The dianionic porphyrin macrocycle is abbreviated as a parallelogram with nitrogens at the corners, in this and subsequent figures. Oxy-P-450 (*4*) is shown as a complex of ferric porphyrin and superoxide anion, but could also be described as an adduct of neutral dioxygen and ferrous porphyrin. States *6* and *7* are hypothetical intermediates whose structures have not been established. Structures *1*, *2*, and *7* are neutral (the dot and the positive charge on *7* indicate the radical state and electron deficiency of the π electron system of the porphyrin ring), while the overall charge on structures *3*, *4*, and *5* is minus one and on structure *6* is minus two. Adapted from Ref. [22]

The cytochromes P-450 are also known, and in fact named, for their novel spectral properties relative to other heme systems. Specifically, this derives from the ~450-nm Soret band in the electronic absorption spectrum of the ferrous–CO complex. The ferrous–CO derivatives of most heme enzymes display this feature at ~420 nm [20–29, 36].

All P-450 enzymes share the common reaction cycle displayed in Fig. 3 [20–29, 37, 38]. The cycle is initiated by substrate binding to the low-spin, hexacoordinate, native ferric form (*1*) of P-450, converting it to the high-spin, pentacoordinate ferric complex, *2*. Reduction of *2* by one electron yields the high-spin, pentacoordinate ferrous derivative, *3*. State *3* subsequently binds dioxygen to form a "semi-stable" low-spin, hexacoordinate ferrous-dioxygen adduct, *4*. States *1–4* of the P-450 cycle are isolable and well characterized. The low-spin, hexacoordinate ferrous–CO inhibitor complex of P-450, *5* (mentioned above), is also shown in Fig. 3. Beyond oxy-P-450, it is often speculated that species such as *6*, a ferric peroxide complex, and *7*, a high-valent oxo-iron adduct, are formed although their existence must be viewed as hypothetical [20, 39]. (The properties of known high-valent oxo-iron porphyrin complexes will be discussed in greater detail in the Section 1.2.2) Finally, oxygen atom transfer from *7* to the substrate occurs to give the organic product and regenerate state *1*. This last step probably follows a radical abstraction–recombination mechanism [20, 25].

The study of "model compounds" or simply, "models" of heme proteins is very helpful in elucidating structure–function relationships. "Models" are compounds with low molecular weight that imitate structural, spectroscopic, or functional details of the original enzymes. The latter are macromolecules and hence more difficult to study. Synthetic models for states *1–5* must be thiolate-ligated. Such models have been prepared and extensively characterized. The models from several laboratories have recently been reviewed [22]. A model system having a ferric-peroxide composition, as is present in 6, has also been described [40]. Relevant models are listed in the tables (see Sects. 3.1 and 4.1.1). Model chemistry has been extremely important in characterizing these intermediates.

1.2.1.2 Chloroperoxidase

Chloroperoxidase, isolated from the marine fungus *Caldariomyces fumago* [41], is an enzyme that has "classical" peroxidase and catalase activities [22, 42], as well as a novel halogenation activity. Thus, chloroperoxidase can either oxidize substrates with concurrent reduction of H_2O_2 to water (in two one-electron steps), or it can disproportionate H_2O_2 to O_2 and H_2O (in one two-electron step). In addition, chloroperoxidase catalyzes the halogenation (I^-, Br^-, Cl^-, but not F^-) of β-keto acids and a range of additional substrates, in a reaction that involves concomitant reduction of H_2O_2 to water (Eq. 2) [42].

$$\text{A–H} + X^- + H^+ + H_2O_2 \rightarrow \text{A–X} + 2H_2O \qquad (2)$$

Other heme-containing peroxidases (vide infra) can iodinate or brominate β-diketones and similar halogen acceptors with the halide ion as the source of the halogen, but cannot catalyze the chlorination reaction. Chloroperoxidase can also use chlorite, in the absence of chloride and H_2O_2, as the source of chlorine for chlorinations [43]. This latter reaction can be catalyzed by horseradish peroxidase [43], but not by the mammalian enzyme myeloperoxidase which may have an iron chlorin macrocycle [44–49]. Most recently, chloroperoxidase has been shown to be capable of catalyzing P-450-like mono-oxygenation reactions under certain conditions [22]. Many of the spectral properties of chloroperoxidase are similar to those of cytochrome P-450 [20, 22, 42]. This led to suggestions of an underlying structural similarity between the two enzymes. However, the catalytic cycles of P-450 and chloroperoxidase are not identical.

The catalytic cycle of chloroperoxidase (Fig. 4) begins at state *2* (the high-spin, pentacoordinate ferric enzyme) and goes directly to state *7* upon the addition of hydrogen peroxide and other oxygen atom donors. Three reactivity paths are available, depending on the nature of the substrates and the presence or absence of a halogen source. In the peroxidase mode, state *7* is reduced in two separate one-electron steps (with concomitant substrate oxidation) to form state *8*, also a high-valent oxo-iron species, and then regenerate state *2*. In the catalase mode, state *7* carries out a two-electron oxidation of hydrogen peroxide to form dioxygen and regenerate *2*. Finally, in the halogenation mode, it is proposed that

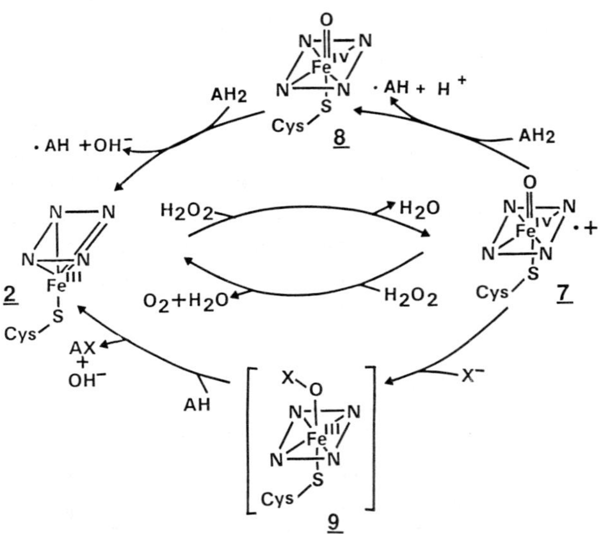

Fig. 4. Catalytic cycle of chloroperoxidase and the postulated structures of intermediates. The structures of the intermediates in the peroxidase (*2* → *7* → *8* → *2*) and catalase (*2* → *7* → *2*) modes have been partially characterized. The structure of intermediate *9* in the halogenation mode (*2* → *7* → *9* → *2*) is hypothetical. Structures *2* and *7* are neutral (the dot and the positive charge on *7* indicate the radical state and electron deficiency of the π electron system of the porphyrin ring), while the overall charge on structures *8* and *9* is minus one. Adapted from Ref. [22]

state *7* reacts with the halide source to form a ferric–hypohalite adduct, *9* (also known as Compound X), which then transfers an "activated" halogen to the substrate and regenerates state *2*. The involvement of state *9* in the halogenation pathway has been a matter of some controversy [22]. Stable chloroperoxidase complexes analogous to P-450 states *3*, *4*, and *5* (Fig. 3) can also be formed quite readily, but have no apparent functional significance.

Although the exact sequence of intermediates seen in the P-450 reaction cycle is not observed with chloroperoxidase, one feature of the chloroperoxidase reaction cycle (Fig. 4) does occur for the P-450 system (Fig. 3). Addition of oxygen atom donors such as peroxides or iodosobenzene to P-450 state *2* (the enzyme–substrate complex) results in the formation of product, in a reaction that probably has state *7* as an intermediate. The first step of this alternative, short-circuit cycle, also called the peroxide shunt, is essentially identical to the first step of the chloroperoxidase catalytic pathway.

1.2.2 High-Valent Oxo-Iron Porphyrin Systems

1.2.2.1 Peroxidases

Horseradish peroxidase is one of a class of heme enzymes (also including chloroperoxidase, vide supra) that catalyze the overall two electron oxidation of organic substrates with H_2O_2 as the oxidant or electron acceptor (Eq. 3) [50]. Unlike P-450 and chloroperoxidase, the axial fifth ligand to the heme iron of horseradish peroxidase is a nitrogen donor (histidine).

$$A\text{–}H_2 + H_2O_2 \rightarrow A + 2H_2O \tag{3}$$

The catalytic cycle of peroxidases (Fig. 5) begins with the oxidation of the high-spin, pentacoordinate ferric native enzyme (*10*) by hydrogen peroxide to form a semi-stable intermediate called Compound I (*11*). Compound I is a high-valent *oxo*-iron complex that is two oxidation equivalents above ferric horseradish peroxidase. Although formally an Fe^V heme, Compound I is generally thought to be an Fe^{IV} porphyrin π-cation radical [51, 52].

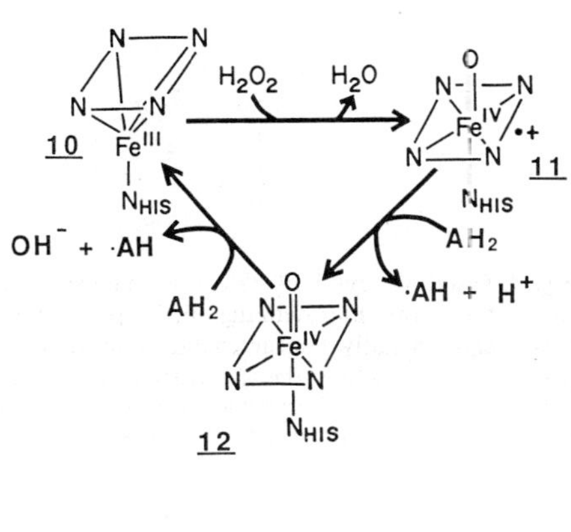

Fig. 5. Catalytic cycle of horseradish peroxidase. The overall charge on the resting state *10* and Compound I (*11*) is plus one (the dot and the positive charge on *11* indicate the radical state and electron deficiency of the π electron system of the porphyrin ring), while Compound II (*12*) is neutral. Adapted from Ref. [20]

The next step of the peroxidase reaction pathway involves the one-electron reduction of Compound I by the organic substrate. This produces a second intermediate called Compound II (*12*) that is still one oxidation equivalent above the ferric state, and is thus an Fe^{IV} heme. Finally, Compound II is reduced back to the native ferric state (*10*) with concomitant one-electron substrate oxidation. Two one-electron oxidized substrate molecules non-enzymatically disproportionate to give one two-electron oxidized product and an unoxidized substrate molecule. As will be discussed, model complexes for the high-valent states of horseradish peroxidase have been reported from the laboratories of Groves, [53, 54] Balch [55, 56] and others [57, 58]. Recent work by Ortiz de Montellano and co-workers strongly suggests that the substrate oxidation reactions catalyzed by horseradish peroxidase take place at the heme edge and not at the oxo-ferryl group [59].

Compounds I and II of horseradish peroxidase have been studied by a variety of methods. Evidence for the Fe^{IV} oxidation state has come from Mossbauer spectroscopy of both intermediates [60, 61]. Investigation of Compound I with magnetic susceptibility [62] has been interpreted in terms of a ferromagnetically coupled combination of a low-spin Fe^{IV} $(S=1)$ and a porphyrin π-radical cation $(S=1/2)$. Electronic absorption and NMR studies have provided additional evidence in support of the presence of the porphyrin π-radical cation [51, 63]. A single oxygen atom has been shown to be bound to the heme iron of Compound I and Compound II by labeling studies [64, 65]. Although the oxo formulation is generally accepted for Compound I, both oxo and hydroxyl assignments have been suggested for Compound II. Resonance Raman studies reported by Terner and Kitagawa and their co-workers [66–70] strongly support the *oxo* assignment. The evidence obtained with EXAFS spectroscopy concerning the structure of Compound II will be discussed in Sect. 4.

Although horseradish peroxidase is commonly studied as a “normal” or “reference” peroxidase, there is another peroxidase with properties that differ from those of horseradish peroxidase both spectrally and structurally: cytochrome *c* peroxidase (CCP) [71, 72]. The function of this enzyme is to oxidize cytochrome *c* (Cyt-*c*). At first glance, the catalytic mechanism of cytochrome *c* peroxidase (Eq. 4–6) is very similar to that of horseradish peroxidase (Fig. 5).

$$\mathrm{CCP} + \mathrm{H_2O_2} \rightarrow \mathrm{CCP\ Compound\ I} + \mathrm{H_2O} \tag{4}$$

$$\mathrm{CCP\ Compound\ I} + \mathrm{Cyt}\text{-}c[\mathrm{Fe^{II}}] + \mathrm{H^+} \rightarrow \mathrm{CCP\ Compound\ II} + \mathrm{Cyt}\text{-}c[\mathrm{Fe^{III}}] \tag{5}$$

$$\mathrm{CCP\ Compound\ II} + \mathrm{Cyt}\text{-}c[\mathrm{Fe^{II}}] + \mathrm{H^+} \rightarrow \mathrm{CCP} + \mathrm{Cyt}\text{-}c[\mathrm{Fe^{III}}] + \mathrm{H_2O} \tag{6}$$

However, the spectral properties of cytochrome *c* peroxidase Compound I, also known as Compound ES, are clearly different from those of horseradish peroxidase Compound I. The results of numerous spectral studies indicate that the electronic structure of cytochrome *c* peroxidase Compound I is most likely $[Fe^{IV}{=}O]R^*$, where R^* is a protein-centered radical [71–80]. Thus, the Compound I and II derivatives of cytochrome *c* peroxidase both have high-valent *oxo*-iron structures, but differ in the presence of the amino acid radical in Compound I.

1.2.2.2 Catalases

A second class of heme enzymes that has a high-valent *oxo*-iron intermediate is the catalase group [81]. Most catalases have iron protoporphyrin IX as the prosthetic group (Fig. 1) and axial tyrosinate ligation [82–86]. However, both the catalase from *Neurospora crassa* [87, 88] and the HPII catalase from *Escherichia coli* [89] are likely to have iron chlorins as prosthetic groups [87–91].

The reaction cycle of the catalases (Fig. 6), like that of the peroxidases, begins with the high-spin ferric state (*13*) which reacts with a molecule of hydrogen peroxide to form the Compound I intermediate (*14*). Next, however, oxidation of a second hydrogen peroxide molecule yields dioxygen, with the concomitant return of catalase Compound I to the native resting state. Catalases can be made to produce a Compound II intermediate that is generally described as an $Fe^{IV}{=}O$ complex like Compound II of the peroxidases.

Dolphin and Felton originally suggested that the differences in reactivity between catalases and peroxidases might be derived from the different electronic ground states for the two Compound I forms of the enzymes [52]. This was based on the fact that the electronic absorption spectral properties of catalase Compound I resemble the spectrum of a model porphyrin π-cation radical complex having a $^2A_{1u}$ ground state. In contrast, the absorption spectrum of horseradish peroxidase Compound I was similar to that of a model porphyrin π-cation radical complex with a $^2A_{2u}$ ground electronic state [52]. More recently, Browett et al. have carefully examined the variable temperature magnetic circular dichroism properties of horseradish peroxidase Compound I and conclude that "a single set of electronic transitions can account for the complete

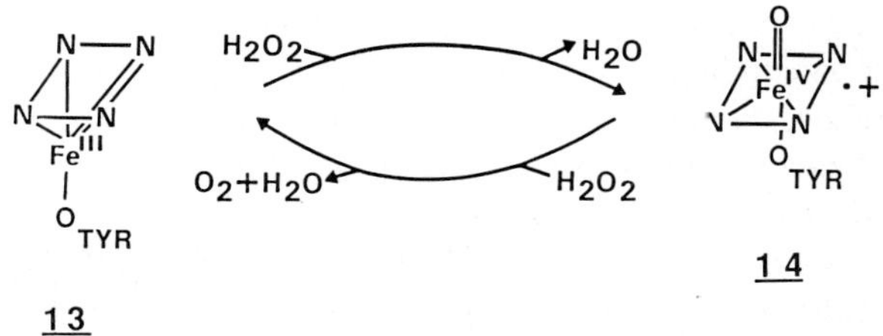

13

14

Fig. 6. Catalytic cycle of catalase. The resting state *13* and Compound I (*14*) are neutral (the dot and the positive charge on *14* indicate the radical state and electron deficiency of the π electron system of the porphyrin ring)

magnetic circular dichroism and absorption spectral envelopes of *both* horseradish peroxidase and catalase Compound I." They propose that both intermediates have ground states consisting of admixtures of $^2A_{1u}$ and $^2A_{2u}$ configurations [92]. (See Note in Proof No. 1.)

The absorption spectrum of the Compound I form of chloroperoxidase is different from that of horseradish peroxidase Compound I, and is more closely analogous to that of catalase Compound I. This suggests that it may also have a $^2A_{1u}$ ground state [22, 50]. However, the EPR spectrum of chloroperoxidase Compound I indicates that there is electron density at the *meso* carbons; this finding is inconsistent with a $^2A_{1u}$ ground electronic state [50, 93]. Thus, the different absorption spectral properties of the Compound I intermediates of peroxidases may not derive solely from differences in orbital symmetry. Rather, *other* factors such as the nature of the axial ligand or the macrocycle stereochemistry may be responsible for these spectral differences.

1.3 Some Questions on Structure–Function Relationships

A question of critical importance to understanding the catalytic activities of heme systems is a precise knowledge of the structural details of the heme coordination sphere, including the identity of the axial ligand(s) to the central iron. For the cytochromes P-450, strong spectroscopic evidence including the EXAFS studies described herein has been amassed over the past two decades suggesting thiolate ligation from cysteine to the heme iron in states *1–5* of the catalytic cycle (Fig. 3) [20–29, 94, 95]. Thus the specific identification of sulfur donor ligation to the iron of cytochrome P-450, and especially the evaluation as to whether the sulfur is neutral (thiol, thioether, or disulfide) or anionic (thiolate) throughout the accessible reaction states, has been a focus of particular attention in the application of EXAFS spectroscopy to this system. The presence of cysteine as a ligand has recently been confirmed by X-ray crystallography [96–99].

Spectral similarities between P-450 and chloroperoxidase originally led to suggestions that both enzymes had thiolate ligation [20, 22, 42]. However, the two systems displayed clear differences in their catalytic activities. Furthermore, at the time when EXAFS studies of chloroperoxidase were initiated, it was not clear whether the enzyme had a free (non-disulfide linked) cysteine available to coordinate to the heme iron [100]. Also, the unusually low pH optimum of the chloroperoxidase halogenation reaction, ~pH 3.0 for peroxidative formation of a carbon–halogen bond [42], raised questions concerning possible protonation of the axial heme ligand(s).

The precise structural identities of the high-valent *oxo*-iron states of heme systems are also of interest. Recent work by Mayer [101] indicates that the $Fe^{IV}{=}O$ bond of an oxo iron (IV) complex is ~0.1 Å longer than expected in comparison with other metal oxo complexes. The oxygen-binding respiratory proteins hemoglobin and myoglobin will each form a relatively stable derivative upon addition of H_2O_2 that is spectrally very similar to the Compound II complex of horseradish peroxidase. However, this myoglobin state has no "normal" functional relevance. Similarly, ferrous horseradish peroxidase can form an "oxy"-complex (Compound III), analogous to oxy-hemoglobin and oxy-myoglobin, although this species has no known role in the normal peroxidase catalytic cycle (Fig. 5). These, and other observations, have led investigators to address the structural nature of the functional differences between peroxidases and respiratory proteins, with a specific focus on the catalytically significant states: Compound I and Compound II.

2 The EXAFS Experiment—Data Analysis

The theory of EXAFS spectroscopy and the methods of data analysis have been extensively reviewed [1–19]. The recent review by Penner-Hahn and Hodgson has particularly good coverage of iron porphyrins [1]. Briefly, the X-ray absorption spectrum (Fig. 7) consists of three regions: the pre-edge, the edge, and the EXAFS. The pre-edge region is the background X-ray absorption for atoms of lower atomic number than the specific element being studied. The edge region occurs at an energy specific to the element under study, and arises from the transitions of bound core electrons to unfilled atomic orbitals (e.g. $1s \rightarrow 3d$). Because the energy required to remove an electron increases as the oxidation state of the atom increases, the absorption edge reflects the oxidation state of the absorber [2]. The geometry and the ligand field strength of the donor atoms also affect the position of the edge.

The third spectral region is the EXAFS, where the core electron goes into the continuum. As the selected atom absorbs X-rays, an inner shell electron is ejected, producing an outgoing photoelectron wave. This wave is backscattered by the surrounding shell(s) of atoms to yield a new wave with an energy-dependent phase difference with respect to the out-going wave (Fig. 2). This results in either an increase or a decrease of the absorption coefficient of the

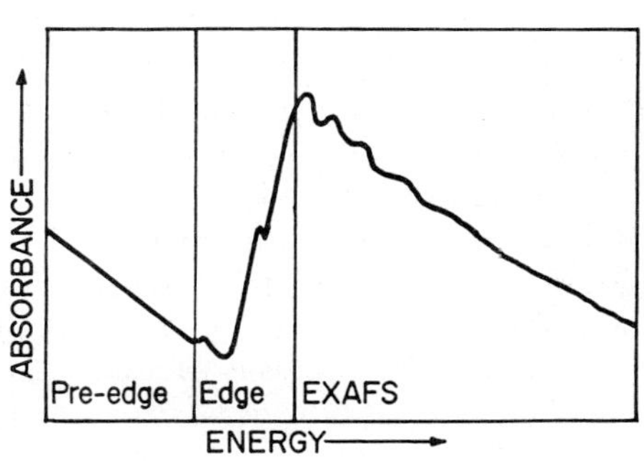

Fig. 7. A typical X-ray absorption spectrum. Reproduced with permission from Ref. [13]

absorber. Subtraction of the pre-edge and the background from the X-ray absorption data yields the oscillatory EXAFS spectrum (Fig. 8) which is plotted vs. the k vector ($Å^{-1}$) [102]. The data are usually plotted with k^2 or k^3 weighting in order to enhance the signal at high k. The frequency, phase, and amplitude of this damped sine wave depend on the M–L distance and on the nature (i.e. atomic type) and number of backscatterers. Specific features of the EXAFS cannot be directly correlated with interactions between the scatterer and absorber. Instead, one must examine the entire EXAFS spectrum.

Fourier transformation of the EXAFS data permits it to be replotted as a function of distance (Fig. 9). This aids visualization of the data, since each peak in the Fourier transform in principle represents a shell of atoms. However, because a phase shift of about 0.4 Å [1] appears in the Fourier-transformed data, it is not possible to use transformed data to accurately determine M–L distances. Nonetheless, it is possible to use the transformed data to make an initial "guess" as to the radial distribution function of atoms surrounding the metal. The Fourier transform can also be used to check the background subtraction procedure and the noise level of the spectrum. The presence of peaks of significant intensity at very low R (Å) suggests that errors were made in the subtraction process; peaks at high R result from especially noisy data.

Two basic methods of EXAFS data analysis have been developed, one based primarily on theoretical principles [9] and the other based on "transferable" phase and amplitude parameters derived from the study of structurally defined model compounds [1, 13]. Both methods have been successfully applied to the

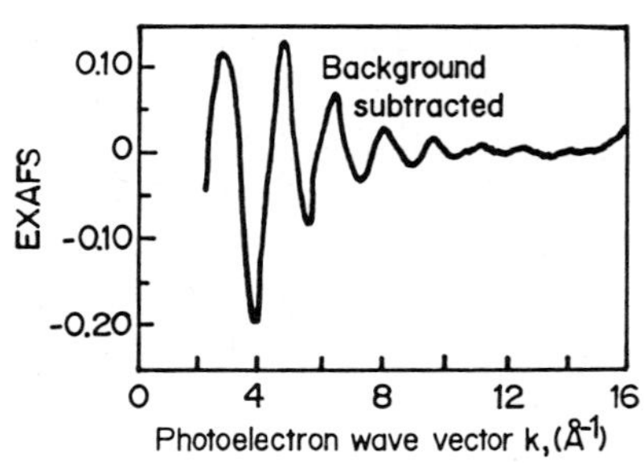

Fig. 8. A typical EXAFS spectrum following background subtraction. Reproduced with permission from Ref. [15]

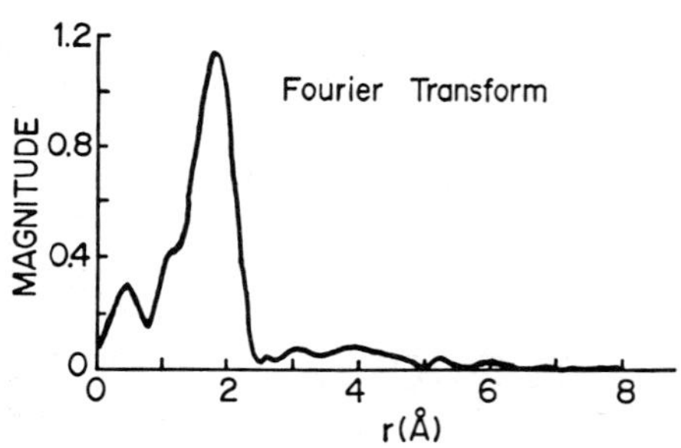

Fig. 9. Fourier transform of the EXAFS data in Fig. 8. Reproduced with permission from Ref. [15]

study of metalloproteins and to heme systems. Most often, the different methods of data analysis produce very similar results. Thus, when disagreements do occur, they can typically be ascribed to differences in the samples or in the measurement of the data, and not to the method of data analysis [2].

The theoretically based method [9] suffers from the use of a large number of adjustable parameters in the data analysis. However, an alternate theoretical model has recently been proposed which addresses some of the deficiencies [104]. Specifically, the multiple-scattering method incorporates interactions that occur between the absorbing metal and groups of backscattering atoms, enabling simulation of unfiltered experimental EXAFS data [103–105].

The more empirical approach suffers from the requirement for model compounds to develop the phase and amplitude parameters. Model systems for this type of EXAFS analysis are defined in a broader sense than is commonly used for other bioinorganic and biophysical methods. EXAFS models consist of compounds having the appropriate absorber/backscatterer atoms (e.g., metal/ligand or metal/metal) present at a known distance. For this reason, it becomes possible to determine metal–ligand bond distances in enzyme states for which direct structural analogs do not exist.

Figure 10 illustrates the single damped sine wave expected for an iron absorber with a single shell of nitrogen backscattering atoms at various fixed distances. Note that both the phase and amplitude of the sine wave changes as the distance of the scatterer (first shell) from the absorber varies. As shown in

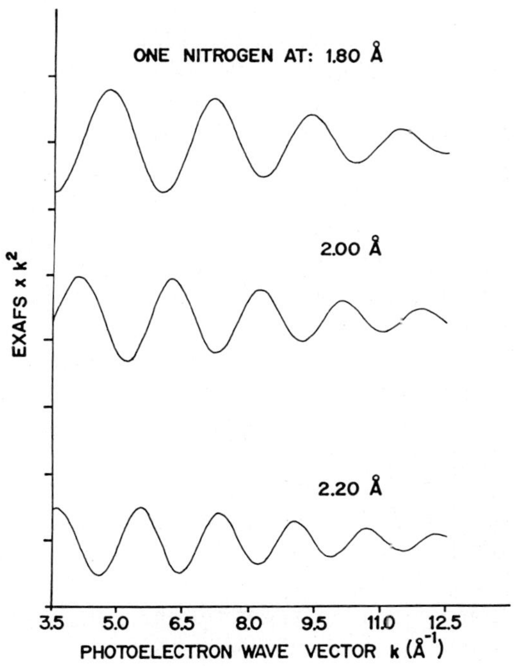

Fig. 10. Phase and amplitude effects for bonds from iron to nitrogen for three distances. Reproduced with permission from Ref. [122]

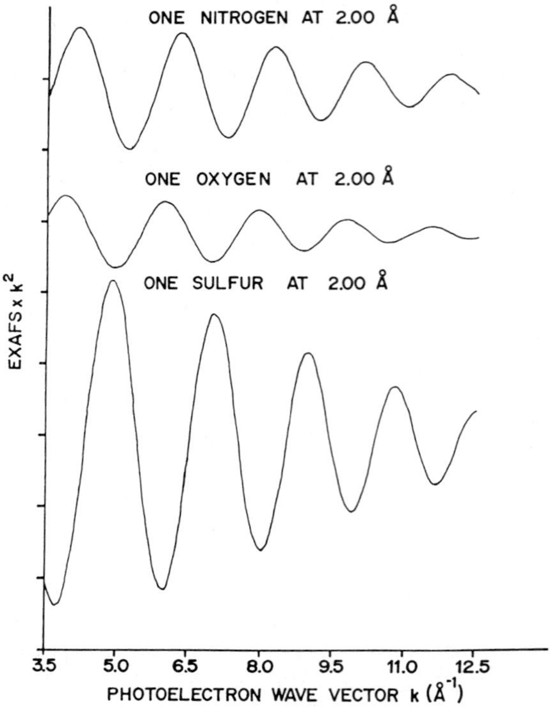

Fig. 11. Phase and amplitude effects for bonds from iron to nitrogen, oxygen, or sulfur. Reproduced with permission from Ref. [122]

Fig. 11, alterations in the type of backscattering atom also will alter the phase and the amplitude of the EXAFS spectrum, even when the interatomic distance is fixed. The spectral pattern of the sine wave for a sulfur scatterer and iron absorber is dramatically different from that of oxygen or nitrogen scatterers with an iron absorber. Thus, sulfur as a first shell atom from iron is easily identified, whereas it is not possible to distinguish oxygen from nitrogen.

The sine wave pattern becomes more complex when the types of scattering atoms are combined, as shown in Fig. 12. The sine wave for an iron absorber with four first shell nitrogens and one first shell sulfur is a combination of the individual EXAFS spectral sine waves of nitrogen and sulfur atoms. This figure begins to mimic what might be expected for the central iron of a porphyrin (coordination to four pyrrole nitrogens) with a single axial sulfur ligand. The differences between the hypothetical EXAFS data displayed in Fig. 12 and the actual data for a thiolate-ligated heme iron system (see Fig. 13) result from additional backscattering from the carbon atoms on the ligands.

The final stage of the data analysis involves curve fitting of the observed data using the phase and amplitude functions alluded to above [1]. One knows in advance that the porphyrin macrocycle will provide four equatorial nitrogen ligands within a certain range of bond distances (Fig. 1) and that the overall structure will be pentacoordinate or hexacoordinate. Imposition of these "boundary" conditions helps to eliminate chemically unreasonable structures

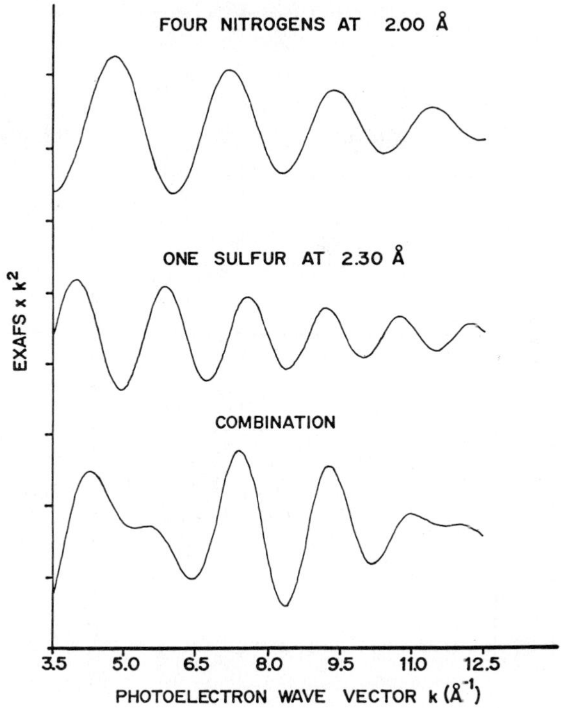

Fig. 12. Phase and amplitude effects for nitrogen and sulfur shells at iron. Reproduced with permission from Ref. [122]

from consideration. For complicated metal complexes having multiple sets of backscatterers, an additional stage of analysis called Fourier filtering is often applied [1, 7]. Fourier filtering involves the back-transformation of an individual peak of the Fourier transform to give a filtered EXAFS spectrum that contains only those frequency elements that produce the particular peak of the Fourier transform. Curve fitting of the filtered data often produces better looking fits, although the derived structural parameters are not necessarily more accurate [1].

Thus, analysis of an EXAFS spectrum permits: (a) determination of the interatomic distances between an absorber and the backscattering atoms in the surrounding shell(s); (b) identification of the backscattering atoms, when they have atomic numbers that differ by more than 2; and (c) determination of the number of backscattering atoms in the surrounding shell(s). Under favorable circumstances, extraction of interatomic distance information for first shell backscatterers has an accuracy of ± 0.02 Å. However, the accuracy in determination of the backscatterer number may vary by as much as 20–30%. The limitation of EXAFS with regard to the atomic number of the backscatterer means that a shell listed as nitrogen (N) could just as well be C or O; likewise, S

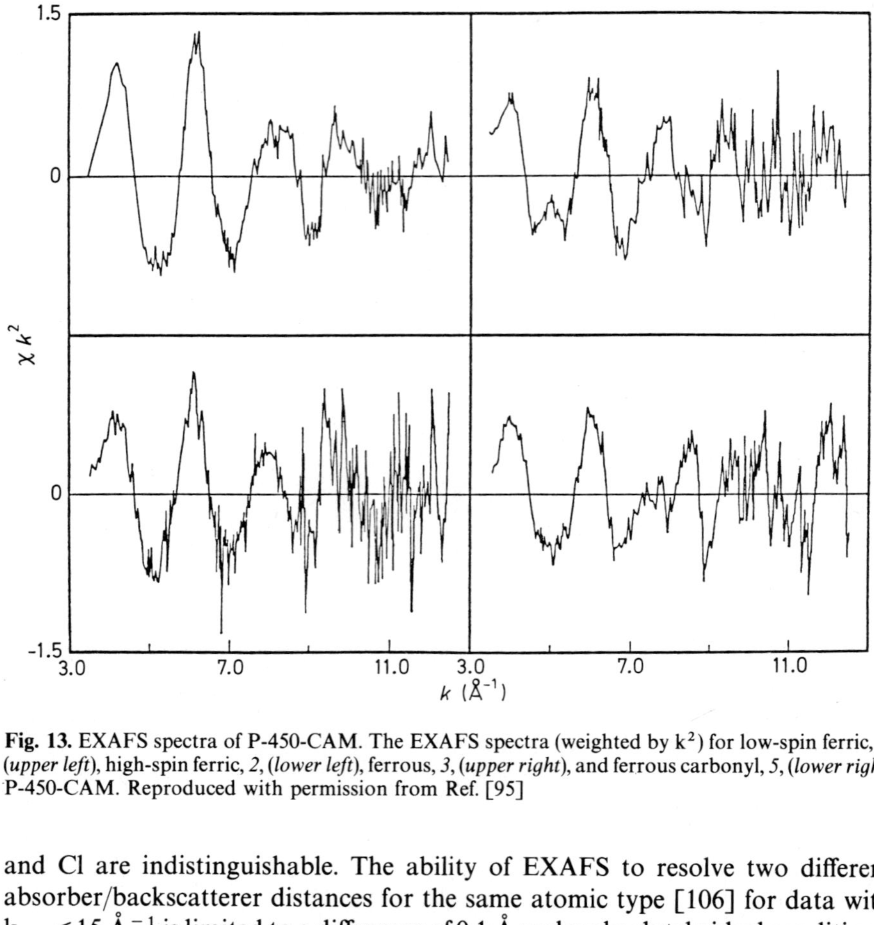

Fig. 13. EXAFS spectra of P-450-CAM. The EXAFS spectra (weighted by k^2) for low-spin ferric, *1*, (*upper left*), high-spin ferric, *2*, (*lower left*), ferrous, *3*, (*upper right*), and ferrous carbonyl, *5*, (*lower right*) P-450-CAM. Reproduced with permission from Ref. [95]

and Cl are indistinguishable. The ability of EXAFS to resolve two different absorber/backscatterer distances for the same atomic type [106] for data with $k_{max} \leq 15$ Å^{-1} is limited to a difference of 0.1 Å under absolutely ideal conditions. This limitation arises from the fact that resolution of two M–L distances in such cases requires the measurement of data to a high enough energy that the waves generated for each M–L interaction become out-of-phase. As can be inferred from Fig. 10, to resolve M–L distances that differ by only 0.1 Å requires data out to much higher than $k = 12.5$ Å^{-1}. In practice, an effective resolution of 0.2 Å is more realistic due to the normal levels of noise in the data [107]. In other words, the improvement in the fit to the data that may result from inclusion of the additional shell of atoms at a slightly different distance will not be great enough to argue convincingly against the presence of a larger number of donor atoms at an averaged distance.

Despite these limitations, the accuracy with which EXAFS can determine M–L bond distances for metalloproteins is greater than in the case of protein X-ray crystallography. High quality EXAFS data can typically be obtained in about 12 hours of scanning using solutions of $\geq$2–3 mM in the absorber atom. This compares very favorably with the days to weeks of data collection necessary for X-ray crystallography of proteins. In addition, by studying frozen solutions at cryogenic temperatures, it is possible to structurally characterize unstable intermediates and to avoid denaturation with labile protein samples. Finally, although additional useful information can be obtained by doing EXAFS on crystals, one of the overall advantages of the technique is that accurate metal–ligand bond distances can be obtained on concentrated solutions of metalloproteins and models without the need for crystalline samples. The experimental conditions for producing X-ray diffraction quality crystals have often involved high salt and/or the presence of precipitating agents until the recent work of Walter et al. [108]. In contrast, it is generally possible to study biological molecules with EXAFS spectroscopy under solvent conditions that more closely match the physiological state.

3 Thiolate-Ligated Heme Systems

3.1 EXAFS Spectroscopy

The initial application of EXAFS spectroscopy to thiolate-ligated heme systems was a combined study of iron porphyrin model complexes, ferric cytochrome P-450, and ferric chloroperoxidase by Cramer et al. [109]. This study reported the development of methods of EXAFS spectral analysis for iron porphyrin model complexes. Analysis of the EXAFS spectral data for a variety of structurally defined model iron porphyrins demonstrated that a fit of the EXAFS spectra using 3 waves ($Fe–N_p$, $Fe–C_\alpha$, and $Fe–X_{ax}$) led to determination of axial Fe–X distances with an accuracy of better than 0.025 Å. $Fe–N_p$ bond distances were determined with even greater accuracy.

The procedure used for the model complexes was then extended to the proteins. For low-spin ferric cytochrome P-450, state *1*, the results were consistent with an Fe–S bond distance of 2.19 ± 0.03 Å [109]. The results for high-spin ferric chloroperoxidase, state *2*, indicated an Fe–S bond distance of 2.30 ± 0.03 Å. An acceptable fit to the EXAFS spectra of ferric P-450 and chloroperoxidase could not be obtained without inclusion of a sulfur atom. Thus, this report was the first *direct* observation of sulfur donor ligation to the heme iron in each of these two proteins. EXAFS was also the first technique to yield quantitative information about Fe–S bond lengths in these proteins. The Fe–S distance determined for native high-spin chloroperoxidase is 0.024 Å shorter than the known Fe–S bond distance in the high-spin model complex, Fe^{III}-(PPIXDME) (SC_6H_4-*p*NO_2) [110].

Table 1 contains a summary of the $Fe–S_{ax}$ and $Fe–N_p$ bond lengths for all P-450 and chloroperoxidase states that have been examined by EXAFS to date. Relevant EXAFS and X-ray crystallographic data on model compounds are also tabulated.

Table 1. Structural details for cytochrome P-450, chloroperoxidase, and relevant model complexes[a]

System	Method	Fe–N(porphyrin) R (Å)	Fe–N(porphyrin) N[b]	Fe–S(axial) R (Å)	Fe–S(axial) N[b]	Ref.
A. Ferric						
		Low-Spin				
P-450-CAM	EXAFS	2.00	5.0	2.22	0.6	[95]
P-450-LM2	EXAFS	2.00	4.8	2.19	0.8	[109]
P-450-CAM[c]	X-RAY	—	4	2.20	1	[96, 97]
$[Fe(TPP)(SC_6H_5)_2]^-$	X-RAY	2.008	4	2.336	1	[111]
$Fe(TPP)(HSC_6H_5)(SC_6H_5)$	X-RAY	—	4	2.27(RS^-) 2.43(RSH)	1 1	[112]
		High-Spin				
P-450-CAM	EXAFS	2.06	5.2	2.23	0.8	[95]
Chloroperoxidase	EXAFS	2.05	4.2	2.30	0.9	[109]
P-450-CAM[d]	X-RAY	2.05	4	2.20	1	[97, 98]
$Fe(PPIXDME)(SC_6H_4NO_2)$	X-RAY	2.064	4	2.324	1	[113]
B. Ferrous						
		High-Spin				
P-450-CAM	EXAFS	2.08	3.0	2.34[e]	0.6	[95]
$Fe(OEP)(SPr)^-$	EXAFS	2.05	3.8	2.33	0.4[f]	[114]
$Fe(TPP)(SEt)^-$	X-RAY	2.096	4	2.360	1	[115]
	Low-Spin Carbon Monoxide Complex					
P-450-CAM	EXAFS	1.98	3.3	2.32	1.0	[95]
$Fe(OEP)(SPr)(CO)^-$	EXAFS	2.00	4.4	2.33	0.2[f]	[114]
$Fe(TPP)(SEt)(CO)^-$	X-RAY	1.993	4	2.352	1	[115]
Fe(OEP)(PrSH)(CO)	EXAFS	2.01	5.1	2.41	0.8	[114]
Fe(OEP)(THT)(CO)	EXAFS	2.00	5.2	2.41	0.4[f]	[114]
Fe(OEP)(MeSSMe)(CO)	EXAFS	2.03	5.9	2.40	0.7	[114]
	Low-Spin Dioxygen Complex					
P-450-CAM[g]	EXAFS	2.00	7.8[h]	2.37	1.3	[116]
Chloroperoxidase[i]	EXAFS	2.00	7.4[h]	2.37	1.4	[116]
$[Fe(TpPP)(SC_6HF_4)(O_2)^-]$[k]	X-RAY	1.990	4	2.369	1	[117]
$Fe(TpPP)(THT)(O_2)$[m]	X-RAY	1.99–2.00	4	2.49	1	[118]

[a] EXAFS data were obtained by curve fitting. Abbreviations: TPP, tetraphenylporphyrin; PPIXDME, protoporphyrin IX dimethyl ester. OEP, octaethylporphyrin; SPr, n-propanethiolate; SEt, ethanethiolate; PrSH, n-propanethiol; THT, tetrathiophene; MeSSMe, dimethyldisulfide; TpPP, *meso*-tetrakis (α,α,α,α-*o*-pivalamidophenyl)porphyrin;
[b] The number (N) of atoms at the distance indicated;
[c] Data at 2.2 Å resolution. The iron is found to be 0.29 Å out of the plane of the four pyrrole nitrogen atoms toward the cysteinate axial ligand. The sixth ligand was found to be water (or hydroxide);
[d] Data at 1.7 Å resolution. The iron is found to be 0.43 Å out of the plane of the four pyrrole nitrogen atoms toward the cysteinate axial ligand. There is no sixth ligand. The $C_\beta S_\gamma Fe$ bond angle is 105.9°;
[e] Best fit to filtered EXAFS data. $Fe–S_{ax} = 2.38$ Å when unfiltered EXAFS data were analyzed;
[f] Analysis of solution data using parameters derived from the solid-state EXAFS of structurally defined model complexes may result in low values for $N(S_{ax})$ due to Debye-Waller effects (see Ref. 114);
[g] Fe–O(dioxygen) = 1.78 Å; $N(O_{ax}) = 1.1$;
[h] Analysis of low temperature data using parameters derived from the study of model complexes at room temperature may result in high N values due to Debye-Waller effects (see Ref. 116);
[i] Fe–O(dioxygen) = 1.77 Å; $N(O_{ax}) = 1.3$;
[k] Fe–O(dioxygen) = 1.818 Å;
[m] "Semiquantitative" structural analysis of X-ray crystal data.

An additional observation reported in the initial EXAFS study was that the trough at ~9 Å^{-1} could be used as an indicator of the geometry of the heme system [109]. This spectral feature is dominated by the interference between the Fe–N_p and Fe–C_α components, and is relatively insensitive to Fe–X. For porphyrins having the iron in-plane (P-450 state *1* in this study), this trough was observed at $k > 9$ Å^{-1}. However, for systems in which the iron is out-of-plane (chloroperoxidase state *2*), it was seen at $k < 9$ Å^{-1}. This correlation has also been seen in more recent studies (see Figs. 13, 15 and 16).

Given the wealth of spectroscopic data indicating cysteine ligation to ferric P-450, it came as no surprise that the first EXAFS data also supported the presence of an axial cysteine ligand. For chloroperoxidase, however, the unequivocal demonstration of an Fe–S interaction was inconsistent with the previously published chemical analyses of the enzyme [100] in which the only two cysteine residues present in the protein were reported to form a disulfide bridge. The conclusions of the chemical analysis had already been challenged in a comparative study of the magnetic circular dichroism properties of chloroperoxidase, P-450, and relevant model complexes [119]. This dilemma has recently been resolved by determination of the amino acid sequence of chloroperoxidase directly from the gene and from cDNA [120]. The analysis has revealed the presence of a third cysteine available for coordination to the heme iron. Even more recently, the chemical analysis of the enzyme has been reinvestigated and the new data also supports the conclusion that the heme iron is ligated by cysteine sulfur [121].

In 1982, EXAFS spectra of cytochrome P-450-CAM were reported for the low-spin ferric state (*1*), the high-spin ferric, substrate-bound complex (*2*), the high-spin ferrous state (*3*), and for the ferrous-CO adduct (*5*) (Table 1) [95, 122]. The EXAFS spectra of these four states are displayed in Fig. 13. The Fourier transform and least squares fit of the data for the low-spin ferric state are shown in Figs. 14 and 15, respectively. With all four states, acceptable fits to the data could only be obtained by including a sulfur atom in the analysis. Furthermore, the Fe–S distances determined from the EXAFS spectral data were consistent with thiolate ligation for all four states of P-450, *1–3* and *5* (Fig. 3) with bond distances equal to or shorter than those observed for thiolate-ligated iron porphyrin model complexes (Table 1). Indeed, for Fe^{III}-(TPP) (HSC_6H_5) (SC_6H_5), where both axial Fe–S(thiol) and axial Fe–S(thiolate) bonds are present (112), only the Fe–S distance for the *thiolate* matched that of low-spin ferric P-450 (Table 1). The ~2.20 Å Fe–S thiolate bond distances obtained from EXAFS spectroscopy of P-450-CAM states *1* and *2* [95, 122] are closely analogous to those subsequently obtained for the enzyme by X-ray crystallography [96–99].

Although the EXAFS experiment does not directly provide geometrical information, extensive investigations of model heme complexes with X-ray crystallography have shown that determination of the Fe–N_p bond distance coupled with prior knowledge of the spin state can indirectly provide evidence for the coordination number and therefore the geometry [123, 124]. In this

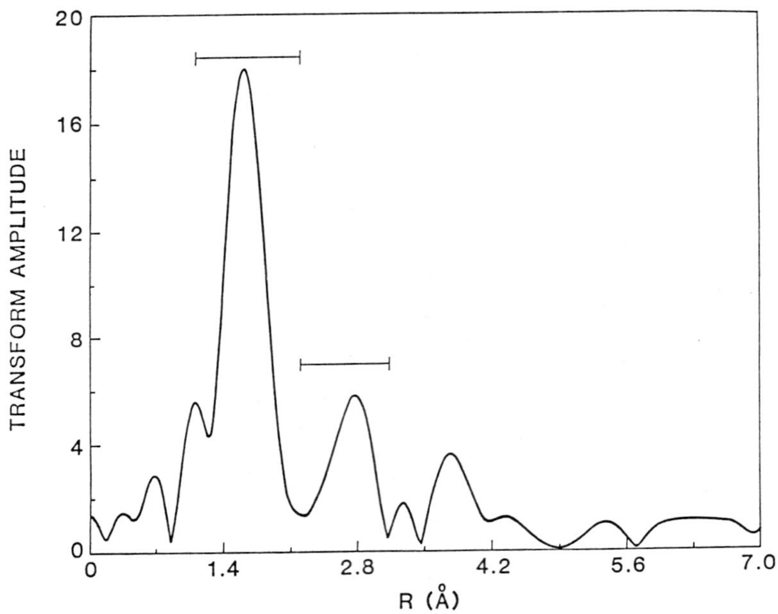

Fig. 14. Fourier transformation of the EXAFS data of low-spin ferric P-450-CAM. The horizontal bars indicate the width of the window used for back-transforming (filtering) the data from the first shell (N_p and X_{ax}) and second shell (porphyrin α- and *meso*-carbon atoms). The contribution from the porphyrin β-carbons (peak at ca. 3.8 $Å^{-1}$) is clearly visible. The other P-450 transforms have qualitatively similar appearances. Reproduced with permission from Ref. [95]

fashion, the EXAFS study of P-450-CAM states *1*, *2*, *3*, and *5* [95, 122] provided corroborating support for the coordination structures (six-, five-, five-, and six-coordinate, respectively) shown for the four intermediates in Fig. 3.

In a detailed EXAFS study of low-spin ferrous-CO porphyrin model complexes [114], thiolate sulfur vs. non-thiolate sulfur axial ligation to the iron was examined. A variety of ferrous heme complexes with sulfur donor ligation were examined: five-coordinate with a thiolate ligand; six-coordinate with a thiolate fifth ligand and CO as the sixth ligand; and six-coordinate with a non-thiolate sulfur donor fifth ligand and CO as the sixth ligand (Table 1). Comparison of the pentacoordinate $Fe(OEP)(SPr)^-$ and hexacoordinate $Fe(OEP)(SPr)(CO)^-$ complexes as well as the respective P-450 protein states (*3* and *5*) by EXAFS analysis showed there to be no change in the ~2.33 Å $Fe–S_{ax}$ bond distance. However, the $Fe–N_p$ distance dropped upon CO ligation, as expected for conversion of a pentacoordinate complex to hexacoordinate. An increase in the $Fe–S_{ax}$ bond distance from ~2.33 to ~2.41 Å was found upon replacement of a thiolate sulfur donor ligand with a non-thiolate sulfur donor (Table 1). These data clearly demonstrated that the π donor character of the thiolate ligand leads to a more extensive orbital interaction with the heme iron [114, 125] and therefore to a shorter bond length. These data demonstrate once

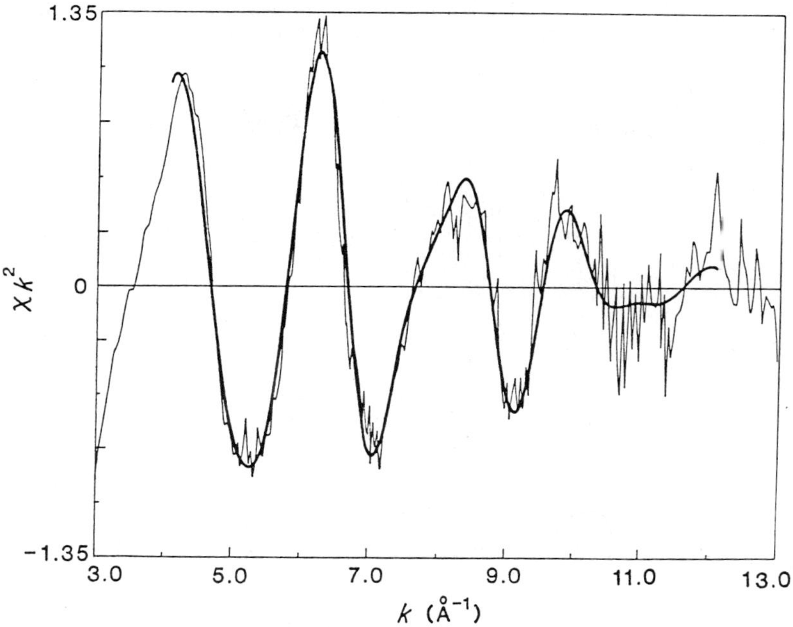

Fig. 15. Curve-fitting result for the EXAFS data of low-spin ferric P-450-CAM. The least squares fit (dark line) to the measured data (light line) for structure determination. Three waves (N, S, C[α, *meso*]) were used. Fitting was over a range of k = 4–12 Å^{-1}. The best fits to the other P-450 data were qualitatively similar. Numerical results of all P-450 curve fittings are summarized in Table 1. Reproduced with permission from Ref. [95]

again that the sulfur donor present in ferrous-CO P-450 is a thiolate sulfur as proposed.

Finally, recent comparative EXAFS spectroscopy of oxy-P-450 and oxy-chloroperoxidase (state *4*, Fig. 3) provides clear evidence for thiolate ligation to the heme iron in both cases (Fig. 16) [116, 126]. As can be seen in Fig. 17, the curve fitting analyses of the data for oxy-P-450-CAM (and oxy-chloroperoxidase as well) only work when a sulfur is included as an axial ligand. Oxy-P-450 is the last identified intermediate in the P-450 reaction cycle (Fig. 3) and the state about which the least is known. An Fe–S distance of 2.37 Å was observed for both oxy-P-450 and oxy-chloroperoxidase. This bond length corresponds very closely with the Fe–S bond distance found in the oxygenated form of an anionic model complex, $[Fe(TpPP)(SC_6H_4F)(O_2)]^-$ (see Table 1), prepared by Weiss and co-workers [57, 127]. It is also 0.12 Å shorter than the Fe–S bond length in $Fe(TpPP)(THT)(O_2)$ (see Table 1) [118]. The strong similarity—indeed, near identity—of the EXAFS data for the two oxy-ferrous enzymes (Table 1) provides further evidence that the two systems have identical heme coordination spheres [116]. Thus, reported electronic spectral differences between the two oxy-ferrous enzymes [128–130] must derive from differences in the active-site protein

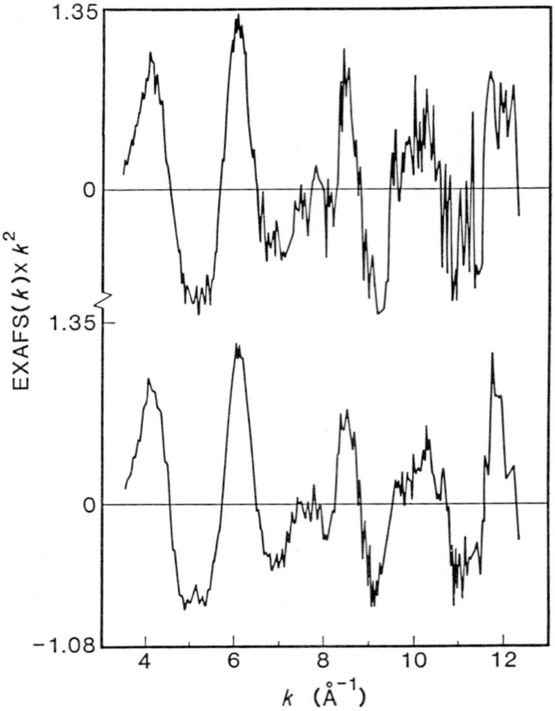

Fig. 16. EXAFS spectra of oxygenated cytochrome P-450 at pH 7.4 (*top*) and oxygenated chloroperoxidase at pH 6.0 (*bottom*) obtained at −80°C. A mixed solvent was employed consisting of ethylene glycol (65% v/v) and 0.035 M potassium phosphate buffer (plus 4 mM camphor for P-450-CAM). Spectra have been multiplied by k^2 to enhance the visibility of oscillations at high k. Reproduced with permission from Ref. [116]

environment (see below). The Fe–N_p bond distance of 2.00 Å for both oxyferrous enzymes once again provided corroborative evidence for a six-coordinate heme, as shown in Figure 3.

In summary, EXAFS spectroscopy has provided direct and compelling evidence demonstrating that the proximal ligand to the P-450 heme is a thiolate in all isolable reaction states (Fig. 3, *1–5*). The same conclusion has been reached for states *2* and *4* of chloroperoxidase. Determination of the Fe–N_p bond lengths for these seven enzyme states has provided corroborative evidence for the coordination numbers displayed in Figs. 3 and 4. The structural similarities seen between parallel derivatives of P-450 and chloroperoxidase (Table 1) also provide support for the use of various derivatives of chloroperoxidase, such as Compounds I and II, as structural models for as yet uncharacterized states of P-450.

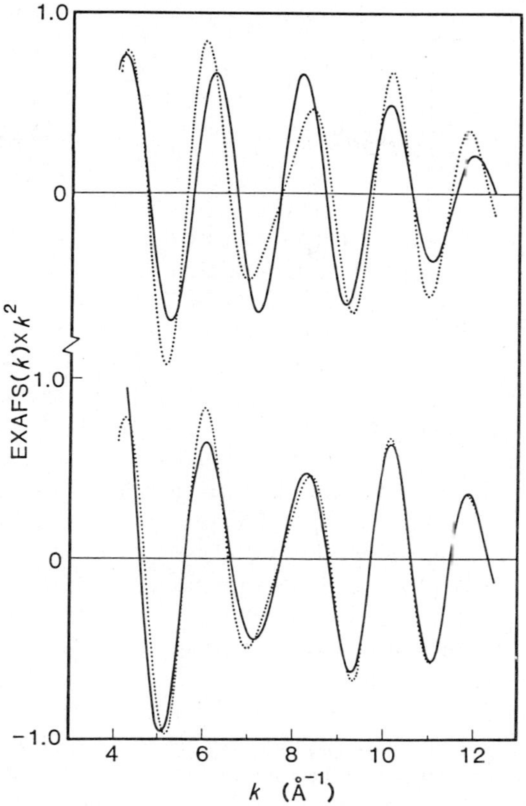

Fig. 17. Curve-fitting result for the EXAFS data of oxy-P-450-CAM. The least-squares fit (*solid line*) to the filtered data of the first shell (*dotted line*) without (*top*) and with (*bottom*) inclusion of the Fe–S_{ax} shell. Fitting was over a range of $k = 4–12$ Å^{-1}. The best fits to the data for both oxy-P-450-CAM and oxy-chloroperoxidase were qualitatively similar. Numerical results are summarized in Table 1. Reproduced with permission from Ref. [116]

3.2 Catalytic Role of the Axial Thiolate: Speculations

Given the clear evidence for thiolate ligation to the iron in all of the isolable states of cytochrome P-450 and chloroperoxidase, the functional significance of the thiolate ligand must then be addressed. In its catalytic cycle, cytochrome P-450 must not only bind dioxygen, as performed by the histidine-ligated heme proteins hemoglobin and myoglobin, but it must also activate the dioxygen for insertion into substrates. With such similar structures at the heme iron, the differences in functional properties between cytochrome P-450 and chloroperoxidase must be derived from differences in the protein environment around the heme moiety, from differences in substrate and solvent accessibility to the central metal ion, or from both.

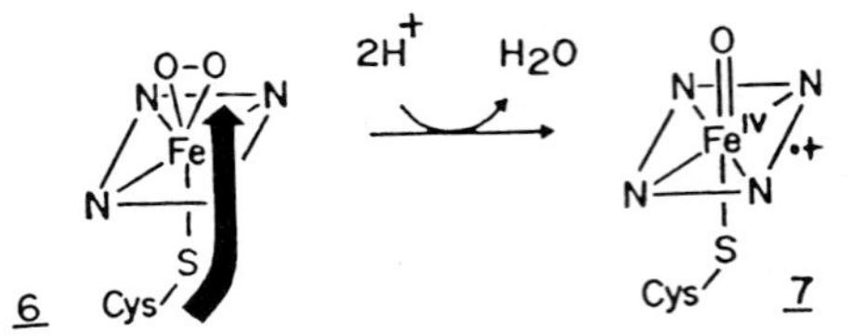

Fig. 18. Proposed role for the thiolate ligand in the catalytic mechanism of cytochrome P-450 (see Figure 3 for the entire reaction cycle)

Dawson et al. [131] have suggested that the ferric and ferrous iron of P-450 is unusually electron-rich, relative to that of hemoglobin and myoglobin, due to the iron-thiolate bond of P-450. Comparative ligand-binding and spectroscopic studies of P-450-CAM and myoglobin have quantitatively verified the increased electron density at the iron of P-450 [132–134]. The catalytically-active species of P-450 has been suggested to be a high valent oxo-iron complex (see also Section 4 of this review) [20–29, 131, 135–137]. The presence of the electron-rich thiolate might aid in stabilization of the iron in such states. It has also been proposed that the proximal thiolate of P-450 may act as an electron-releasing ligand and facilitate cleavage of the peroxide O–O bond in proposed intermediate *6* (Fig. 18) [20, 22, 131–133].

What, then, is the functional significance of the axial thiolate ligation of chloroperoxidase, for which the catalytic reactivity is so clearly unlike that of cytochrome P-450? Sono et al. [138] demonstrated that the active site environment of chloroperoxidase contains polar amino acid residues. The polar environment clearly affects ligand binding and could also be involved in catalysis. Indeed, such properties are typical of a "peroxidase-type" active site environment, like that of histidine-ligated horseradish peroxidase and cytochrome *c* peroxidase [139–142]. Thus, it appears that chloroperoxidase combines the spectral and structural properties of cytochrome P-450, that arise from the thiolate-ligated iron, with the active-site environment of "normal" (non-thiolate-ligated) peroxidases to produce its unique reactivity.

4 High-Valent Oxo-Iron Porphyrin Systems

4.1 EXAFS Spectroscopy

4.1.1 Ferryl States

As briefly summarized in Section 1.2.2.1, extensive evidence has been reported indicating that horseradish peroxidase Compound I is an oxo-ferryl [Fe^{IV}=O] porphyrin π-cation radical and that Compound II is an oxo-ferryl porphyrin. Groves and co-workers have reported an inorganic model complex for Compound I [53, 54] and Balch and co-workers have described a Compound II model [55, 56]. These models each appear to have the expected compositions for the respective enzyme states that they are designed to mimic.

The first application of EXAFS spectroscopy to the ferryl states of heme systems was reported by Penner-Hahn et al. in 1983 [143]. This work included a comparative study of the Groves and Balch model complexes, and of horseradish peroxidase Compounds I and II. The EXAFS spectra and corresponding Fourier transforms of the four high-valent systems (two proteins and two models), taken from a subsequent, more complete, analysis of the data [107], are displayed in Figs. 19 and 20. Table 2 contains a summary which shows the Fe–O(oxo) and Fe–N_p bond lengths for a variety of oxidized heme proteins and their models.

From the energies of the X-ray absorption edge, it was concluded that horseradish peroxidase Compounds I and II, and the respective models, were all Fe^{IV} species. Furthermore, there was essentially no difference in the EXAFS data of the two protein states and their respective model complexes (compare Figs. 19 and 20). Curve-fitting analyses of the data for all four species suggested the presence of one set of oxygen (or nitrogen) atoms at a distance of ~1.6 Å [143]. This was consistent with the presence of a short Fe=O bond, as expected for an oxo-ferryl moiety. A second set of atoms at ~2.0 Å corresponded to the pyrrole

Table 2. Structural details for high-valent *oxo*iron (IV) states of horseradish peroxidase, myoglobin, cytochrome *c* peroxidase and relevant porphyrin model complexes[a]

System	Method	Fe–N(porphyrin) R (Å)	Fe–O(oxo) R (Å)	Ref.
A. Compound I				
Horseradish peroxidase[b]	EXAFS	1.99–2.00	1.61–1.64	[107, 143]
Horseradish peroxidase[c,d]	EXAFS	2.02	1.64	[144]
Cytochrome *c* peroxidase[c,e]	EXAFS	2.02	1.67	[145]
$[Fe^{IV}O(TMP^{\bullet})L]^{+}$[b]	EXAFS	2.02–2.04	1.62–1.66	[107, 143]
B. Compound II				
Horseradish peroxidase[b]	EXAFS	1.99–2.00	1.60–1.64	[107, 143]
Horseradish peroxidase[c,f]	EXAFS	2.00	1.93	[144]
Myoglobin[c,g]	EXAFS	1.98	1.69	[146]
$Fe^{IV}O(TTP)(NMeIm)$[b]	EXAFS	2.02–2.03	1.64–1.66	[107, 143]
$Fe^{IV}O(TpPP)(THF)$[h]	X-RAY	2.005	1.604	[147]

[a] EXAFS data analysis procedures are described in the listed references. Abbreviations: L, solvent ligand (methanol in the case listed; $TMP^{\bullet}$, *meso*-tetramesitylporphyrinato(−1) radical; NMeIm, N-methylimidazole; TTP, *meso*-tetratolylporphyrin; THF, tetrahydrofuran; TpPP, *meso*-tetrakis(α,α,α,α-*o*-pivalamidophenyl)porphyrin;

[b] The range of EXAFS data reported results from the use of two different analysis methods (see Ref. 107). The value reported for Fe–N_p actually represents an average value for Fe–N_p and Fe–N_{ax};

[c] Separate values for Fe–N_p and for Fe–N_{ax} reported;

[d] Fe–N_{ax} = 1.93 Å;

[e] Fe–N_{ax} = 1.91 Å; Note cytochrome *c* peroxidase compound I is also known as compound ES;

[f] Fe–N_{ax} = 2.10 Å;

[g] Fe–N_{ax} = 2.11 Å;

[h] Preliminary structural characterization. Although the structure suffers from disorder, the Fe–O bond length is reported with an accuracy of ±0.019 Å.

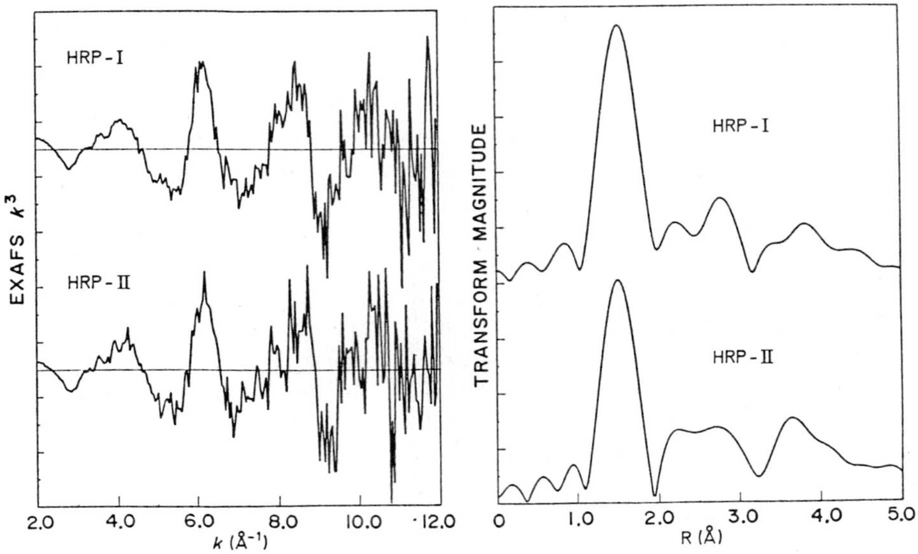

Fig. 19. EXAFS spectra (left) and Fourier transforms of the data (right) for horseradish peroxidase Compounds I and II. EXAFS data are weighted by k^3 to enhance the amplitude of high k oscillations. Reproduced with permission from Ref. [107]

nitrogen atoms (Table 2). This initial EXAFS study provided the first direct evidence of a short Fe=O bond (a double bond) in both Compounds I and II of horseradish peroxidase and confirmed the proposed oxo-ferryl structures of both the Groves and Balch models [143].

The curve-fitting analysis procedure is quite complex for iron porphyrin systems with short bonds. Background removal artifacts could potentially be misinterpreted [107]. This is because short bonds give only a few EXAFS oscillations over the observable energy range of the spectrum (see Fig. 10). The initial report of Penner-Hahn et al. [143] was followed by a much more thorough investigation of the EXAFS data by the same investigators [107]. The subsequent study employed K_2FeO_4 (Fe=O, 1.67 Å [148] and an oxo-chromium porphyrin adduct (Cr=O, 1.57 Å [149]) as model M=O complexes, in addition to the model complexes of Groves and Balch described above (Table 2) [53–56]. The data analysis procedure utilized a Fourier filter to isolate only the EXAFS arising from atoms in the first coordination sphere. Results of the curve-fitting analysis for the structurally defined models indicated that the data analysis was accurate to ± 0.02 Å [143]. As shown in Table 2, an average Fe=O bond distance of 1.64 ± 0.03 Å was obtained for all four high-valent oxo-ferryl porphyrins (horseradish peroxidase Compounds I and II and their respective models). Weiss and co-workers have provided additional support for the short Fe=O bond of horseradish peroxidase Compound II by their recent preparation and preliminary crystallographic characterization of a Compound II model

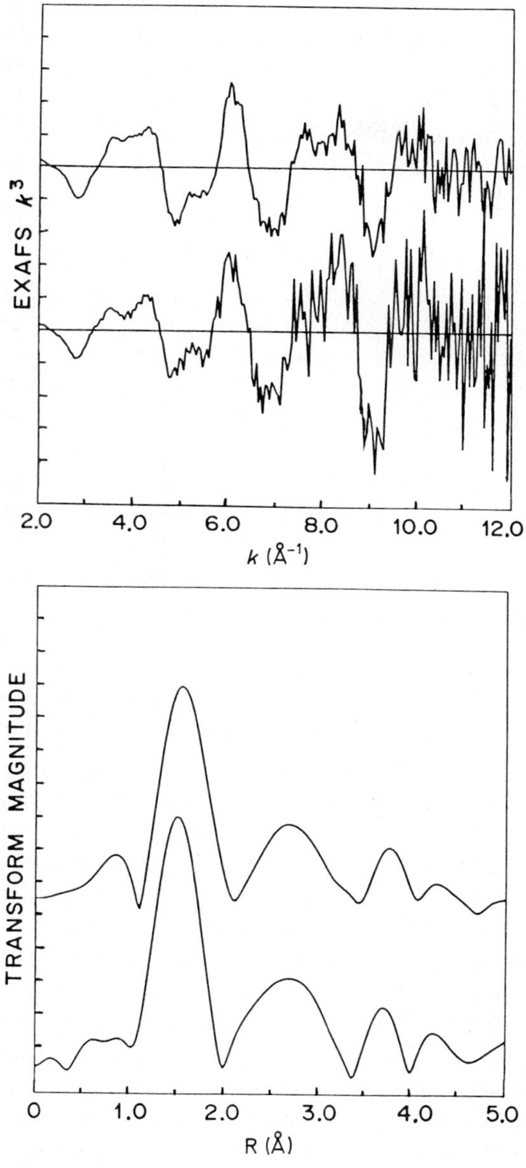

Fig. 20. EXAFS spectra (top figure) and Fourier transforms of the data (bottom figure) for the models of Compound I (top) and Compound II (bottom) prepared by Groves and Balch, respectively (see text). EXAFS data are weighted by k^3 to enhance the amplitude of high k oscillations. Reproduced with permission from Ref. [107]

complex (an analog of the Balch Compound II model [55, 56]) with an Fe=O bond length of 1.604 Å [147].

Chance et al. have also studied the EXAFS properties of the high-valent oxoferryl states of horseradish peroxidase, cytochrome *c* peroxidase, and myoglobin [144–146]. A two-atom-type constrained amplitude ratio fit and a three-atom-type consistency test were used for the analysis of the EXAFS data [144, 146]. These analytical methods differ from that used by Hodgson and co-workers

[143]. Chance et al. concluded that the valence states for the central iron of horseradish peroxidase Compounds I and II were both more highly oxidized than Fe^{III} [144]. The identical conclusion had been reached in the earlier study of high-valent horseradish peroxidase complexes [143]. Furthermore, an Fe=O bond distance of 1.64 ± 0.02 Å was determined by Chance et al. for horseradish peroxidase Compound I [144]. This finding was essentially identical to that of Penner-Hahn et al. [143].

In contrast, a significantly longer Fe–O bond length (1.93 ± 0.02 Å) was reported for horseradish peroxidase Compound II [144]. The apparent lengthening of the Fe=O bond between horseradish peroxidase Compounds I and II led these investigators to conclude that the Fe=O double bond of Compound I is converted to a single bond upon formation of Compound II. This result is clearly at odds with the previous EXAFS study of Compound II [143]. It is also in conflict with an extensive body of evidence that suggests similar Fe sites for horseradish peroxidase Compounds I and II [60, 61], and that favors oxo ligation to the Compound II intermediate [66–70, 150]. The data analysis of Chance et al. for horseradish peroxidase Compound II is also unusual in that it includes sets of similar atomic type atoms [O(oxo), N_p, N_{ax}] at very similar distances (1.93, 2.00, and 2.10 Å, respectively) [144]. Theory suggests that such a refinement will only be possible with considerably more extensive data than were reported ($k_{max} = 12$ Å^{-1}) [106, 107].

Recently, Terner and Kitagawa and their respective co-workers have examined the resonance Raman properties of horseradish peroxidase Compound II [66–70] and have found the value of ν(Fe=O) to vary with pH. For example, Sitter et al. [67] observed a shift from 788 cm^{-1} at pH 8.9 to 775 cm^{-1} at neutral pH. These observations have been interpreted to indicate the presence of a hydrogen bond in the neutral-to-low-pH form between the ferryl O atom and a titrable residue such as a protonated distal imidazole. Makino et al. reported similar results [151] indicating the existence of two forms of Compound II that are interconvertible with pH. In addition, Kitagawa and coworkers have noted that the neutral pH form of Compound II exchanges its O atom with $H_2{}^{18}O$ while the alkaline derivative does not [70]. Because the resonance Raman frequency of the Fe=O bond varies by less than 15 cm^{-1}, the hydrogen bonding is presumably weak [69]. Only the non-hydrogen-bonded (alkaline) form of Compound II is thought to be catalytically important. The pKa for this interconversion varies with the horseradish peroxidase isozyme [66–70, 152].

The functional importance of the alkaline transition in Compound II is intriguing. Hayashi and Yamazaki [153] have shown that the ferryl/ferric redox potential is dramatically decreased at high pH. Terner and co-workers [154] recently observed that the resonance Raman oxidation state marker frequency (ν_4 [155, 156]) of alkaline pH ferric horseradish peroxidase was quite similar to that of Fe^{IV} hemes. They proposed that oxidation of alkaline ferric horseradish peroxidase (Fe^{III}–OH) to the Fe^{IV}=O state is promoted by the distal histidine acting as a base catalyst [154]. Likewise, the higher ferryl/ferric redox potential at lower pH [153] is consistent with the idea that hydrogen bonding to the oxo oxygen of Compound II facilitates its reduction to the ferric state, as proposed by Penner-Hahn et al. [107].

Thus, a possible explanation for the two different Fe=O bond lengths obtained for horseradish peroxidase Compound II could be that the shorter one of ~1.65 Å [143] corresponds to the alkaline state, while the longer one of ~1.9 Å [144] derives from the lower pH, hydrogen-bonded form. However, this explanation seems unlikely since a 0.3 Å change in Fe=O bond length, and conversion to a single-bonded Fe–O, would be expected to yield more than a 13 cm^{-1} shift in ν(Fe–O). Nonetheless, it is worth noting that while both laboratories began the preparation of Compound II from the native protein at pH 7.0, the exact pH of the samples after peroxide and ascorbate addition was not reported. It is therefore possible that some of the difference in the samples could have resulted from changes in pH. The EXAFS data of Chance et al. for the two high-valent states of horseradish peroxidase are distinctly different from one another [144]. In contrast, the data of Penner-Hahn et al. [107] for the two protein derivatives are virtually identical to each other (Fig. 19). Additional and more detailed EXAFS studies of horseradish peroxidase Compound II will be necessary to resolve this dilemma.

EXAFS data for the proposed Fe^{IV}=O myoglobin derivative have also been reported by Chance et al. [146]. A short Fe=O bond distance of 1.69 Å was reported, together with evidence that the iron had been oxidized to Fe^{IV}. The data clearly indicate that this myoglobin derivative has the expected Fe^{IV}=O structure. (See Note in Proof No. 2.)

Chance et al. have also investigated cytochrome *c* peroxidase Compound I (Compound ES) with EXAFS spectroscopy and found that it, too, has a short Fe–O bond of 1.67 ± 0.04 Å [145]. As discussed earlier, cytochrome *c* peroxidase Compound I is thought to contain an Fe^{IV}=O complex with a protein-centered radical [Fe^{IV}=O]R* [71]. Comparative crystallography of cytochrome *c* peroxidase Compound I and the native ferric enzyme [154] have been interpreted in terms of a short, strong Fe=O double bond just as indicated by the results of EXAFS spectroscopy [145]. Thus, consensus has been reached that short Fe=O bonds (~1.65 Å) are present for the Compound I derivative of horseradish peroxidase, the Compound I intermediate of cytochrome *c* peroxidase, and the related myoglobin complex (Table 2).

EXAFS analysis of a peroxide compound of beef heart cytochrome *c* oxidase has also revealed the presence of a short Fe=O bond with a bond length of 1.71 Å [157]. A catalytic role for the ferryl-oxo species of cytochrome *c* oxidase has been postulated [158–161]. In this case, the prosthetic group is no longer protoporphyrin IX, but is instead heme *a* [162]. The observation of an Fe=O bond for this intermediate of cytochrome oxidase further illustrates the *generality* of the short, ~1.65 Å, Fe^{IV}=O bond for high-valent oxo-iron states (Table 2).

The Fe–N_{ax} bonds of the Compound I states of horseradish peroxidase and cytochrome *c* peroxidase were reported to be 1.93 and 1.91 Å, respectively, vs. 2.11 Å for the oxo-iron(IV) derivative of myoglobin [144]. It must again be noted that there is disagreement [107] as to whether EXAFS data of

k_{max} 12.5 Å^{-1} can resolve Fe–N_{ax} distances that are as similar in value to the Fe–N_p distances reported ($\Delta R = 0.09$, 0.11, and 0.13 Å, respectively). Nonetheless, the authors suggested that the Fe–N_{ax} bond length serves to control the heme protein function [145]. A similar conclusion has been derived from studies of the deoxyferrous proteins with resonance Raman spectroscopy. In particular, the value of ν[Fe^{II}–N(His)] is higher (248 cm^{-1}) for the peroxidases than for hemoglobin and myoglobin (~222 cm^{-1}) [71, 72, 80]. In addition, the frequency of ν[Fe^{IV}=O] for heme proteins and enzymes ranges from a high of 797 cm^{-1} for the oxo iron state of myoglobin to a low of ~767 cm^{-1} for cytochrome *c* peroxidase Compound I [164]. This ~30 cm^{-1} variability of ν(Fe=O) is suggested to correlate inversely with the ligand field strength of the *trans*-ligand strength (i.e., histidine vs histidinate) [164]. (See Note in Proof No. 3.)

4.1.2 *Native States*

The EXAFS spectra of the ferric states of catalase, horseradish peroxidase, and cytochrome *c* peroxidase have been found to be highly similar [144]. Analysis of the data for ferric catalase led Chance et al. to suggest an aquo sixth ligand with an Fe–O distance of 2.09 Å. This conclusion is surprising given the fact that the crystal structure of ferric bovine liver catalase indicates that the heme site is pentacoordinate [82]. Electron density possibly suggesting an axial aquo ligand has been observed in the X-ray crystallographic study of ferric *Penicillium vitale* catalase [83, 84]. However, the resonance Raman properties of native ferric *Aspergillus niger*, bovine liver, and *Micrococcus luteus* catalases all indicate pentacoordination, suggesting that this may be a generalizable property of catalases [86].

A weakly interacting aquo sixth ligand at ~2.35 Å was reported for both horseradish peroxidase and cytochrome *c* peroxidase. The presence or absence of a weakly coordinating (aquo) sixth ligand to ferric cytochrome *c* peroxidase has also been the subject of some controversy. However, the recent detailed analysis of this system by resonance Raman spectroscopy clearly indicates that in freshly prepared enzyme the heme iron is pentacoordinate [72]. The heme iron of native ferric horseradish peroxidase is also generally thought to be pentacoordinate [165]. Thus the aquo sixth ligand observed by Chance et al. [144] for native ferric horseradish peroxidase, cytochrome *c* peroxidase, and catalase is inconsistent with other evidence for these systems. The EXAFS data analysis of native ferric catalase by Chance et al. [144] was also unusual in that separate sets of similar atomic type atoms (i.e., Fe–O_{ax} and Fe–N_p) whose M–L bond lengths differ by less than 0.1 Å were reported (vide supra).

Significant differences in the Fe–N_{ax} bond distance between the native ferric states of horseradish peroxidase (~1.92 Å) and myoglobin (~2.09 Å) have been reported [144, 146, 166]. These variations in bond lengths were proposed to correlate with the respective functional activities of the two heme proteins. Specifically, it was suggested that the shorter Fe–N_{ax} bond distance of horseradish peroxidase, likely the result of hydrogen bonding of the proximal histidine to an adjacent base, might help stabilize the porphyrin π-cation radical state through electron delocalization to the proximal ligand [146]. Once again, however, it must be emphasized that the reported difference in Fe–N_{ax} and Fe–N_p bond lengths for ferric horseradish peroxidase and myoglobin (0.14 and 0.07 Å, respectively) may be less than can accurately be resolved with the available EXAFS data (vide supra). Interestingly, Dasgupta et al. [72] have reported a pH-dependent conversion of deoxyferrous cytochrome *c* peroxidase to a species spectrally similar to myoglobin.

Hydrogen bonding to the proximal histidine of cytochrome *c* peroxidase [167, 168] has been proposed to play a role in the catalytic mechanism of the peroxidases. This idea is supported by the model studies of Traylor, Groves, and Bruice [169–173]. In particular, an increase in peroxidase activity is observed for a model heme system when the imidazole axial ligand is hydrogen bonded [173]. Valentine and co-workers [174] have also shown altered ligand affinities for imidazole-ligated heme systems when hydrogen bonding occurs at the imidazole. These observations are likely the result of the increased electron density at the heme iron that occurs when the axial imidazole is partially deprotonated [175–177]. It has also been proposed that a proximal histidinate may stabilize higher oxidation states of the heme iron [178, 179]. In contrast, Traylor and Popovitz-Biro concluded that hydrogen bonding to the proximal imidazole was not of great importance for reversible oxygen binding by respiratory heme proteins [173]. This latter finding parallels that proposed by Ondrias et al. for deoxyhemoglobins in 1982 [180].

Extending the proposed role of a partially deprotonated imidazole axial ligand in facilitating O–O bond cleavage of bound peroxide, Traylor and Popovitz-Biro suggested that complete deprotonation of the proximal ligand, as occurs with the thiolate proximal ligand of cytochrome P-450, should have an even greater effect [173]. Such a role for the thiolate ligand in the mechanism of action of P-450 was discussed above. Indeed, we note that those enzymes whose catalytic cycles likely involve Compound I or Compound II intermediates *ALL* have an anionic (or strongly hydrogen bonded) proximal ligand [86, 181]. Specifically, this includes the thiolate of cytochrome P-450 and chloroperoxidase [20, 22, 95, 109, 116, 126], the tyrosinate of heme catalases (and possibly of chlorin catalases) [82–86, 90, 91], and the imidazolate (strongly hydrogen-bonded imidazole) of horseradish peroxidase and cytochrome *c* peroxidase [71, 72, 182–188].

4.2 Mechanistic Implications of the Oxo-Iron Structure

Given the strong evidence for an oxo-iron structure containing a short Fe=O double bond, of ~1.65 Å in high-valent states of a number of heme proteins, one then questions the functional significance of this species as an enzymatic intermediate. The close similarity in structure between horseradish peroxidase Compounds I and II may facilitate rapid reduction of Compound I by minimizing the reorganization energy barrier for this reaction step. The extent to which the Fe=O bond length of the oxo iron unit will be influenced by the trans ligand and by hydrogen bonding to the oxo oxygen remain to be understood. Clearly, the Fe=O bond length in iron oxo systems is not sensitive to whether or not the porphyrin is a π-cation radical.

An intriguing resonance Raman report by Paeng and Kincaid [189] indicates that $\nu[Fe^{IV}{=}O]$ of horseradish peroxidase Compound I is at 737 cm^{-1}, a 39-cm^{-1} decrease from that of neutral-to-low pH Compound II. This is a surprisingly large shift given the similarity in the Fe=O bond length of both derivatives as determined by EXAFS [107, 143]. It could be that the EXAFS responds *only* to the M–L bond, while the resonance Raman frequency is sensitive to the extensive overlap of the metal and porphyrin π systems [190]. Oertling and Babcock [191] have reported the position of $\nu[Fe^{IV}{=}O]$ to be at 791 cm^{-1} for horseradish peroxidase Compound I. They suggested, however, that the species they observed was a previously undetected $[Fe^{IV}{=}O]R^*$ transient, similar to cytochrome *c* peroxidase Compound I. These data also suggest that, at neutral pH, the oxo group is *not* hydrogen-bonded to the distal histidine [191]. Alternatively, for Compound I there may be considerable delocalization of the unpaired electron to the axial histidine. This latter interpretation is supported by a recent NMR study by La Mar and co-workers [192]; the former proposal is favored by Oertling and Babcock [191]. Clearly, the relationship between oxo iron structure and enzyme function remains an area of active investigation, with numerous unresolved issues.

Finally, the similarity between the peroxidases, especially chloroperoxidase, and cytochrome P-450 in their reactivity with peroxide suggests that the active oxygen species in P-450 may also be a ferryl species, i.e., an oxo iron (IV) complex. Evidence both for [193] and against [194] the involvement of a Compound I-type intermediate in the reaction cycle of P-450 has appeared. As of yet, there exists no direct evidence for the nature of the intermediates beyond oxy-P-450 in the reaction cycle.

5 Non-Heme Tetrapyrroles

The application of X-ray absorption spectroscopy (XAS), X-ray absorption near-edge structure (XANES), and EXAFS to tetrapyrroles that are not iron porphyrins is as yet relatively limited. Studies include EXAFS of 3-propenamide-zinc(II)-*meso*-tetraphenylporphyrin complexes [201], XANES of vanadyl-phthalocyanine and vanadyl-*meso*-tetraphenylporphyrin [202], and XANES of iron(III)-phthalocyanine and its CO adduct [203].

The largest body of work is devoted to nickel (II) F-430, the hydrocorphin cofactor of methyl coenzyme M reductase from methanogenic bacteria

[204–209]. EPR spectroscopy of F-430 has indicated the presence of nickel(I) in the catalytic cycle [208]. EXAFS and XAS of F-430, its mono- and di-epimers, and of tetrapyrrolic nickel(II) model complexes have begun to provide detailed information about the macrocycle [210–216]. Key findings include an 8336 eV pre-edge feature that is indicative of tetracoordinate, square-planar geometry for nickel(II) macrocycles, but is absent from pre-edge spectra of six-coordinate nickel(II) [210]. The hexacoordinate nickel(II) complexes also have long nickel-ligand bonds ($\sim$2.1 Å), suggesting that the macrocycle is generally planar [213]. However, for the tetracoordinate nickel(II) species, shorter $\sim$1.9 Å nickel–nitrogen bonds suggest a ruffled macrocycle [213]. Most recently, Furenlid et al. [216] have used EXAFS to probe the functional properties of F-430, comparing the one-electron reduction products of nickel(II)-porphycene, -chlorin, and -isobacteriochlorin (iBC) with the neutral species. The porphycene and chlorin form nickel(II) π-anion complexes, for which the metal–nitrogen bond lengths are essentially identical with those of the nickel(II) complexes. In contrast, one-electron reduction of the nickel(II)iBC yields a nickel(I) anion having metal–nitrogen bond lengths that vary by as much as $\pm$0.1 Å from the neutral species [216]. These data demonstrate that some flexibility of the macrocycle is required for metal vs. macrocycle reduction in nickel(II) systems, of key importance in understanding the biological function and reactivity of F-430.

6 Concluding Remarks and Unresolved Issues

The use of EXAFS spectroscopy as a structural probe of heme-containing mono-oxygenases and peroxidases and of relevant model complexes has produced a considerably more detailed picture of the metal coordination sites in such systems. In the case of cytochrome P-450, analysis of EXAFS spectra has directly demonstrated that the proximal ligand is a sulfur donor, as had been predicted by other spectral methods, in the low-spin ferric, high-spin ferric, high-spin ferrous, oxy-ferrous, and ferrous-CO states (*1–5*, Fig. 3). These findings have recently been confirmed by X-ray crystallography for the first two states. Further, the Fe–S bond distances determined for these five P-450 derivatives by EXAFS are equal to or shorter than those in appropriate model complexes determined by crystallography (Table 1), as expected if the sulfur donor ligand is a thiolate. For chloroperoxidase, EXAFS investigations of the high-spin ferric and oxy-ferrous states has also provided strong evidence for the presence of a thiolate ligand to the heme iron, despite the initial lack of supporting chemical evidence. The presence of such a ligand has recently been corroborated by genetic as well as chemical studies of the enzyme.

For the high-valent Compound I intermediate of the peroxidases and the appropriate model complex, EXAFS spectroscopy has unequivocally demonstrated the presence of a short $\sim$1.65 Å Fe=O bond. The published data are somewhat contradictory for the Compound II intermediate with both short (~1.65 Å) and long (~1.90 Å) Fe–O bond lengths having been reported. However, studies of Compound II model complexes with EXAFS and X-ray crystallography and of high-valent iron oxo derivatives of myoglobin, cytochrome *c* peroxidase, and cytochrome *c* oxidase consistently have revealed the presence of short (~1.65 Å) Fe=O bonds (Table 2). This suggests that a short Fe=O bond may be a general property of such systems.

Finally, there remain several unresolved questions. For P-450, the major issue concerns the structural identity of proposed intermediates following reduction of the oxy-enzyme. Until it is possible to trap these species for spectroscopic study by EXAFS and other techniques, their identities will remain hypothetical. For chloroperoxidase, a key question is the possible role of a ferric hypochlorite complex known as Compound X [22, 42, 195, 196] in the halogenation reaction. Structural characterization of any such species would significantly advance our understanding of how the enzyme works. Because chloroperoxidase has a thiolate proximal ligand and also forms high-valent intermediates, it bridges the gap between P-450 and the peroxidases. Consequently, EXAFS examination of the high-valent intermediates of the enzyme is of double importance in further testing the generality of the conclusions reached about the structural properties of high-valent oxo-iron systems, and because such intermediates may serve as models for the analogous P-450 states.

The Compound I and Compound II derivatives of catalase have not been studied by EXAFS spectroscopy. The question of interest here involves the effect of the tyrosinate proximal ligand on the length of the Fe=O bond. Further experiments with horseradish peroxidase Compound II are also warranted. In particular, it would be interesting to probe the effect of hydrogen bonding to the oxo-oxygen by investigating the EXAFS as a function of pH. A similar study of Compound I might also be revealing. Finally, lignin peroxidase and manganese peroxidase from the white-rot fungus *Phanerochaete chrysosporium* [197–200] have recently been reported to form high-valent derivatives with spectroscopic properties that are fairly similar to those of analogous states of horseradish peroxidase. Investigation of these intermediates by EXAFS would provide a further test of the apparent generality of the short Fe=O bond in such states.

Acknowledgements. J.H.D. gratefully acknowledges the National Science Foundation (Grant DMB-86:05876) for support of the research from his laboratory described in this review. These studies have been possible because of the fruitful collaboration with Keith Hodgson and his talented co-workers: Steve Cramer, Lung-Shan Kau, and, in particular, James Penner-Hahn. The important contributions of Lowell Hager to the work with chloroperoxidase are appreciated. J.H.D. wishes to especially thank present and former members of his research group who have contributed to the results described herein: Masanori Sono, Kim Smith Eble, Ed Svastits, Grant Bruce, Kecia Courtney, Ian Davis, Marty Ross, Cheryl Shigaki, and Susan Tibedo. J.H.D. also wishes to express his appreciation to William H. Orme-Johnson for the warm hospitality extended to him during a sabbatical leave spent at MIT.

L.A.A.'s research is supported by grants from the National Institutes of Health (GM 34468), the Donors of the Petroleum Research Fund, administered by the American Chemical Society (17319-G3), and by the Medical Research Foundation of Oregon (MRF 8712). L.A.A. appreciates the encouragement of Thomas M. Loehr.

Finally, we both wish to acknowledge helpful discussions and constructive comments concerning this manuscript from Johann W. Buchler, Thomas M. Loehr, William H. Orme-Johnson, James Penner-Hahn, W. A. (Tony) Oertling, and Ursula Simonis.

7 Abbreviations

EXAFS	extended X-ray absorption fine structure
P-450-CAM	the P-450 enzyme from *Pseudomonas putida* (grown on camphor as a sole carbon source)
CCP	cytochrome *c* peroxidase
Cyt *c*	cytochrome *c*
N_p	the pyrrole nitrogen of a porphyrin
C_α	the α carbon of the pyrrole ring of a porphyrin
X_{ax}	an axial ligand of unspecified atom type
S_{ax}	an axial sulfur donor ligand
O(Oxo)	oxo oxygen atom
N_{ax}	an axial nitrogenous ligand
O_{ax}	an axial oxygen donor ligand
PPIX	protoporphyrin IX
PPIXDME	the dimethyl ester of protoporphyrin IX
TPP	*meso*-tetraphenylporphyrin
TpPP	*meso*-tetrakis (α,α,α,α-*O*-pivalamido)phenylporphyrin

(see also Tables 1 and 2)

Notes Added in Proof

1. The work of Oertling et al. [217] demonstrates that both the electronic absorption and resonance Raman spectra of the model compound, $Co^{III}OEP^+(ClO_4^-)_2$, whose spectrum resembles that of horseradish peroxidase compound I, is a $^2A_{1u}$ radical. Their data further indicate that spectral differences previously reported between $^2A_{1u}$ and $^2A_{2u}$ states may derive from differences in porphyrin stereochemistry. Using ENDOR spectroscopy, Babcock and co-workers have recently shown that two porphyrin π-cation radical model compound with disparate optical spectra both have $^2A_{1u}$ ground states [218].

2. Recent variable temperature magnetic circular dichroism studies by Foote et al. [219] have shown that the $Fe^{IV}{=}O$ myoglobin derivative exists in two forms, depending on the pH. The observed spectral differences were tentatively ascribed to deprotonation of the proximal histidine at higher pH.

3. The recent resonance Raman work of Reczak et al. [220] suggest an even lower value for ν ($Fe^{IV}{=}O$) of Compound I of cytochrome *c* peroxidase: 753 cm^{-1}.

8 References

1. Penner-Hahn JE, Hodgson KO (1989) Iron Porphyrins, Part Three (Lever ABP, Gray HB, eds.), pp. 235–304, VCH Publishers, Weinheim, FRG
2. Penner-Hahn JE (1988) ACS Symposium Series: 372: 28
3. Cramer SP (1988) Chem Anal (N.Y.): 92: (X-ray Absorpt.): 257
4. Hasnain SS (1987) Life Chem Reports 4: 273
5. Hasnain SS, Garner CD (1987) Prog Biophys Mol Biol 50: 47
6. Garner CD (1986) J Physique Colloque C8: 1111
7. Scott RA (1985) Meth Enzymol 117: 414
8. Powers L (1982) Biochim Biophys Acta 683: 1
9. Teo B-K (1980) Acc Chem Res 13: 412
10. Teo B-K, Lee PA (1979) J Am Chem Soc 101: 2815
11. Teo B-K, Atonio MP, Averill BA (1983) J Am Chem Soc 105: 3751
12. Kincaid BM, Shulman RG (1980) Adv Inorg Biochem 2: 303
13. Cramer SP, Hodgson KO (1979) Prog Inorg Chem 25: 1
14. Sandstrom DR, Lytle FW (1979) Ann Rev Phys Chem 30: 215
15. Chan SI, Gamble RC (1978) Meth Enzymol 54: 323
16. Chan SI, Hu VW, Gamble RC (1978) J Mol Struc 45: 234
17. Shulman RG, Eisenberger P, Kincaid BM (1978) Ann Rev Biophys Bioenerg 7: 559
18. Eisenberger P, Kincaid BM (1978) Science 200: 1441
19. Stern EA, Sayers DE, Lytle FW (1975) Phys Rev B 11: 4836
20. Dawson JH (1988) Science 240: 433
21. Ortiz de Montellano PR (ed.) (1986) Cytochrome P-450: Structure, Mechanism, and Biochemistry, Plenum, New York
22. Dawson JH, Sono M (1987) Chem Rev 87: 1255
23. Unger BP, Sligar SG, Gunsalus IC (1986) in 'The Bacteria' Vol. 10 (Sokatch JR, ed.), pp. 557–589, Academic Press, Orlando
24. Dawson JH, Eble KS (1986) Adv Inorg Bioinorg Mech 4: 1
25. Groves JT (1985) J Chem Educ 62: 928
26. Black SD, Coon MJ (1987) Adv Enzymol Rel Areas Mol Biol 60: 35
27. Mansuy D (1987) Pure Appl Chem 59: 759
28. Weiner LM (1986) Crit Rev Biochem 20: 139
29. White RE, Coon MJ (1980) Ann Rev Biochem 49: 315
30. Hedegaard J, Gunsalus IC (1965) J Biol Chem 240: 4038
31. Alberta JA (1986) Ph.D. Thesis, University of South Carolina
32. Alberta JA, Dawson JH (1987) J Biol Chem 262: 11857
33. Dawson JH, Crull GB, Alberta JA, Sono M (1989) in Cytochrome P-450—Biochemistry and Biophysics (Schuster I, ed.) pp. 77–84, Taylor and Francis, London
34. Alberta JA, Andersson LA, Dawson JH (1989) J Biol Chem 264: 20467
35. Eady RR, Large PJ (1969) Biochem J 111: 37p
36. Dawson JH, Andersson LA, Sono M (1983) J Biol Chem 258: 13637
37. Dawson JH, Andersson LA, Sono M (1982) in Cytochrome P-450: Biochemistry, Biophysics, and Environmental Implications (Hietanen E, Laitinen M, Hanninen O, eds.) pp. 523–530, Elsevier/North Holland Biomedical Press
38. Dawson JH, Andersson LA, Sono M (1982) J Biol Chem 257: 3606
39. Groves JT (1979) Adv Inorg Biochem 1: 119
40. McCandlish E, Mikostai AR, Nappa M, Sprenger AQ, Valentine JS, Strong JD, Spiro TG (1980) J Am Chem Soc 102: 4268
41. Morris DR, Hager LP (1966) J Biol Chem 241: 1763
42. Hewson DW, Hager LP (1978) in The Porphyrins (Dolphin D, ed.) Vol. 7, pp. 295–332, Academic Press, New York
43. Hollenberg PF, Rand-Meir T, Hager LP (1974) J Biol Chem 249: 5816
44. Sibbett SS, Hurst JK (1984) Biochemistry 23: 3007
45. Ikeda-Saito M, Argade PV, Rousseau DL (1985) FEBS Lett 184: 52
46. Babcock GT, Ingle RT, Oertling WA, Davis JC, Averill BA, Hulse CL, Stufkens DJ, Bolscher BGJM, Wever R (1985) Biochim Biophys Acta 828: 58
47. Andersson LA, Loehr TM, Lim AR, Mauk AG (1984) J Biol Chem 259: 15340

48. Andersson LA, Loehr TM, Chang CK, Mauk AG (1985) J Am Chem Soc 107: 182
49. Ikeda-Saito M, Sono M, Dawson JH (1985) Biophys J 47: 85a
50. Marnett LJ, Weller P, Battista JR (1986) in Cytochrome P-450: Structure, Mechanism, and Biochemistry (Ortiz de Montellano PR, ed.) pp. 29–76, Plenum, New York
51. Dolphin D, Forman A, Borg DC, Fajer J (1971) Proc Natl Acad Sci USA 68: 614
52. Dolphin D, Felton RH (1974) Acc Chem Res 7: 26
53. Groves JT, McMurry TJ (1985) Rev Port Quim 27: 102
54. Boso B, Lang G, McMurry TJ, Groves JT (1983) J Chem Phys 79: 1122
55. Chin DH, La Mar GN, Balch AL (1980) J Am Chem Soc 102: 4344
56. Chin DH, Balch AL, La Mar GN (1980) J Am Chem Soc 102: 1446
57. Schappacher M, Chottard G, Weiss R (1986) J Chem Soc Chem Comm 93
58. Gold A, Jayaraj K, Doppelt P, Weiss R, Chottard G, Bill E, Ding X, Trautwein AX (1988) J Am Chem Soc 110: 5756
59. Ator MA, Ortiz de Montellano PR (1987) J Biol Chem 262: 1542
60. Schulz CE, DeVaney PW, Winkler H, Debrunner PG, Doan N, Chiang R, Rutter R, Hager LP (1979) FEBS Lett 103: 102
61. Moss TH, Ehrenberg A, Bearden AJ (1969) Biochemistry 8: 4159
62. Theorell H, Ehrenberg A (1952) Arch Biochem Biophys 41: 442
63. La Mar GN, De Ropp JS, Smith KM, Langry KC (1981) J Biol Chem 256: 237
64. Schonbaum GR, Lo S (1972) J Biol Chem 247: 3353
65. Adediran SA, Dunford HB (1983) Eur J Biochem 132: 147
66. Terner J, Sitter AJ, Reczek CM (1985) Biochim Biophys Acta 828: 73
67. Sitter AJ, Reczek CM, Terner J (1985) J Biol Chem 260: 7515
68. Sitter AJ, Reczek CM, Terner J (1986) J Biol Chem 261: 8638
69. Hashimoto S, Teraoka J, Inubushi T, Kitagawa T (1986) J Biol Chem 261: 11110
70. (a) Hashimoto S, Tatsuno Y, Kitagawa T (1986) Proc Natl Acad Sci USA 83: 2417; (b) Kitagawa T, Ozaki Y (1987) Struct Bonding 64: 71
71. Mauro JM, Miller MA, Edwards SL, Wang J, Fishel LA, Kraut J (1989) Metal Ions Biol Sys 25: 477
72. Dasgupta S, Rousseau DL, Anni H, Yonetani T (1989) J Biol Chem 264: 654
73. Yonetani T, Schleyer H, Ehrenberg A (1966) J Biol Chem 241: 3240
74. Wittenberg BA, Kampa L, Wittenberg JB, Blumberg WE, Peisach J (1968) J Biol Chem 243: 1863
75. Hoffman BM, Roberts JE, Brown TG, Kang CH, Margoliash E (1979) Proc Natl Acad Sci USA 76: 6132
76. Hoffman BM, Roberts JE, Kang CH, Margoliash E (1981) J Biol Chem 256: 6556
77. Lang G, Spartalian K, Yonetani T (1976) Biochim Biophys Acta 451: 250
78. Yonetani T, Anni H (1987) J Biol Chem 262: 9547
79. Edwards SL, Xuong N-H, Hamlin RC, Kraut J (1987) Biochemistry 26: 1503
80. Smulevich G, Mauro JM, Fishel LA, English AM, Kraut J, Spiro TG (1988) Biochemistry 27: 5477
81. (a) Deisseroth A, Dounce AL (1970) Physiol Rev 60: 319 (b) Schonbaum GR, Chance B (1976) The Enzymes 13: 363
82. Murthy MRN, Reid TJ, III; Sicignano A, Tanaka N, Rossmann MG (1981) J Mol Biol 152: 465
83. Vainshtein BK, Melik-Adamyan WR, Barynin VV, Vagin AA, Grebenko AI (1981) Nature (London) 293: 411
84. Vainshtein BK, Melik-Adamyan WR, Barynin VV, Vagin AA, Grebenko AI, Borisov VV, Bartels KS, Fita I, Rossmann MG (1986) J Mol Biol 188: 49
85. Frew JE, Jones P (1984) Adv Inorg Bioinorg Mech 3: 175
86. Sharma KS, Andersson LA, Loehr TM, Goff HG, Terner J (1989) J Biol Chem 264: 12772
87. Jacob GS, Orme-Johnson WH (1979) Biochemistry 18: 2967
88. Jacob GS, Orme-Johnson WH (1979) Biochemistry 18: 2975
89. Loewen PC, Switala J (1986) Biochem Cell Biol 64: 638
90. Andersson LA (1989) Proc SPIE-Int Soc Opt Eng 1055: 279
91. Andersson LA, Zeitler CM, Dawson JH, Loewen PC, in preparation
92. Browett WR, Gasyna Z, Stillman MJ (1988) J Am Chem Soc 110: 3633
93. Rutter R, Valentine M, Hendrich MP, Hager LP, Debrunner PG (1983) Biochemistry 22: 4769
94. Sato R, Omura T (eds.) (1978) Cytochrome P-450, Academic Press, New York
95. Hahn JE, Hodgson KO, Andersson LA, Dawson JH (1982) J Biol Chem 257: 10934

96. Poulos TL, Finzel BC, Howard AH (1986) Biochemistry 25: 5314
97. Poulos TL, Finzel BC, Howard A (1987) J Mol Biol 195: 687
98. Poulos TL, Finzel BC, Gunsalus IC, Wagner GC, Kraut J (1985) J Biol Chem 260: 16122
99. Poulos TL (1988) Adv Inorg Biochem 7: 1
100. Chiang R, Makino R, Spomer WE, Hager LP (1975) Biochemistry 14: 4166
101. Mayer JM (1988) Inorg Chem 27: 3899
102. Lytle FW, Sayers DE, Stern EA (1975) Phys Rev B 11: 4825
103. Blackburn NJ, Strange RW, McFadden LM, Hasnain SS (1987) J Am Chem Soc 109: 7162
104. Blackburn NJ, Strange RW, Farooq A, Haka MS, Karlin KD (1988) J Am Chem Soc 110: 4263
105. Knowles PF, Strange RW, Blackburn NJ, Hasnain SS (1989) J Am Chem Soc 111: 102
106. Lee PA, Citrin PH, Eisenberg P, Kincaid BM (1981) Rev Mod Phys 53: 769
107. Penner-Hahn JE, Eble KS, McMurry TJ, Renner M, Balch AL, Groves JT, Dawson JH, Hodgson KO (1986) J Am Chem Soc 108: 7819
108. Walter M, Tykodi S, Uhm A, Westbrook E, Sabat M, Margoliash E (1989) Biophys J 55: 54a
109. Cramer SP, Dawson JH, Hodgson KO, Hager LP (1978) J Am Chem Soc 100: 7282
110. Koch S, Tang SC, Holm RH, Frankel RB, Ibers JA (1975) J Am Chem Soc 97: 916
111. Byrn MP, Strouse CE (1981) J Am Chem Soc 103: 2633
112. Collman JP, Sorrell TN, Hodgson KO, Kulrestha AK, Strouse CE (1977) J Am Chem Soc 99: 5180
113. Tang SC, Koch S, Papaefthymiou GC, Foner S, Frankel RB, Ibers JA, Holm RH (1976) J Am Chem Soc 98: 2414
114. Kau L-S, Svastits EW, Dawson JH, Hodgson KO (1986) Inorg Chem 25: 4307
115. Caron C, Mitschler A, Riviere G, Ricard L, Schappacher M, Weiss R (1979) J Am Chem Soc 101: 7401
116. Dawson JH, Kau L-S, Penner-Hahn JE, Sono M, Eble KS, Bruce GC, Hager LP, Hodgson KO (1986) J Am Chem Soc 108: 8114
117. Ricard L, Schappacher M, Weiss R, Monteil-Montoya R, Bill E, Gonser U, Trautwein A (1983) Nouv J Chim 7: 405
118. Jameson GB, Robinson WT, Collman JP, Sorrell TN (1978) Inorg Chem 17: 858
119. Dawson JH, Trudell JR, Barth G, Linder RE, Bunnenberg E, Djerassi C, Chiang R, Hager LP (1976) J Am Chem Soc 98: 3709
120. Fang G-H, Keningsberg P, Axley MJ, Nuell M, Hager LP (1986) Nucleic Acids Res 14: 8061
121. Blanke SR, Hager LP (1988) J Biol Chem 263: 18739
122. Dawson JH, Andersson LA, Davis IM, Hahn JE (1980) in Biochemistry, Biophysics, and Regulation of Cytochrome P-450 (Gustafsson J-A, Carlstedt-Duke J, Mode A and Rafter J, eds.) pp. 565–572, Elsevier/North Holland Biomedical Press, Amsterdam
123. Scheidt WR, Reed CA (1981) Chem Rev 81: 543
124. Scheidt WR, Lee YS (1987) Struct Bond 64: 1
125. Hanson LK, Eaton WA, Sligar SG, Gunsalus IC, Gouterman M, Connell CR (1976) J Am Chem Soc 98: 2672
126. Kau L-S, Svastits EW, Sono M, Dawson JH, Hodgson KO (1986) Journal de Physique C8: C8-1151
127. Schappacher M, Ricard L, Fischer J, Weiss R, Bill E, Monteil-Montoya R, Winkler H, Trautwein AX (1987) Eur J Biochem 168: 419
128. Sono M, Eble KS, Dawson JH, Hager LP (1985) J Biol Chem 260: 15530
129. Lambeir A-M, Dunford HB (1985) Eur J Biochem 147: 93
130. Nakajima R, Yamazaki I, Griffin BW (1985) Biochem Biophys Res Commun 28: 1
131. Dawson JH, Holm RH, Trudell JR, Barth G, Linder RE, Bunnenberg E, Djerassi C, Tang SC (1976) J Am Chem Soc 98: 3707
132. Sono M, Andersson LA, Dawson JH (1982) J Biol Chem 257: 8308
133. Sono M, Dawson JH (1982) J Biol Chem 257: 5496
134. Andersson LA, Sono M, Dawson JH (1983) Biochim Biophys Acta 748: 341
135. Groves JT (1979) Adv Inorg Biochem 1: 119
136. Ullrich V (1979) Top Curr Chem 83: 67
137. Gunsalus IC, Sligar SG (1978) Adv Enzymol Rel Areas Mol Biol 47: 1
138. Sono M, Dawson JH, Hall K, Hager LP (1986) Biochemistry 25: 347
139. Dunford HB, Alberty RA (1967) Biochemistry 6: 447
140. Ellis WD, Dunford HB (1988) Biochemistry 7: 2054
141. Erman JE (1974) Biochemistry 13: 34

142. Erman JE (1974) Biochemistry 13: 39
143. Penner-Hahn JE, McMurry, TJ, Renner M, Latos-Grazynsky L, Eble KS, Davis IM, Balch AL, Groves JT, Dawson JH, Hodgson KO (1983) J Biol Chem 258: 12761
144. Chance B, Powers L, Ching Y, Poulos TL, Yamazaki I, Paul KG (1984) Arch Biochem Biophys 235: 596
145. Chance M, Powers L, Poulos T, Chance B (1986) Biochemistry 25: 1266
146. (a) Chance M, Powers L, Kumar C, Chance B (1986) Biochemistry 25: 1259 (b) Powers L, Sessler JL, Woolery GL, Chance B (1984) Biochemistry 23: 239
147. Schappacher M, Weiss R, Monteil-Montoya R, Trautwein A, Tabard A (1985) J Am Chem Soc 107: 3736
148. McGinnety JA (1972) Acta Crystallogr B28: 2845
149. Groves JT, Kruper WJ, Jr, Haushalter RC, Butler WM (1982) Inorg Chem 21: 1363
150. La Mar GN, de Ropp JS, Latos-Grazynski L, Balch AL, Johnson RB, Smith KM, Parish DW, Cheng R-J (1983) J Am Chem Soc 105: 782
151. Makino R, Uno T, Nishimura Y, Iizuka T, Tsuboi M, Ishimura Y (1986) J Biol Chem 261: 8376
152. Yamazaki I, Nakajima R (1988) in (King TS, Mason HS, Morrison M, Oxidases and Related Redox Systems, Alan R Liss, eds.) pp. 451–462, New York
153. Hayashi Y, Yamazaki I (1979) J Biol Chem 254: 9101
154. Sitter AJ, Shifflett JR, Terner J (1988) J Biol Chem 263: 13032
155. Yu N-T, Felton RH (1978) in The Porphyrins Vol. 3 (Dolphin D, ed.) pp. 347–393, Academic Press, New York
156. Spiro TG (1983) in Iron Porphyrins, Part II (Lever ABP, Gray HB, eds.) pp. 89–160, Addison-Wesley, Reading (MA)
157. Kumar C, Nagu A, Powers L, Ching Y-C, Chance B (1988) J Biol Chem 263: 7159
158. Blair DF, Witt SN, Chan SI (1985) J Am Chem Soc 107: 7389
159. Wikstrom M (1981) Proc Natl Acad Sci USA 78: 4051
160. Hill BC, Greenwood C, Nicholls P (1986) Biochim Biophys Acta 853: 91
161. Witt SN, Chan SI (1987) J Biol Chem 262: 1446
162. Heme *a* differs by replacement of the *2*-vinyl group of protoporphyrin IX with a farnesyl, and by replacement of the *8*-methyl group of PPIX with a formyl moiety. These changes significantly alter the spectral properties of heme *a*, both as a model complex and in the protein, relative to PPIX-containing systems [163]
163. Smith KM (ed.) (1975) Porphyrins and Metalloporphyrins, Elsevier, Amsterdam
164. Oertling WA, Kean RT, Wever R, Babcock GT (1990) Inorg Chem 29: 2633
165. Evangelista-Kirkup R, Crisanti M, Poulos TL, Spiro TG (1985) FEBS Lett 190: 221
166. Powers L, Chance B, Ching Y, Angiolillo P (1981) Biophys J 34: 465
167. Poulos TL, Kraut J (1980) J Biol Chem 255: 8199
168. Finzel BC, Poulos TL, Kraut J (1984) J Biol Chem 259: 13027
169. Traylor TG, Lee WA, Stynes DV (1984) J Am Chem Soc 106: 755
170. Traylor TG, Lee WA, Stynes DV (1984) Tetrahedron 40: 553
171. Groves JT, Watanabe Y (1986) J Am Chem Soc 108: 7834
172. Zipplies MF, Lee WA, Bruice TC (1986) J Am Chem Soc 108: 4433
173. Traylor TG, Popovitz-Biro R (1988) J Am Chem Soc 110: 239
174. Quinn R, Mercer-Smith J, Burstyn JN, Valentine JS (1984) J Am Chem Soc 106: 4136
175. Walker FA, Lo MW, Ree MT (1976) J Am Chem Soc 98: 5552
176. Doeff MM, Sweigert DA (1982) Inorg Chem 21: 3699
177. Tondreau GA, Sweigert DA (1984) Inorg Chem 23: 1060
178. Poulos TL, Freer ST, Alden RA, Edwards SL, Skogland U, Tako K, Erikson B, Xuong N, Yonetani T, Kraut J (1980) J Biol Chem 255: 575
179. Schonbaum GR, Houtchens RA, Caughey WS (1979) in Biochemical and Clinical Aspects of Oxygen (Caughey WS, ed.) pp. 195–211, Academic Press, New York
180. Ondrias MR, Rousseau DL, Shelnutt JA, Simon SR (1982) Biochemistry 21: 3428
181. Anzenbacher P, Dawson JH, Kitagawa T (1989) J Mol Struct 214: 149
182. de Ropp JS, Thanabal V, La Mar GN (1985) J Am Chem Soc 107: 8268
183. La Mar GN, de Ropp JS (1979) Biochem Biophys Res Commun 90: 36
184. La Mar GN, de Ropp JS (1982) J Am Chem Soc 104: 5203
185. Stein P, Mitchell M, Spiro TG (1980) J Am Chem Soc 102: 7795
186. Teraoka J, Kitagawa T (1981) J Biol Chem 256: 3969
187. Desbois A, Mazza G, Stretzkowski F, Lutz M (1984) Biochim Biophys Acta 785: 161

188. Mincey T, Traylor TG (1979) J Am Chem Soc 101: 765
189. Paeng KJ, Kincaid JR (1988) J Am Chem Soc 110: 7913
190. Buchler JW, Kokisch W, Smith PD (1978) Struct Bond 34: 79
191. Oertling WA, Babcock GT (1988) Biochemistry 27: 3331
192. Thanabal V, La Mar GN, de Ropp JS (1988) Biochemistry 27: 5400
193. Wagner GC, Palcic MM, Dunford HB (1983) FEBS Lett 156: 244
194. McCarthy MB, White RE (1983) J Biol Chem 258: 9153
195. Chiang R, Rand-Meir T, Makino R, Hager LP (1976) J Biol Chem 251: 6340
196. Libby RD, Thomas JA, Kaiser LW, Hager LP (1982) J Biol Chem 257: 5030
197. Andersson LA, Renganathan V, Loehr TM, Gold MH (1987) Biochemistry 26: 2258
198. Gold MH, Wariishi H, Valli K (1989) ACS Symp Ser 389: 127
199. Marquez L, Wariishi H, Dunford HB, Gold MH (1988) J Biol Chem 263: 10549
200. Wariishi H, Dunford HB, MacDonald IC, Gold MH (1989) J Biol Chem 264: 3335
201. Goulon J, Goulon C, Niedercorn F, Selve C, Castro B (1981) Tetrahedron 37: 3707
202. Wong J, Lytle FW, Messmer RP, Maylotte DH (1984) Phys Rev B 30: 5596
203. Linkous CA, O'Grady WE, Sayers D, Yang CY (1986) Inorg Chem 25: 3761
204. Ellefson WL, Whitman WB, Wolfe RS (1982) Proc Natl Acad Sci USA 79: 3707
205. Hausinger RP, Orme-Johnson WH, Walsh C (1984) Biochemistry 23: 801
206. Daniels L, Sparling R, Sprott GD (1984) Biochim Biophys Acta 768: 113
207. Fässler A, Kobelt A, Pfaltz A, Eschenmoser A, Bladon C, Battersby AR, Thauer RK (1985) Helv Chim Acta 68: 2287, and references therein
208. Albracht SPJ, Ankel-Fuchs D, Van der Zwaan JW, Fontjin RD, Thauer RK (1986) Biochim Biophys Acta 870: 50
209. Albracht SPJ, Ankel-Fuchs D, Bocher R, Ellerman J, Moll J, Van der Zwaan JW, Thauer RK (1988) Biochim Biophys Acta 955: 86
210. Eidsness MK, Sullivan RJ, Schwartz JR, Hartzell PL, Wolfe RS, Flank A-M, Cramer SP, Scott RA (1986) J Am Chem Soc 108: 3120
211. Diakun GP, Piggot B, Tinton HJ, Ankel-Fuchs D, Thauer RK (1985) Biochem J 232: 281
212. Scott RA, Hartzell PL, Wolfe RS, Legall J, Cramer SP (1986) in Frontiers in Bioinorganic Chemistry (Xavier AV, ed.) pp. 20–26, VCH Publishers, Weinheim, FRG
213. Shiemke AK, Hamilton CL, Scott RA (1988) J Biol Chem 263: 5611
214. Shiemke AK, Kaplan WA, Hamilton CL, Shelnutt JA, Scott RA (1989) J Biol Chem 264: 7276
215. Shiemke AK, Shelnutt JA, Scott RA (1989) J Biol Chem 264: 11236
216. Furenlid LR, Renner MW, Smith KM, Fajer J (1990) J Am Chem Soc 112: 1634
217. Oertling WA, Salehi A, Chang CK, Babcock GT (1989) J Phys Chem 93: 1311
218. Sandusky PO, Salehi A, Chang CK, Babcock GT (1989) J Am Chem Soc 111: 6437
219. Foote N, Gadsby PMA, Greenwood C, Thomson AJ (1989) Biochem J 261: 515
220. Reczek CM, Sitter AJ, Terner J (1989) J Mol Struct 214: 27

Phthalocyaninatometal and Related Complexes with Special Electrical and Optical Properties

Hanna Schultz, Helmut Lehmann, Manfred Rein, Michael Hanack*

Institut für Organische Chemie, Lehrstuhl für Organische Chemie II, Universität Tübingen, Auf der Morgenstelle 18, D-7400 Tübingen, West-Germany

Phthalocyanines and related complexes are important compounds due to their special electrical and optical properties. This article describes, after a more preparative part on the synthesis of porphyrins and phthalocyanines, the different ways to use the macrocycles for the mentioned properties.

Phthalocyanines and related compounds can be assembled in a stacked structure by using the so-called "shish-kebab" approach, taking advantage of the possibility to form discotic mesophases or simply by doping the mononuclear metal complexes. The different systems e.g. main group metal complexes or transition metal complexes are discussed with regard to their structure. The methods for increasing the solubility by using differently substituted macrocycles and the electrical properties of these compounds are described in detail.

A separate section is devoted to phthalocyanines and porphyrins as discotic liquid crystals. The nonlinear optical effects as well as photoconductivity and the possibility of the formation of Langmuir-Blodgett-films of phthalocyanines and derivatives is discussed at some length. Several practical applications of these unconventional materials are mentioned.

* In collaboration with Sonja Deger, Carola Hedtmann-Rein, Armin Lange, Xaver Münz, Hans-Joachim Schulze, Petra Vermehren, Tilman Zipplies

© Springer-Verlag Berlin Heidelberg 1990

1 Introduction

Many conducting and semiconducting organic compounds have been developed during the last fifteen years, e.g. charge-transfer complexes, doped polyacetylene, polypyrrole, polythiophene, polyaniline, and others. Several of them, however, have the serious disadvantage of low thermal and chemical stability thereby often restricting practical applications of these compounds. Thus the search for conducting or semiconducting compounds with higher thermal and chemical stability is an important task for chemists and physicists.

A class of compounds with a comparatively high thermal stability are unsaturated, sometimes aromatic metallomacrocycles, e.g. derivatives of tetraazaporphyrin ($TAPH_2$) of which the most thoroughly investigated are the phthalocyaninatometal (PcM), the tetrabenzoporphyrinatometal (TBPM) complexes, the metal complexes of 1,2- and 2,3-naphthalocyanines (1,2- and 2,3-NcM), and the tetra(2,3-naphtho)porphyrins (2,3-TNPM) (Fig. 1).

In addition octaethylporphyrin ($OEPH_2$), tetramethyl- and tetraphenylporphyrin ($TMPH_2$ and $TPPH_2$), dihydrodibenzotetraaza[14]-annulene ($taaH_2$) and hemiporphyrazine (HpH_2) are other examples of macrocycles which have been investigated in efforts to construct new types of conducting materials. In the following we will concentrate on phthalocyaninatometal complexes, tetrabenzoporphyrins, 1,2- and 2,3-naphthalocyanines and tetra(2,3-naphtho)-porphyrins.

Phthalocyanine (PcH_2) is structurally similar to porphyrin (PH_2) (see Fig. 1). The four isoindoline units are linked together in the 1,3-position by aza bridges to form a cyclic system. Formally, phthalocyanines are tetrabenzo-tetraazaporphyrins.

1.1 Synthesis of Mononuclear Porphyrin and Phthalocyanine Complexes

The advantage of phthalocyaninatometal complexes is in general a facile synthesis starting from inexpensive precursors (see Scheme 1). Their high thermal stability has already been mentioned; phthalocyaninatometal complexes PcM (M = e.g. Cu, Ni, Co) can be heated up to 500 °C in vacuo without decomposition. Phthalocyaninatometal complexes are chemically stable, resistant against non-oxidizing acids, bases, and very often the stability towards photoprocesses is also quite high [1].

Phthalocyanines have been synthesized using more than 60 elements as the central atom: besides main group elements, transition metals, lanthanoids and actinoids as well as semimetals such as B, Si, Ge, As, and also nonmetals, e.g. P, have been employed [1, 2].

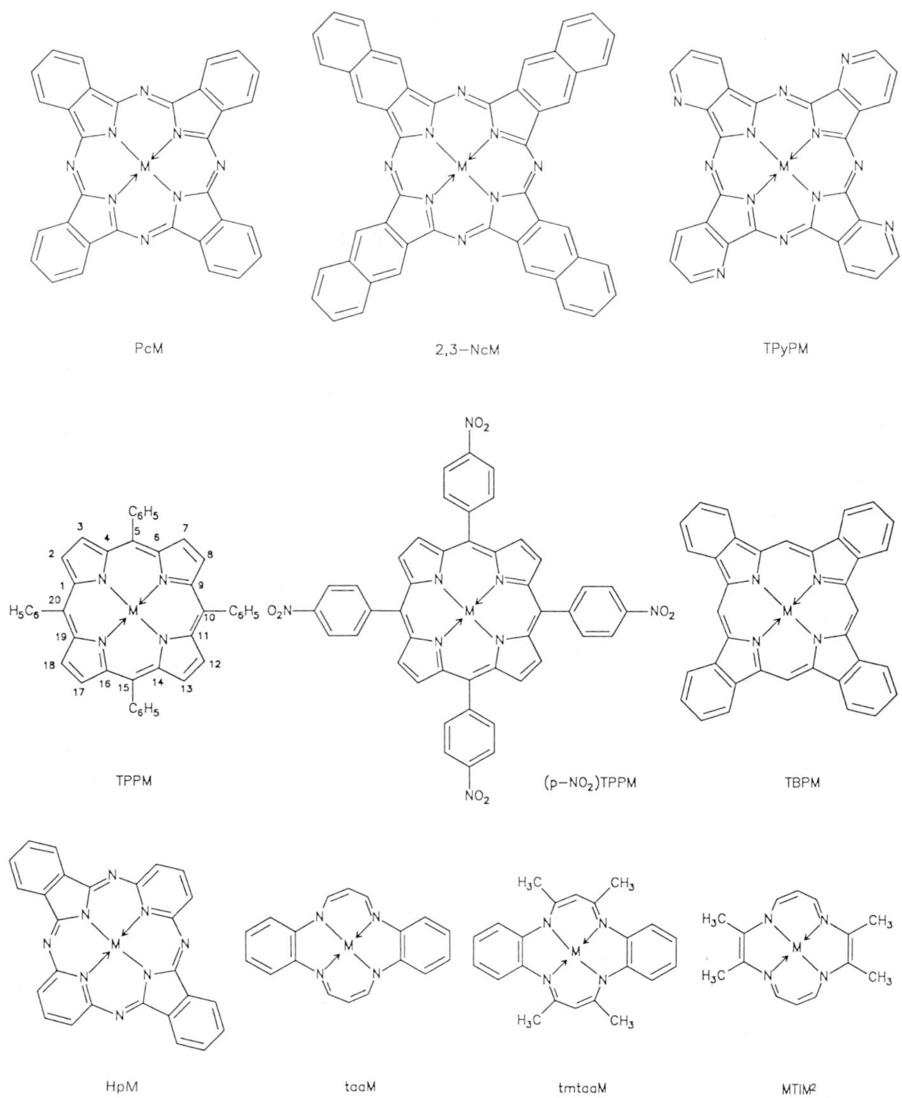

Fig. 1. Macrocyclic metal complexes MacM, used for the synthesis of mono- and polynuclear compounds $MacML_2$ and bridged $[MacML]_n$

Many starting materials can be used to synthesize phthalocyanines. The most common one is phthalonitrile. In Scheme 1 various substrates and synthetical routes to phthalocyanines are depicted.

Phthalocyaninatometal complexes are mostly purified by sublimation, which can lead to crystals or to thin films [3].

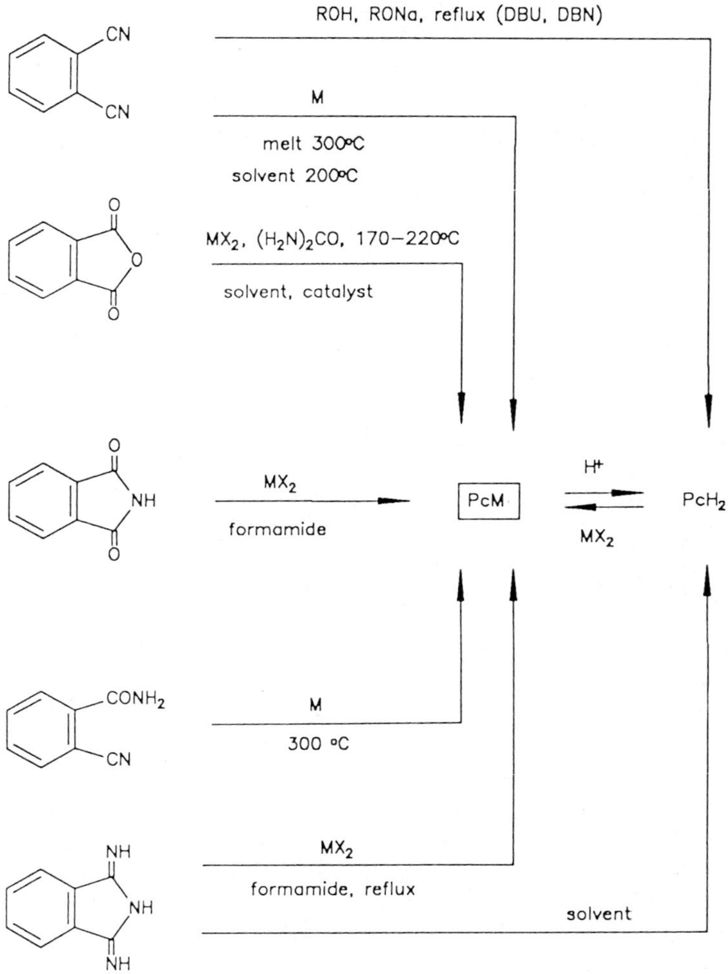

Scheme 1. Synthetical routes to phthalocyanines

The majority of the phthalocyaninatometal complexes are planar molecules and may crystallize in the so-called α- or in the thermodynamically more stable β-modification (see Fig. 2).

Other phthalocyaninatometal complexes can adopt a square pyramidal geometry having the metal positioned above the plane of the ring. Phthalocyanines can adopt a sandwich like structure when the central metals are lanthanoids and actinoids. In these complexes the coordination number of the metal atoms is 8 [4].

The phthalocyaninatometal complexes as well as the other macrocycles shown in Fig. 1 have interesting redox properties. The redox processes can take place either at the macrocycle or the central metal atom. The nature of the

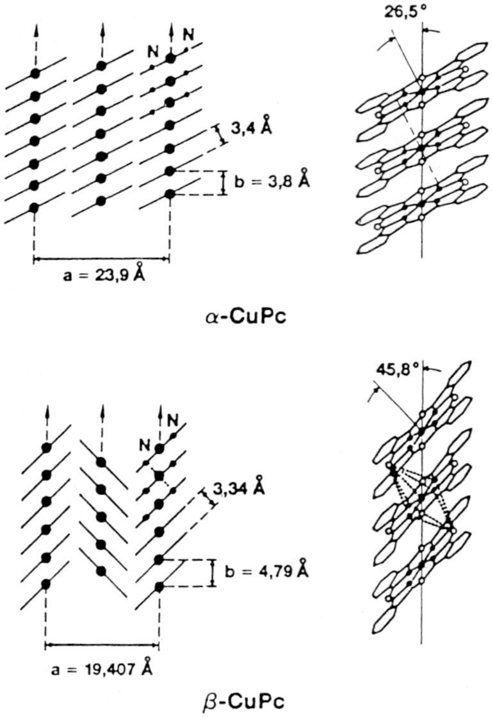

Fig. 2. Crystal modifications of copper(II) phthalocyanines (Permission for printing)

central metal atom is important for the redox properties of the macrocycle, substituents on the macrocycles also influence the redox behavior. Macrocycles often show a stepwise two-electron oxidation and a reversible stepwise many-electron reduction. Two-electron redox processes at the central metal atom have also been observed. In general, the first ring-oxidation step affects the HOMO, the first ring-reduction step affects the LUMO of the phthalocyanine macrocycle. The difference of these potentials (approximately 1.56 V) can be correlated to the molecular band gap [5].

In spite of their structural similarity, tetrabenzoporphyrin ($TBPH_2$) (Fig. 1) is more difficult to synthesize than PcH_2 [1]. Only 11 transition metals and a few rare earth elements have successfully been incorporated into the tetrabenzoporphyrin system [6]. Some of the methods and starting materials are given in Scheme 2.

Contrary to the majority of phthalocyaninatometal complexes, tetrabenzoporphyrinatometal complexes have to be prepared from tetrabenzoporphyrin $TBPH_2$ by treatment with metal salts in a suitable solvent. The preparation of tetrabenzoporphyrin mostly follows one of the routes given in Scheme 2. Tetrabenzoporphyrinatozinc (TBPZn) is prepared first [7]. Subsequent removal of zinc from TBPZn e.g. by treatment with trifluoroacetic acid leads to $TBPH_2$ [8].

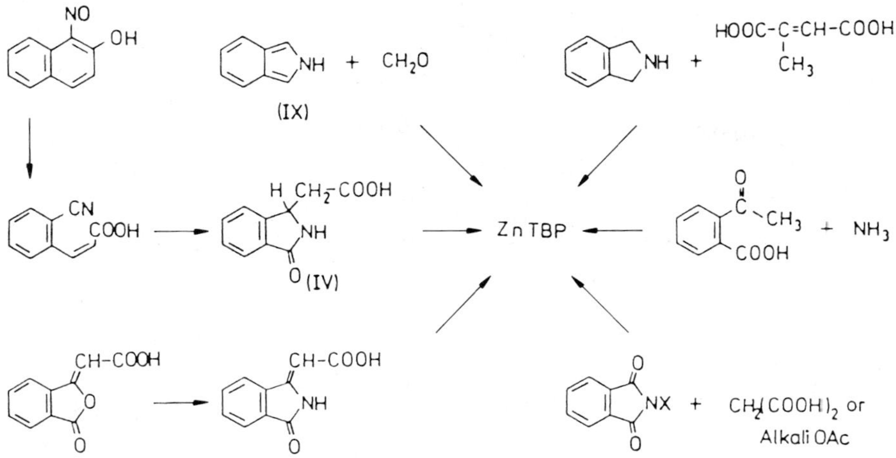

Scheme 2. Syntheses of tetrabenzoporphyrinatozinc

In tetrabenzoporphyrin the methyne bridges widen the inner macrocycle, leading in the center to a N–N-distance of 3.94 Å compared to 3.78 Å in phthalocyanine.

Tetrabenzoporphyrins are chemically and thermally also quite stable. As in case of phthalocyanines, their NMR spectra show large ring current effects. The macrocycle in TBPM can be attacked by electrophiles. Tetrabenzoporphyrinatometal complexes are more easily oxidized than the corresponding phthalocyanines [9].

Starting material for the synthesis of 2,3-naphthalocyaninatometal complexes (2,3-NcM) (Fig. 1) is 2,3-dicyanonaphthalene, which in turn is prepared in a one step reaction from α,α,α′,α′-tetrabromoorthoxylene and fumaronitrile in presence of sodium iodide [10]. The iron compound 2,3-NcFe for example is obtained when $Fe(CO)_5$ is reacted with 2,3-dicyanonaphthalene in 1-chloronaphthalene at 250 °C in the absence of air (see Scheme 3) [10].

Application of the same methods starting from 1,2-dicyanonaphthalene [11] yields 1,2-naphthalocyaninatometal complexes. The magnesium, lead, copper and zinc 1,2-naphthalocyanines (1,2-NcM) were first prepared by Linstead [12]. Compared to the corresponding phthalocyanines the known 1,2-naphthalocyaninatometal compounds exhibit a higher thermal and chemical stability. When 1,2-NcM, is synthesized from 1,2-dicyanonaphthalene four different positional isomers are formed (compare to 2,3-NcM, Fig. 1) [11].

The synthesis of the other mentioned metallomacrocycles, e.g. tetra(2,3-naphtho)porphyrinatometal complexes (2,3-TNPM) or octaethylporphyrins (OEPM), is not as straightforward.

Until recently, the only metal complex of tetra(2,3-naphtho)porphyrin was 2,3-TNPZn [13] which was synthesized starting e.g. from 3-acetyl-2-naphthoic acid [14]. The routes shown in Scheme 4 have improved the synthesis [14].

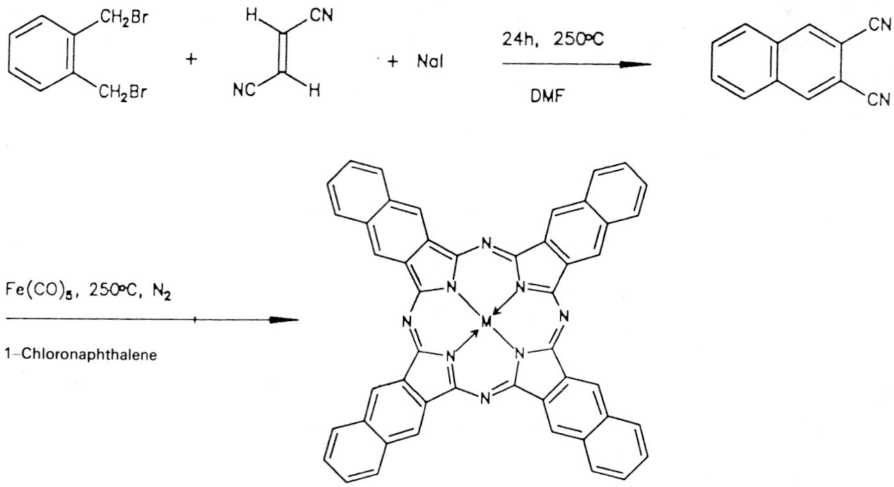

Scheme 3. Synthesis of 2,3-naphthalocyaninatoiron

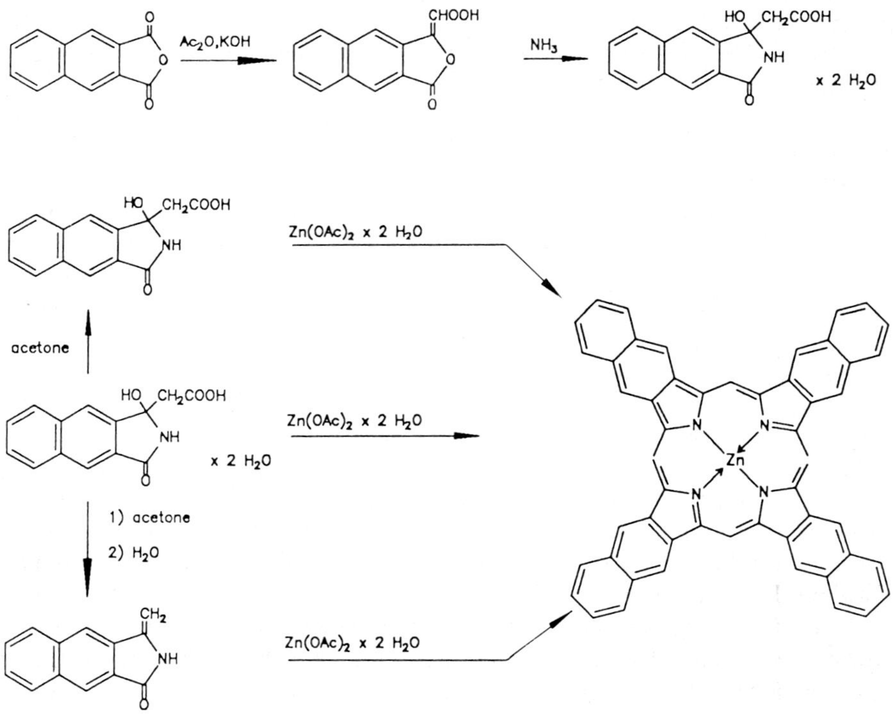

Scheme 4. Syntheses of tetra(2,3-naphthoporphyrinato)zinc (2,3-TNPZn)

2,3-$TNPH_2$ is the key-compound for the synthesis of other 2,3-TNP metal complexes, e.g. 2,3-TNPCo or 2,3-TNPFe. Contrary to $TBPH_2$, which is formed by demetallation of the zinc complex with concentrated sulfuric acid or trifluoroacetic acid, such a treatment fails to produce metal-free $TNPH_2$. The 2,3-TNP system has such a low oxidation potential that acid treatment produces solely the corresponding radical cation. However, demetallation under formation of 2,3-$TNPH_2$ becomes possible even at room temperature using trifluoromethane sulfonic acid. 2,3-TNPCo was obtained by treating 2,3-$TNPH_2$ with $Co(OAc)_2$ in boiling pyridine. 2,3-TNPFe however can be synthesized in larger yields e.g. by reacting potassium naphthalene-2,3-dicarboximide with $Fe(OAc)_2$ [14].

All of the tetra(2,3-naphtho)porphyrinatometal complexes known to date are distinguished from the other macrocycles described so far by their low oxidation potentials [14]. Cyclic voltammetry reveals that the first oxidation of the macrocycle in 2,3-TNPZn already occurs at 0.23 V. The corresponding oxidation in TBPZn or PcZn takes place at 0.47 or 0.68 V, respectively. Comparable results are found for the corresponding iron and cobalt compounds [9].

The synthesis of $OEPH_2$ is shown in Scheme 5 [15].

Hemiporphyrazine (HpH_2) is closely related to phthalocyanine (see Fig. 1). In hemiporphyrazine two of the four isoindoline units present in phthalocyanine are replaced by two pyridine rings. The synthesis which has already been reported by Linstead [16] is carried out starting from 1,3-diiminoisoindoline and 2,6-diaminopyridine or from phthalonitrile and 2,6-diaminopyridine [17]. Contrary to phthalocyanine, hemiporphyrazine is not planar [18]. In HpNi, according to the X-ray structure [19], the four nitrogen atoms which are coordinated to the nickel atom are in one plane, the isoindoline units are bent out of the plane by approximately 25° in one direction, while the pyridine units are bent in the opposite direction approximately about the same angle. Certain central metal atoms cause a flattening of the hemiporphyrazine ring system [20].

1.2 Unconventional Materials

In the following we will discuss some unconventional properties of macrocyclic metal complexes, preferentially semiconductive and liquid crystalline behavior. There are several reviews available on low-dimensional conductive compounds based on these macrocycles [21]. A detailed description of newer developments in the field of bridged macrocyclic metal complexes especially with transition metals was published recently [22]. In order to use the π-electrons in these macrocyclic systems for a conduction pathway, polymerization of the metallo-macrocycles is necessary. A polymerization can be carried out in three different ways as explained in Sections 1.2.1–1.2.3.

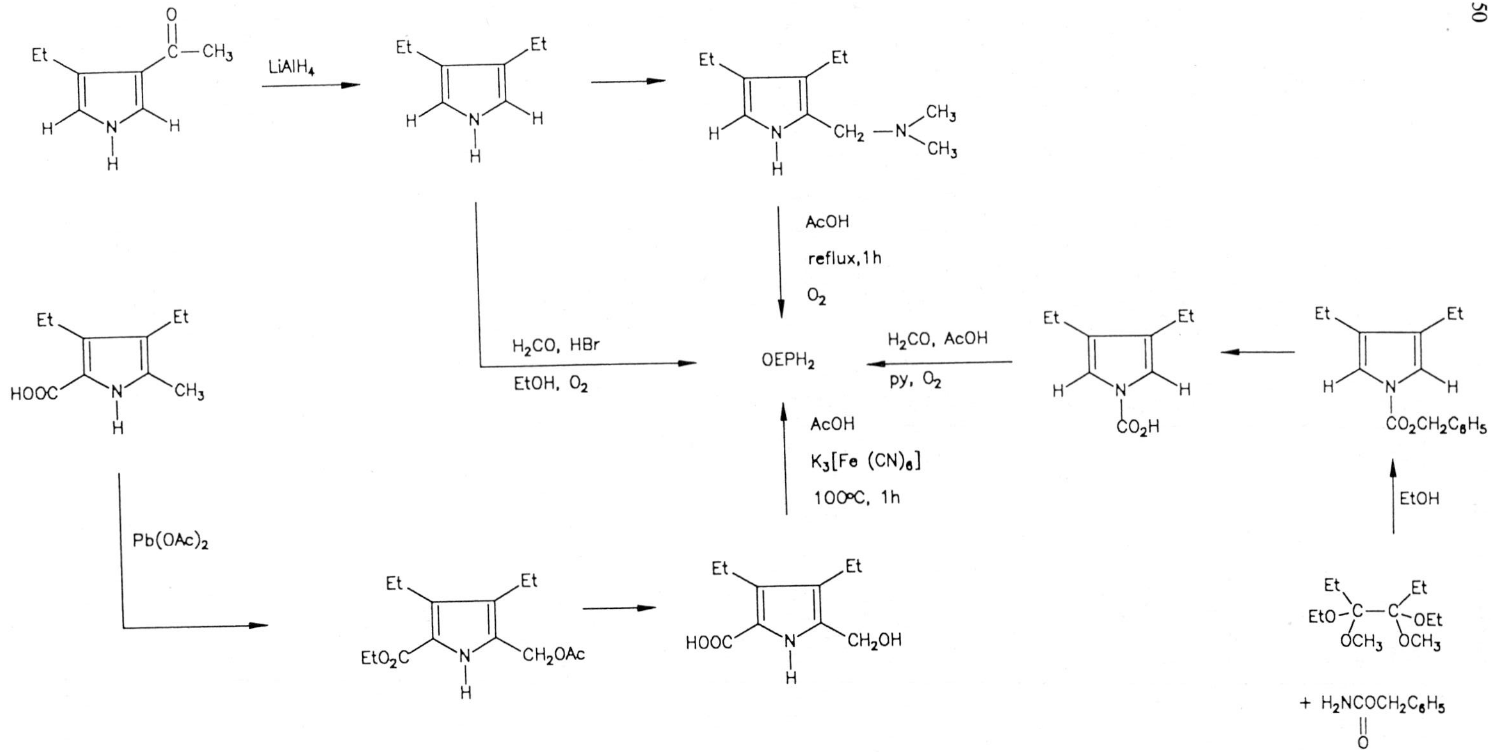

Scheme 5. Synthesis of octaethylporphyrin

1.2.1 "Stacking"

1.2.1.1 Stacking in the Solid State

First e.g. the phthalocyanine can be assembled to form either ladder polymers [23] or plane polymers [23, 24] of which poly-PcCu is mentioned [25]. The third and most interesting mode of assembling macrocyclic metal complexes is the stacked arrangement (see Fig. 3). Assuming a suitable small distance between cofacially arranged planar macrocycles having an extended π-electron system, electron delocalization by π-π-overlap of the perpendicular orbitals in the stacked arrangement should be possible. Partial oxidation (or less frequently reductive doping) of the macrocycles generates charge carriers and conducting or semiconducting quasi one-dimensional materials can be formed. In a few cases a conduction pathway can also be visualized through the central atoms of the macrocycles.

Metallomacrocycles, e.g. phthalocyaninatometal complexes or tetrabenzoporphyrins, however, only very rarely crystallize in the stacked arrangement shown in Fig. 3a. In general, the packing is different as illustrated in Fig. 3b, corresponding schematically to the above-mentioned α- or β-modifications (Fig. 2). This arrangement is not favorable for the formation of a conduction band by π-π-overlap. PcNi, TBPNi, TMPNi and OMTBPNi, for example,

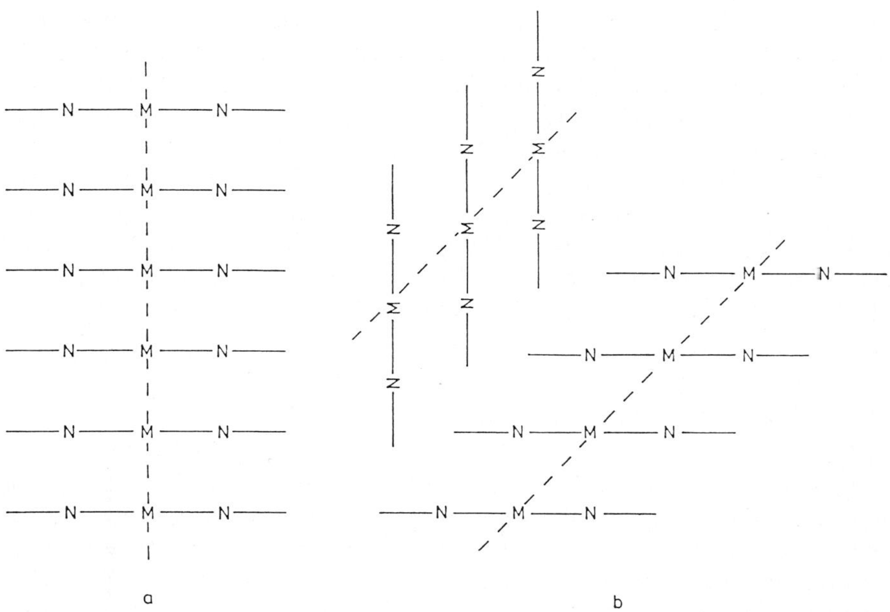

Fig. 3a, b. Stacked arrangement of metallomacrocycles (see text)

crystallize as shown in Fig. 3b. As polycrystalline samples all are insulators with conductivities $\sim 10^{-11}$ S/cm. A stacked arrangement of the metal macrocycles in the crystals as shown in Fig. 3a has only been identified for phthalocyaninatolead, PcPb, in its monoclinic modification [26] which has a room temperature conductivity of $\sim 10^{-4}$ S/cm parallel to the stacking axis [27].

Chemical or electrochemical oxidative doping processes lead to polycrystalline compounds possessing a variety of counter-ions, e.g. I^-, Br^-, quinones, nitrosyl hexafluorophosphate in a wide range of stoichiometries. Oxidative doping often results in highly increased conductivities of the polycrystalline samples. Undoped PcNi shows a conductivity of 1×10^{-11} S/cm, whereas PcNiI exhibits a conductivity of 0.7 S/cm [28]. For many doped, especially iodinated metal complexes the crystal structure is known. Depending upon the stoichiometry they form stacked structures analogous to Fig. 3a. In the stacking direction of the single crystals e.g. of PcNiX (where X = I, Br, ClO_4), TBPNiI, TMPNiI, room temperature conductivities between 40–750 S/cm are measured [28a–c, 29, 30]. As shown by a variety of physical methods the counterions formed by the oxidation process are I_3^- and rarely I_5^- which surround the stacks of the metallomacrocycles in parallel channels containing linear chains of the disordered counterions. Stacked metal complexes in general have been reviewed extensively recently [21b, 22a, 31].

1.2.1.2 Discotic Mesophases

As, with the exception of the mentioned oxidized compounds, the metallomacrocycles do not crystallize forming columnar quasi-one-dimensional structures, one of the prerequisites for conductivity is not met. In addition the stacking repeat distances and the donor–acceptor distances in doped compounds cannot be controlled in any way. By using oxidizing dopants other than halogens, e.g. quinones, integrated stacks can be formed leading to insulators.

J. Simon and co-workers recently worked out a new route to a stacked arrangement of the phthalocyanine macrocycles without using bridging ligands. Substitution with long chain substituents (e.g. $-CH_2-OC_{12}H_{25}$) in peripheral positions of the phthalocyanine ring leads to the formation of discotic mesophases and a stacked arrangement of the macrocycles (see Sect. 4).

1.2.2 "Shish-Kebab" Approach

The so-called "shish kebab" or "Schaschlik" approach allows the construction of stacked macrocyclic metal complexes such as phthalocyaninatometal complexes, metal complexes of tetrabenzoporphyrin, and octaethylporphyrin with variable distances between the planar macrocycles. The macrocycles are linked together by bisaxially metal-bonded bridging ligands thereby combining them

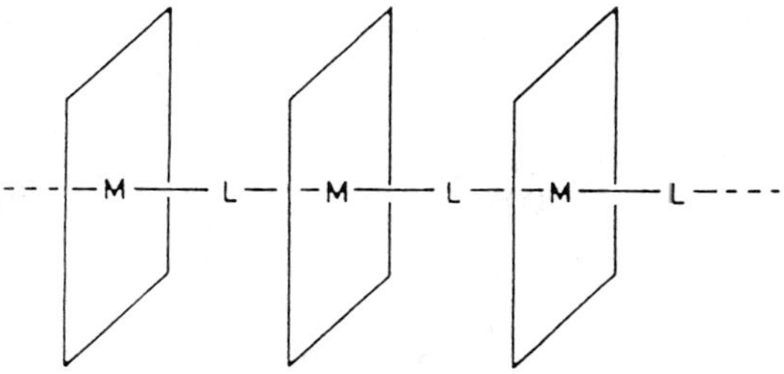

Fig. 4. Macrocyclic metal compounds bridged via ligands L

in a cofacial arrangement. A schematic drawing of such a type of bridged stacks $[MacML]_n$ (Mac = Pc, TBP, 2,3-Nc etc.) is given in Fig. 4.

By using bridging ligands L of different lengths the distance between the cofacial macrocycles can be varied systematically. Theoretical calculations (see Sect. 2) show, that depending upon the interring distances and the conformation of the macrocycles a band structure can be achieved after oxidative doping. The function of the central metal atom and of the bridging ligand L in the polymers $[MacML]_n$ has been studied in some detail. First the main group elements Si, Ge, Sn, Al and others were used as central atoms and the complexes bridged with O^{2-} and F^- (M. E. Kenney and co-workers, T. J. Marks and co-workers) (see Sect. 2). The electronic pathway in the corresponding (doped) polymers predominantly occurs by π-π-overlap of the macrocycles. The bridging ligands are not involved in the charge carrier transport mechanism. They merely build up the stacked cofacial arrangement of the macrocycles.

If, however, as central atoms transition metals preferring an octahedral configuration, and as bridging ligands linear organic molecules containing delocalizable π-electrons are used (M. Hanack and co-workers) an additional electronic pathway along the central axis of the corresponding polymers should open up, and could indeed be verified in some cases. Depending upon the bridging ligand L, these systems exhibit comparatively high semi-conducting properties even without external oxidative doping (see Sect. 3).

1.2.3 Intrinsic Semiconducting Materials

An intrinsic semiconductor is characterized by a small band gap and a low density of highly mobile intrinsic charge carriers. Electrons as well as holes contribute to the conductivity which increases with temperature. Phthalocyanine radicals such as the sandwich type Pc_2Lu or PcLi carry intrinsic charges. Their facile oxidation and reduction suggests that intrinsic conductivity should be possible. The electrical properties of these materials, especially as thin films incorporated in various devices, have been studied [32].

2 Main Group Metal Complexes

2.1 Oxo-bridged Complexes of Group 14 Elements with Macrocyclic Ligands

One of the best investigated type of cofacially joined metallomacrocycles are the polymetalloxanes $[PcMO]_n$ (M = Si, Ge, Sn), first prepared by M. E. Kenney [33] and investigated in detail by T. J. Marks and his group as well as by Kenney's group [34].

The synthesis of $[PcMO]_n$ (M = Si, Ge, Sn) is carried out starting with $PcMCl_2$ (M = Si, Ge, Sn), which is synthesized by standard procedures [31, 33, 35] (see Scheme 6). Hydrolysis of $PcMCl_2$ leads to $PcM(OH)_2$ (M = Si, Ge, Sn). The polycondensation is achieved by dehydration, either by heating $PcM(OH)_2$ in vacuo at 325–440 °C or by heating it in refluxing 1-chloronaphthalene or quinoline. A topotactic polymerization mechanism has been proposed [34f]. Random reaction of all end-groups with each other [35] has also been discussed. Dehydration in vacuo provides the highest degrees of polymerization (vide infra).

Both $[PcSiO]_n$ and $[PcGeO]_n$ have high thermal and chemical stabilities. In fact, $[PcSiO]_n$ can be dissolved in concentrated H_2SO_4 or CF_3SO_3H and is recovered without change.

Estimation of the average molecular weights for $[PcMO]_n$ (M = Si, Ge, Sn) by IR end-group analysis, tritium labeling and laser light scattering experiments

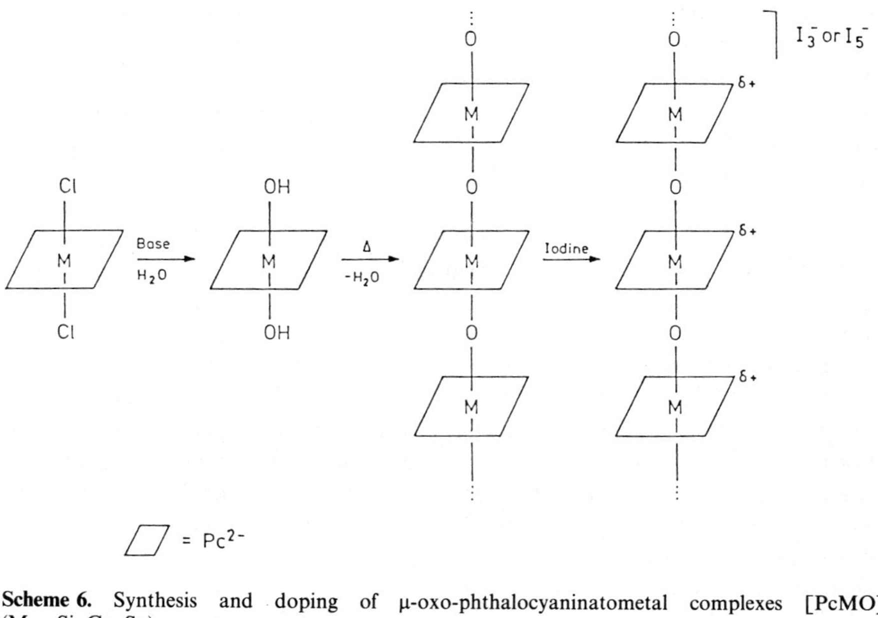

Scheme 6. Synthesis and doping of μ-oxo-phthalocyaninatometal complexes $[PcMO]_n$ (M = Si, Ge, Sn)

yields a degree of polymerization of 70–140 subunits for $[PcSiO]_n$ and somewhat lower values for $[PcGeO]_n$ and $[PcSnO]_n$. Longer polymerization times and higher temperatures seem to increase the molecular weights [34a]. Based on a model structure for $[PcMO]_n$, in analogy to the known structures of PcNiI and the isoelectronic $[PcGaF]_n$ [36] a one-dimensional stacking of the PcM^{2+} subunits, linked by O^{2-} bridges is derived from powder diffraction data by computer simulation techniques [34a]. The M–O–M distances vary from 333 pm for M = Si to 353 pm for M = Ge and 382 pm for M = Sn. The best fit of the data indicates a staggering angle of 39° for $[PcSiO]_n$ and 0° for $[PcGeO]_n$ and $[PcSnO]_n$. These data are confirmed by ^{13}C-CPMAS-NMR spectroscopy [37], electron diffraction [38], and electron transmission spectroscopy [39].

To achieve conductivity, charge carriers must be generated, either by oxidation (p-doping) or reduction (n-doping). Only very little experimental material for n-doped phthalocyanines is available [40]. The doping method used most is oxidation with iodine, which can be carried out in different ways: heterogeneous with iodine vapor (gas phase/solid), by treatment with iodine solutions (liquid/solid) or by grinding of both components (solid/solid). Soluble materials can be doped homogeneously with iodine solutions.

Partial oxidation (doping) of $[PcMO]_n$ (M = Si, Ge) was achieved in addition to iodine with a wide range of other electron acceptors, e.g. chlorine, bromine, quinones and nitrosyl compounds [41] or by electrochemical methods [35, 41e]. Oxidation leads to well-defined, air stable, conducting polymers of thermal stability up to 120 °C. The best investigated compounds are doped with iodine leading to stoichiometries $[(PcMO)I_y]_n$ (M = Si, Ge) with an y_{max} of about 1.1, which represents a degree of maximum partial oxidation of 1/3. As in the case of iodine doping of MacNi, iodine is thereby reduced to I_3^- or I_5^-. This is proved by resonance Raman spectroscopy and ^{129}I-Mößbauer studies. Chains of iodine counterions are disordered in channels parallel to the c-axis. Increasing the interring distance leads to the formation of I_5^- counterions [34b]. Doping of $[PcSnO]_n$ leads to destruction of the polymeric structure [42]. Electrochemical oxidation using counterions such as BF_4^- or ClO_4^- leads to little higher conductivities so far [35].

^{13}C [37b] as well as ^{15}N [37c] solid state NMR spectroscopy were used to investigate local architecture and electronic structure in phthalocyanine based molecular metals. For the partially oxidized materials, large, locally resolved conduction electron knight shifts with dispersions as large as 400 ppm and multiplicities in accord with crystallographic site symmetries are observed in the ^{13}C spectra [37b]. Similarly ^{15}N knight shifts can be observed [37c].

Analysis of powder diffraction data of $[(PcMO)I_y]_n$ (M = Si, Ge) in comparison with the model compound PcNiI points to similarities with this compound. In all cases a staggered arrangement of the metallomacrocycles (staggering angle 39–40°) and parallel chains of I_3^- counterions (disordered along the c-axis) are evident. Doping also leads to a decrease in interring distances of 3–5 pm [34b].

The room temperature conductivities of polycrystalline samples of $[(PcMO)I_y]_n$ (M = Si, Ge) for various stoichiometries are given in Table 1. The nature of the dopant e.g. bromine, iodine, quinones etc. has no significant effect on the conductivities [34b, 41b, 41d].

Voltage shortened compaction measurements indicate a "metal-like" charge transport behaviour in polycrystalline $[(PcSiO)I_y]_n$ samples, and this is supported by optical reflectance spectra, showing a plasma-like edge [34b]. Analysis using a Drude model yields conductivity values, which indicate a conductivity along the stacking axis being in the order of 10^2–10^3 S/cm at room temperature [41d]. Single crystal data are not available for lack of crystals of suitable size.

The main charge transport pathway in $[PcSiO]_n$ is via the phthalocyanine π-system. This is proved by photoelectron spectra of a dinuclear unit R_3Si–O(SiPc)–O–(SiPc)–O–SiR_3 [34d, 34h]. Its crystal structure is in good agreement with the results given for $[PcSiO]_n$ [34b, 34d].

For the explanation of conductivity in stacked phthalocyanine systems, extended Hückel band calculations were carried out [43], but vastly truncated phthalocyanine models were utilized. The bandwidths obtained were at considerable variance with experimental results. The experimentally found correlation between interring distance, staggering angle and room temperature conductivity has been explained by these calculations [43a]. Other charge transport mechanisms, e.g. percolation theory and fluctuation induced carrier tunneling through potential barriers separating metallic regions, have also been discussed [43c].

It is possible to compound $[PcSiO]_n$ with polymers, e.g. kevlar, in CF_3SO_3H solution and to produce wet spun fibres. These fibres show, after doping, conductivities of up to 2 S/cm [44].

Sulphur was used in $[PcGeS]_n$ as bridging ligand, but the Ge–S bond is cleaved on doping [45]. The undoped polymer however shows photoconductivity [46].

The reaction of the dihydroxides $PcSi(OH)_2$, $HpGe(OH)_2$, $TPPGe(OH)_2$, $TPPSn(OH)_2$ or $HpSn(OH)_2$ with diols leads to the corresponding polymers, but the increased interring distance prohibits conductivity [47].

2.1.1 *Peripherally Substituted Phthalocyanines*

The presence of bulky substituents in the periphery of the phthalocyanine ring systems raises their solubilities in common organic solvents drastically. The synthesis of the peripherally alkylated μ-oxo-polymers $[R_4PcMO]_n$, (R = *t*-bu, tms; M = Si, Ge, Sn) were carried out according to Scheme 7 [48].

The polymeric μ-oxo(tetraalkylphthalocyaninato)metal group 14 derivatives are accessible via thermal condensation of the corresponding monomeric $R_4PcM(OH)_2$ (M = Si, Ge, Sn) compounds in high vacuum or in high boiling solvents, e.g. 1-chloronaphthalene or quinoline. The dihydroxides $R_4PcM(OH)_2$ (M = Si, Ge, Sn; R = *t*-bu, tms) were obtained by alkaline hydrolysis of the corresponding dihalogen compounds. R_4PcMCl_2 (M = Si, Ge) were synthesized

Table 1. Room temperature electrical conductivity data (powder, 1 kbar) of doped and nondoped μ-oxo-phthalocyaninatometal(IV) compounds $[PcMO]_n$

Compound	y	Conductivity [S/cm]	Activation Energy [eV]	Interring Distance [pm]
$[PcSiOI_y]_n$	0	5.5×10^{-6}	0.29	333
	1.1	6.7×10^{-1}	0.0089	330
$[PcGeOI_y]_n$	0	2.2×10^{-10}		353
	1.1	1.1×10^{-1}	0.034	348
$[PcSnOI_y]_n$	0	1.2×10^{-9}		387
	1.1	2.2×10^{-6}	1.08	

by reacting the corresponding metal halides with the substituted phthalocyanine precursors [48].

Symmetry considerations reveal that the dihalides R_4PcMCl_2 should be isolated as a mixture of structural isomers with respect to the position of the alkyl groups. Attempts to separate these mixtures by routine column chromatography have not yet been successful. The chain length of $[R_4PcSiO]_n$ was estimated by infrared end group analysis (based on the OH-stretching vibration as the end group sensitive to absorption) to have a minimum average value of $n = 10$. More accurate data were obtained via tritium labeling techniques, which indicated a degree of oligomerization of $n = 25$ [49].

The undoped materials show electrical conductivities which are similar to those of the peripheral unsubstituted $[PcMO]_n$ (M = Si, Ge, Sn) (see Table 2). The somewhat lower conductivities measured for $[R_4PcMO]_n$ (M = Si, Ge, Sn) are associated with the brittleness of the material, which prevents the compression of the pellets.

The doped polymer $[(R_4PcSiO)I_y]_n$ is thermally stable up to 140 °C. Above this temperature a smooth loss of the doping agent occurs, which is finished at about 380 °C. The residue is pure $[R_4PcSiO]_n$.

Doping of the tin polymer with iodine vapor leads to destruction of the polymeric structure [42]. Independently of the doping procedure all silicon and germanium samples $[R_4PcMO]_n$ exhibit the characteristic features reported for the conducting $[(PcSiO)I_y]_n$ materials. The infrared spectra of the doped materials are superimposed by electronic absorptions. In the case of $[R_4PcSiO]_n$ the nature of the partially oxidized state was investigated by ESR spectroscopy, which supported a ligand centered oxidation process [48].

The conductivities of the polymers $[R_4PcMO]_n$ (see Table 2) reach limiting values of 10^{-3} S/cm and show no significant variation with the doping procedure. This suggests that the measured conductivities are limited by macroscopic properties (e.g. grain boundaries) and not by the doping method.

Additional substituted μ-oxo-phthalocyaninatosilicon compounds are discussed in Sect. 4.

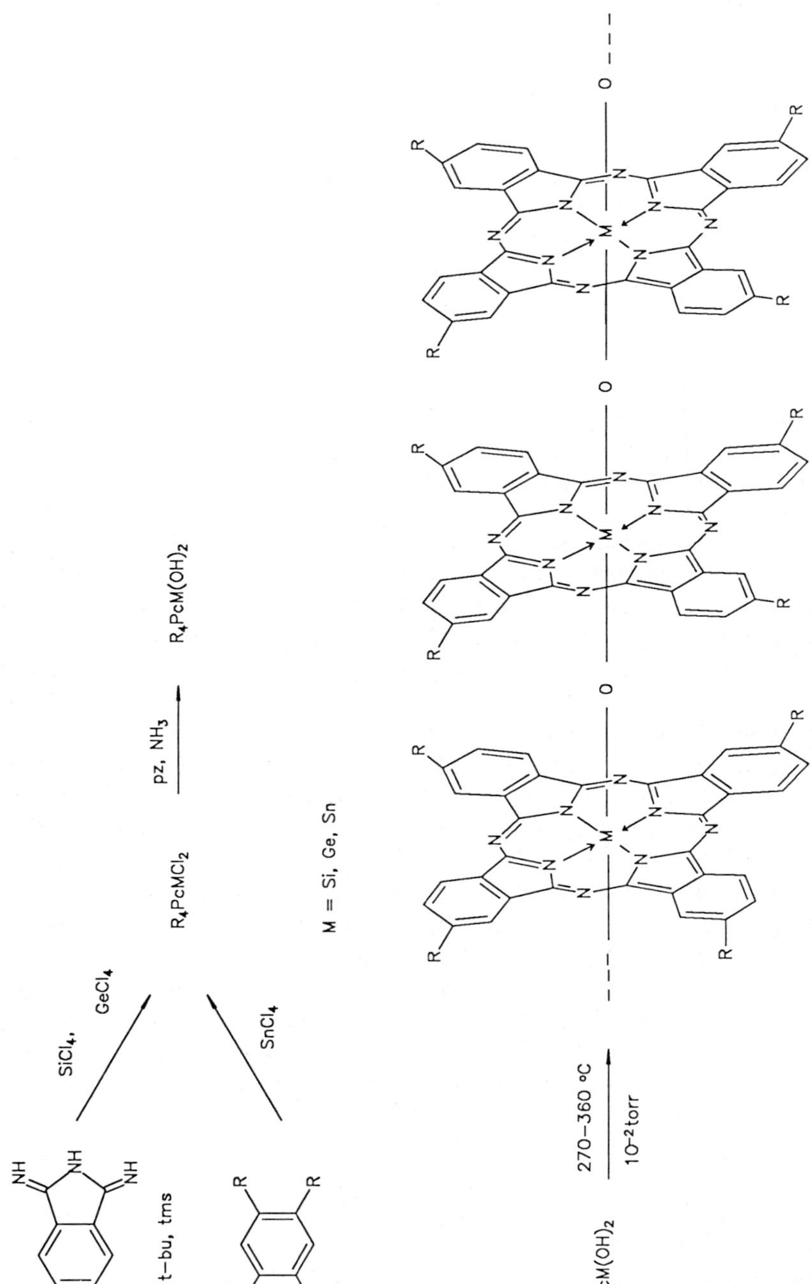

Scheme 7. Peripherally substituted μ-oxo-phthalocyaninatometal complexes $(R_4PcMO)_n$

Table 2. Room temperature electrical conductivity data (powder, 1 kbar) of doped and nondoped μ-oxo-tetrabutylphthalocyaninatometal(IV) compounds $[t\text{-bu}_4\text{PcMO}]_n$ [48].

Compound	y	Conductivity [S/cm]
$[t\text{-bu}_4\text{PcSiOI}_y]_n$	0	8×10^{-8}
	2.0	2×10^{-3}
$[t\text{-bu}_4\text{PcGeOI}_y]_n$	0	6×10^{-11}
	1.9	1×10^{-3}
$[t\text{-bu}_4\text{PcSnOI}_y]_n$	0	4×10^{-12}
	2.0	10^{-6}

2.1.2 Other Macrocyclic Ligands

For a better understanding of the charge carrier mechanisms, it was of interest to extend investigations to systems containing other than phthalocyaninato-macrocycles.

The use of hemiporphyrazine (HpH_2) and tetraphenylporphyrin ($TPPH_2$) for compounds $[\text{MacMO}]_n$ (M = Si, Ge, Sn) is reported [47a, 50]. The hemiporphyrazine compounds can be oxidized, but no significant increase in electrical conductivity is observed (see Table 3). It appears, that iodination is accompanied by destruction of the M–O–M framework [50a]. The 2,3-naphthalocyanine (2,3-Nc) compound $[2{,}3\text{-NcSiO}]_n$ was synthesized, the doped material is described as a "good conductor" [51].

Tetrabenzoporphyrin ($TBPH_2$) as macrocyclic ligand has also been investigated. According to SCF calculations, the TBP radical cation has a larger bandwidth for the free electron in comparison with phthalocyanine [52a]. $[\text{TBPGeO}]_n$ was synthesized as shown in Scheme 8. The compound is of the same type as $[\text{PcGeO}]_n$ with an interring distance of 346 pm as calculated by X-ray powder diffraction data [52b]. The conductivity of the doped material is in the same range as for the analogous phthalocyanine compound (see Table 1). This is in accordance with MO considerations, since the MO mainly responsible for charge carrier properties possesses nodes at the four aza-bridged positions in

Table 3. Room temperature electrical conductivity data (powder, 1 kbar) of doped and nondoped μ-oxo-hemiporphyrazinato- and tetrabenzoporphyrinatometal complexes

Compound	y	Conductivity [S/cm]	Activation Energy [eV]
$[\text{HpMOI}_y]_n$ M = Si, Ge, Sn	0–1.5[a]	1×10^{-12}–1×10^{-10}	
$[\text{TBPGeOI}_y]_n$	0	1×10^{-6}	
	0.75	5×10^{-2}	0.07

[a] Degree of doping not given in Ref. 50a

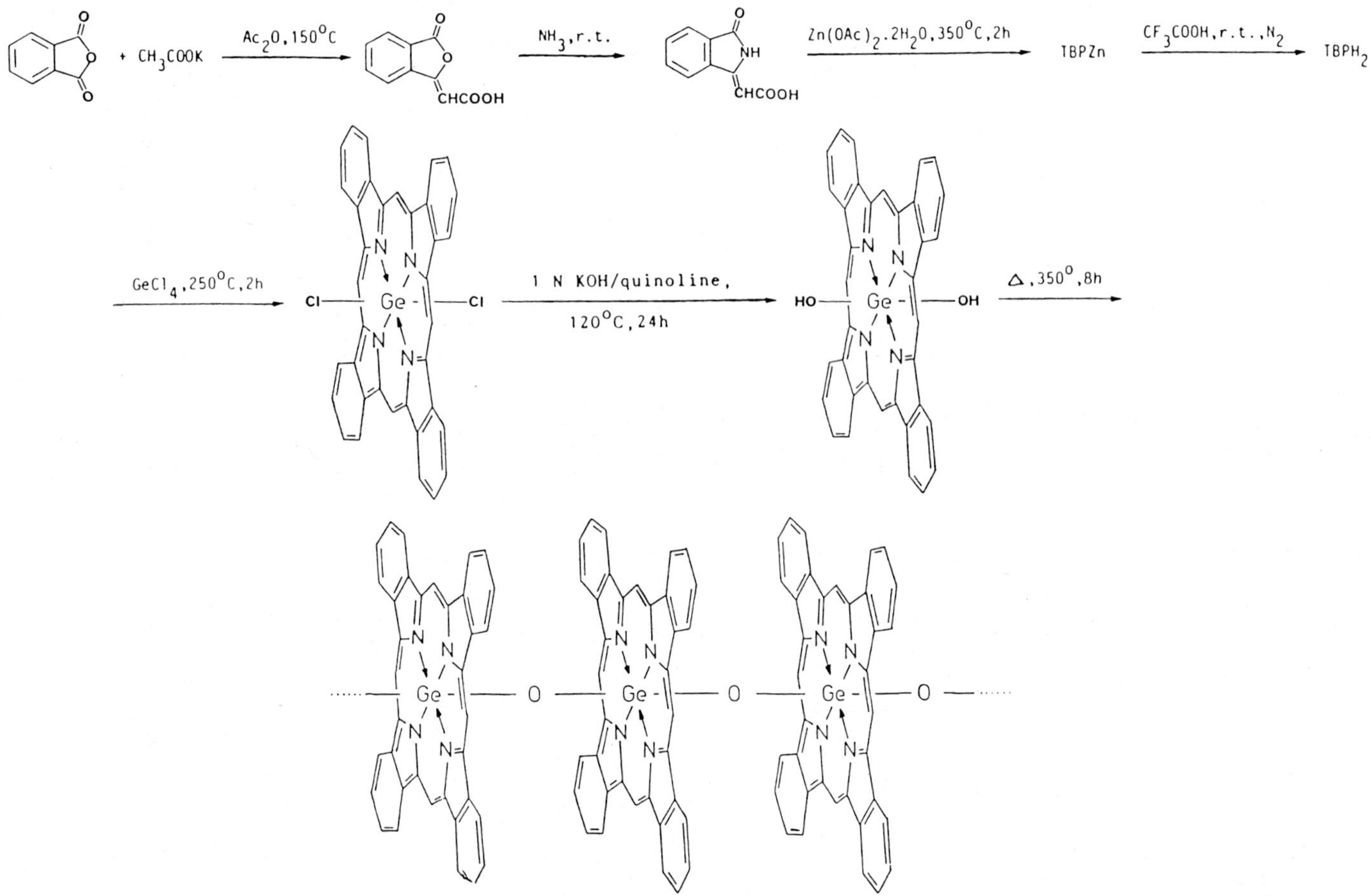

Scheme 8. Synthesis of μ-oxo-tetrabenzoporphyrinatogermanium(IV) $[TBPGeO]_n$

phthalocyanine [52], and therefore no effect should be seen substituting these nitrogens by methyne bridges in phthalocyanine.

The synthesis of a mixed system $[TBPGeOPcGeO]_n$ containing phthalocyaninatogermanium- (PcGe) and tetrabenzoporphyrinatogermanium (TBPGe) subunits in the same chain, linked by oxygen bridges, was reported recently [53]. Iodine doping gave $[TBPcGeOI_{1.1}]_n$ at the maximum doping level. A room temperature DC conductivity $\sigma_{RT} = 8 \times 10^{-2}$ S/cm was measured which lies between the conductivities of the maximally iodine doped unmixed polymers $[PcGeO]_n$ ($\sigma_{RT} = 0.1$ S/cm) and $[TBPGeO]_n$ ($\sigma_{RT} = 3 \times 10^{-2}$ S/cm) [53].

2.1.3 *μ-Oxo-Hemiporphyrazinatoiron*

An example for an oxo-bridged transition metal complex is hemiporphyrazinatoiron $[HpFeO]_n$, of which the structure has been determined (see Fig. 5). The compound crystallizes in space group P 2/n. Distorted hemiporphyrazinatoiron units stack along the b-axis and are linked into polymeric, uniformly spaced, linear chains by axially bound oxygen bridges. Doping does not lead to an increase in conductivity [54].

2.2 *Fluoro-bridged Phthalocyaninatometal Complexes*

Stacks of bridged fluorophthalocyaninatometal complexes $[PcMF]_n$ with M=Al, Ga, Cr were first prepared by M. E. Kenney et al. [55]. For the preparation e.g. PcAlCl and PcGaCl are converted into PcMOH (M=Al, Ga) which reacts with conc. HF to form $[PcMF]_n$ (M=Al, Ga) (Scheme 9).

For further purification $[PcMF]_n$ (M=Al, Ga) can be sublimed in vacuo [36, 55b, 55c]. $[PcGaF]_n$ crystallizes in stacks of nearly eclipsed macrocycles

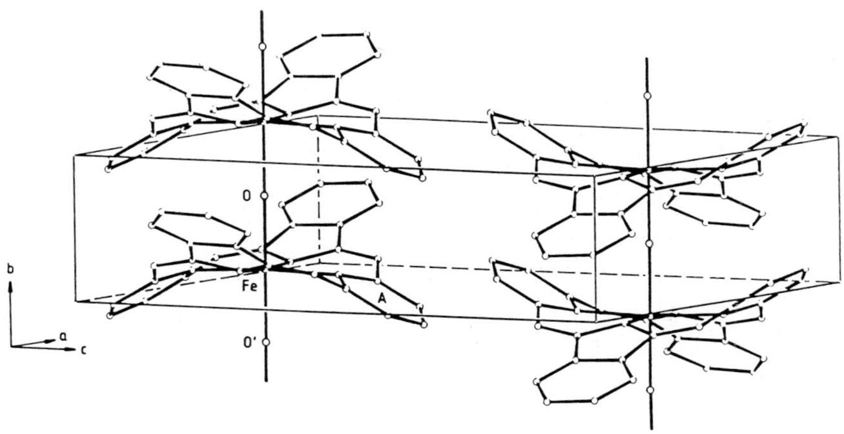

Fig. 5. Unit cell of μ-oxo-hemiporphyrazinatoiron(IV), $(HpFeO)_n$

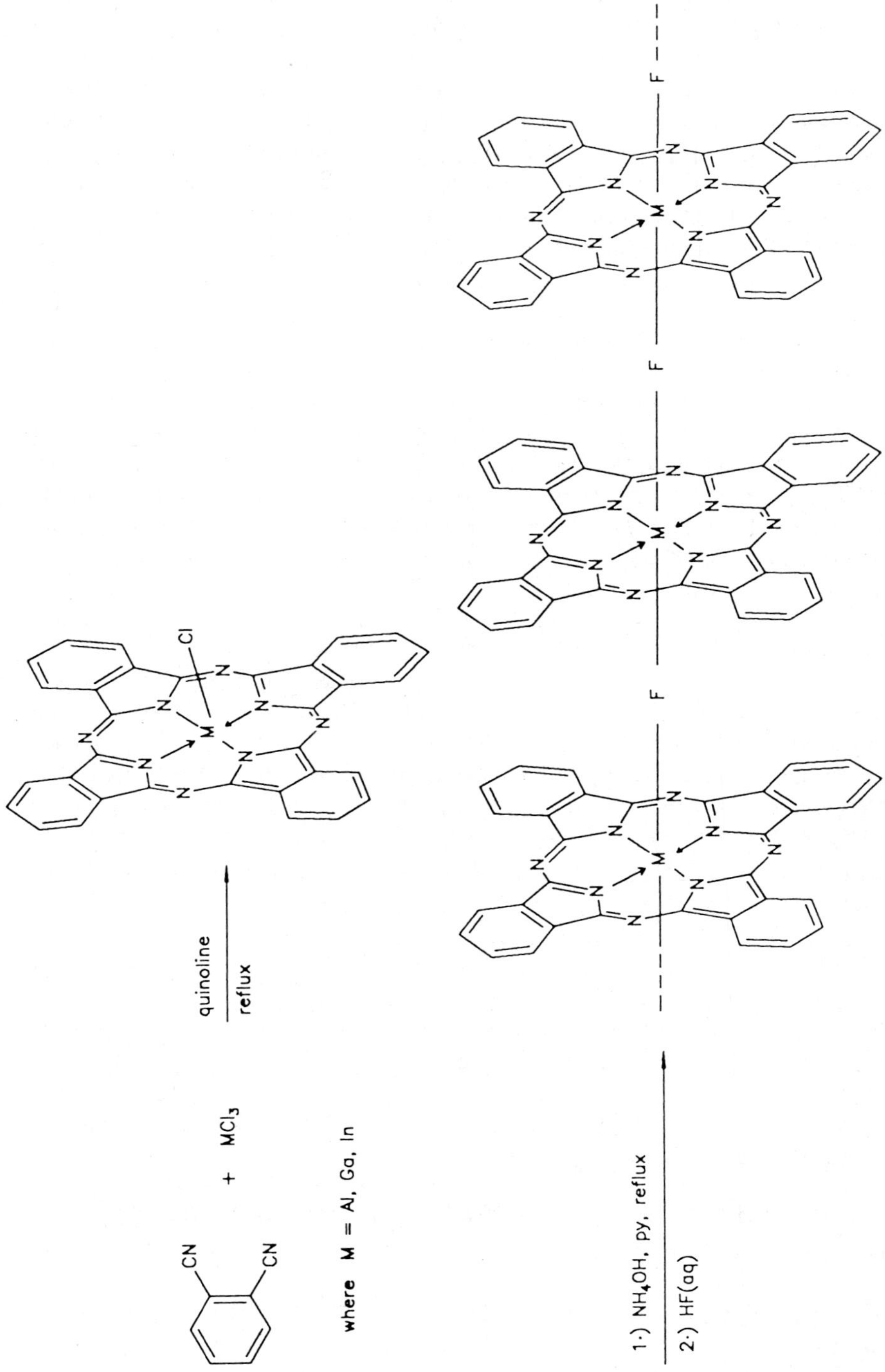

Scheme 9. Synthesis of μ-fluorophthalocyaninatometal(III) $[PcMF]_n$

connected by linear Ga–F–Ga bridges with interplanar distances of 387 pm, as shown by single crystal X-ray analysis [55d, 55e].

All known $[PcMF]_n$-compounds (M = Al, Ga, Cr) can be doped with iodine to yield $[(PcMF)I_y]_n$, where y, depending on M, rises from 0.012 to 3.3 The doped systems contain I_3^- and I_5^- as counterions [55c]. The conductivities of $[(PcMF)I_y]_n$ (M = Ga, Al) rise with increasing iodine content, the highest conductivity being observed for $[(PcAlF)I_{3.3}]_n$ (σ_{RT} = 5 S/cm, activation energy E_a = 0.017 ev) which was prepared from sublimed $[PcAlF]_n$. The higher conductivities at the highest doping level for the Al- versus the Ga-compounds correspond to the greater inter-planar distances for the Ga-compound [55b]. The shorter distances in the Al-compound allow the establishment of a better conductive pathway through interring π-orbital overlap. In general the $[(PcMF)I_y]_n$ (M = Al, Ga) materials have lower thermal stabilities with regard to loss of iodine, compared to $[(PcSiO)I_y]_n$. $[PcMF]_n$ with M = Al, Ga were also oxidized with nitrosyl salts e.g. $NO^+BF_4^-$ to give $[(PcMF)(BF_4)_y]_n$. The conductivities were in the range of 0.3 S/cm [55f].

Thin layers of $[PcAlF]_n$ prepared by sublimation can be reversibly doped and dedoped by I_2/N_2, showing an increase in conductivity of about one order in magnitude [56a]. Due to steric reasons doping of $[PcAlF]_n$ with AsF_5 leads to a rotation of the eclipsed PcAl rings to a staggered conformation. Thus, lower conductivities (10^{-5} S/cm) [56b] in comparison with iodine-doped $[PcAlF]_n$ are observed.

Recently a fluoroaluminium 2,3-naphthalocyanine ($[2,3\text{-}NcAlF]_n$) was prepared. The undoped compound has a conductivity of 3×10^{-3} S/cm [57]. With the help of EXAFS spectroscopy it was possible to demonstrate that fluoro-octamethylporphyrinatogallium(III) forms a bridged structure $[OMPGaF]_n$ [58a]. As chemical doping (e.g. I_2) of $[OMPGaF]_n$ does not yield suitable single crystals for X-ray investigations, electrochemical oxidation of OEPGaF was carried out in a toluene/acetonitrile mixture in the presence of $(n\text{-bu})_4NBF_4$ [58b]. Electrocrystallization afforded single crystals composed of the paramagnetic trinuclear $[OEPGa]_3F_2(BF_4)_2 \cdot C_7H_8$. The two fluorine atoms form a slightly bent bridge between the three macrocycles. The BF_4^- counterions are situated between the trinuclear stacks while the solvating toluene molecules are located on the terminal ends of each stack. Terminal fluorine atoms are missing due to steric hindrance of the OEP rings whereby polymerization cannot take place. Since the large interring distance and the staggered ring conformation reduce π-orbital overlap only very small conductivity values are found.

2.3 *Monomeric and Alkynyl Bridged Phthalocyaninato Element-14 Compounds*

Besides phthalocyaninatometal complexes $[PcMO]_n$, $[PcMF]_n$, and $[PcMS]_n$ in which stacking is warranted by bridging ligands, complexes with macrocyclic and covalently linked alkynyl ligands have been prepared. Though there was

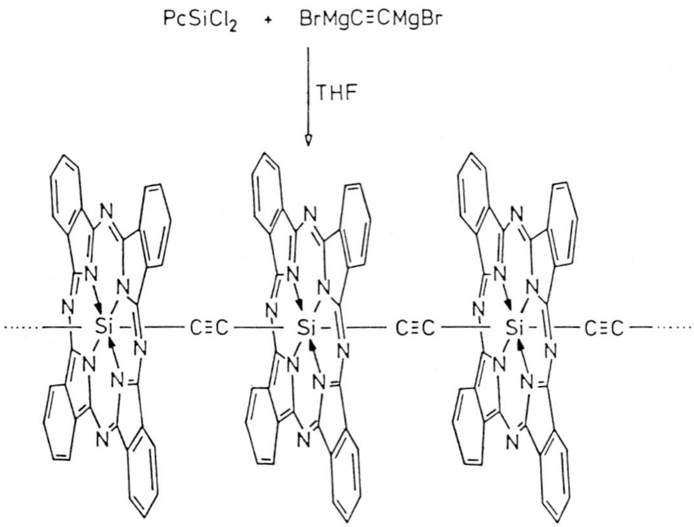

Scheme 10. Synthesis of μ-ethynyl-phthalocyaninatosilicon(IV) $[PcSiC{\equiv}C]_n$

little information available about metal–carbon bonds in phthalocyaninato-metal complexes [59] μ-ethynylphthalocyaninatosilicon $[PcSiC{\equiv}C]_n$ was obtained in nearly quantitative yield by reacting $PcSiCl_2$ with bisbromo-magnesiumacetylene as Grignard reagent (see Scheme 10) [60].

A further bridging ligand, the carbodiimide dianion NCN^{2-} can be used to form a bridged phthalocyaninato group 14 metal complex. Thus, the (carbo-diimido) compound $[PcGeNCN]_n$ was synthesized by thermal reaction of its corresponding monomeric bis(carbodiimido)phthalocyaninatogermanium(IV), $PcGe(NCNH)_2$ [61]. The $[PcGeNCN]_n$ system has been doped with iodine leading to the stable iodine containing compound $[PcGe(NCN)I_{2.1}]_n$ with an enhanced electrical conductivity of 2×10^{-3} S/cm.

3 Bridged Transition Metal Complexes with Macrocyclic Ligands

As already mentioned above, an electronic pathway can be visualized by using transition metal macrocycles in combination with bridging ligands which allow electron migration along the central axis [62]. The π-electron containing bridging ligand L must be linear, or at least forming a sufficiently small M–L–M angle, thereby retaining the quasi one-dimensional arrangement of the bridged system.

The bridging ligand may be a bifunctional organic donor molecule such as pyrazine (pyz), bipyridine (bpy), *p*-diisocyanobenzene (*p*-dib), substituted diisocyanobenzene (dib) e.g. me_4dib, cyanide (CN^-) or thiocyanate (SCN^-). In all cases the interplanar distances of the macrocycles having transition metals as central atoms are larger in comparison with the oxo- or fluoro-bridged compounds discussed in Sects. 2.1.1, 2.1.2, thereby excluding a π-π-overlap of the macrocycles.

The central metal atom of the macrocycle must be a transition metal which prefers an octahedral coordination e.g. Fe, Ru, Co, Rh, Mn or Cr, and which is able to coordinate two bridging ligands in the axial positions.

These metal complexes of macrocyclic ligands can formally be classified according to the oxidation state of the central transition metal atom which can be either + 2 or + 3. The M^{II}-complexes can be axially linked with neutral ligands L like pyz, tz (tetrazine), dib, etc. leading to neutral polymers of an "unsaturated", pentacoordinate fragment MacML (see Fig. 6a). If the central transition metal is in oxidation state + 3, the bridging ligand L can be e.g. CN^-, SCN^-, N_3^- also yielding neutral bridged systems without an external counterion (see Fig. 6b).

The structural variety of these types of transition metal complexes provides an interesting possibility to study systematically the physical properties of such compounds and to develop new semiconducting and conducting materials.

For this purpose a large number of structurally similar, but chemically different complexes have been synthesized [22].

3.1 Complexes with Divalent Metal Ions

3.1.1 Pyrazine and Related Compounds as Bridging Ligands

Linking metallomacrocycles with linear bidentate bridging ligands presumes a detailed knowledge of the coordination behaviour of the employed ligands. Therefore, first a series of mononuclear $PcFeL_2$ adducts with L = pyrazine (pyz) (see Fig. 7), 2-methylpyrazine (mepyz), 2,6-dimethylpyrazine (me_2pyz), 2-ethylpyrazine (etpyz) and 2-chloropyrazine (Clpyz) was synthesized by stirring PcFe in the pure liquid ligand at elevated temperatures [63].

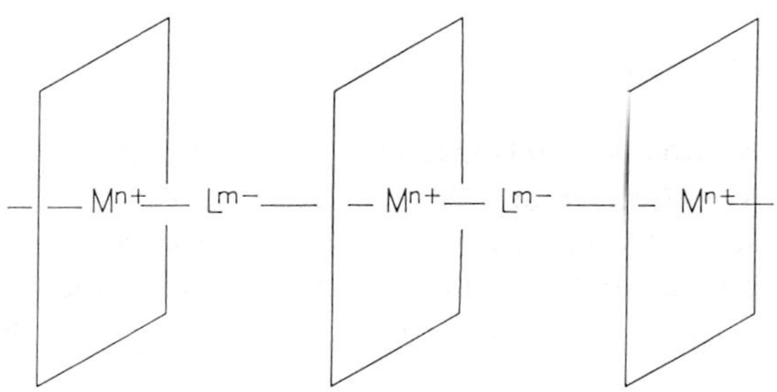

Fig. 6. Different types of neutral polymers: a) n = +2, m = 0, b) n = 3, m = 1

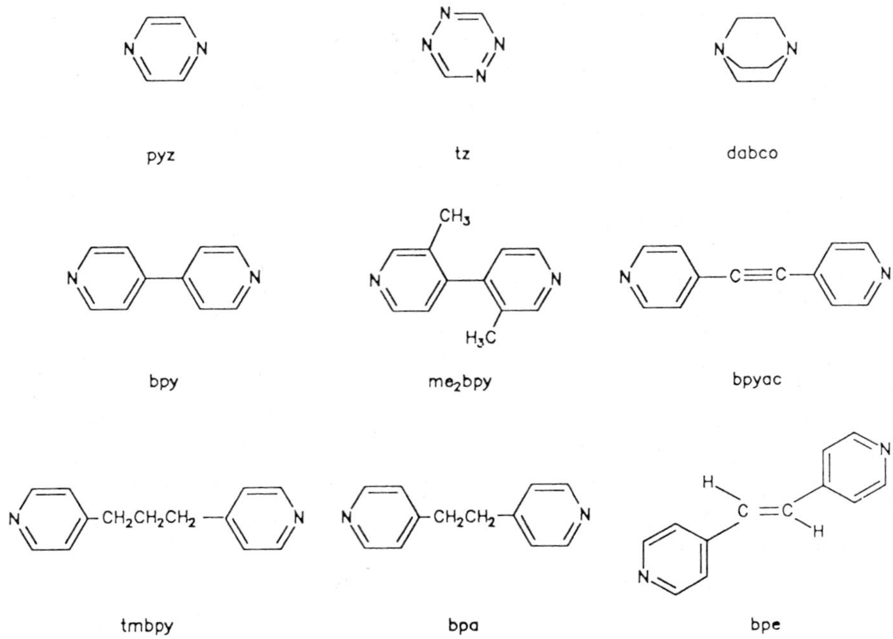

Fig. 7. Selected bidentate bridging ligands

The prepared materials were examined for their stoichiometry by combined TG/DTA measurements, by ^{1}H-NMR spectroscopy and ^{57}Fe Mößbauer spectroscopy. The results show that all adducts have a PcFe:L ratio of 1:2 (see Tables 4–6) [14, 63–74].

The adducts $PcFeL_2$ with L = substituted pyrazines are sufficiently soluble for an investigation by ^{1}H-NMR spectroscopy [63c]. As in the case of other macrocyclic compounds (PcZn, $PcLi_2$) [67] the phthalocyaninato ring protons of $PcFeL_2$ appear as an AA′BB′ pattern at low field, whereas the Pc ring current shifts the proton signals of the axially coordinated pyrazines to higher fields with respect to the non-coordinated ligands. The obtained ^{1}H-NMR spectra show, that only the sterically unhindered nitrogen atom of the substituted pyrazines coordinate to the central metal atom.

^{57}Fe Mößbauer spectroscopy also confirms the hexacoordination of the iron atom. Table 6 [68–74] summarizes the Mößbauer data for some of the synthesized complexes.

Both isomer shifts and quadrupole splittings are lowered with respect to PcFe and comparable to values reported for complexes $PcFeL_2$ with L = substituted pyridines [75]. They confirm the low spin octahedral Fe^{II} environment.

Due to the steric hindrance, substituted pyrazines have so far failed to produce bridged iron complexes. $[PcFe(pyz)]_n$ however is easily obtained either by suspending PcFe in a boiling solution of pyz in chlorobenzene or by cleaving

Table 4. TG/DTA data[a] of mononuclear and polynuclear base adducts of phthalocyaninato-complexes, $PcML_2$ or $[PcM(pyz)]_n$ (M = Fe, Ru)

Compound	Dissociation range of base by TG (°C)	Mass loss% Calc.	Found	T_{max} (endothermic) from DTA signal (°C)	Ref.
$PcFe(pyz)_2$	160–245	22.0	21.6	240	[63]
$PcFe(mepyz)_2$	170–230	24.9	24.4	225	[63]
$PcFe(me_2pyz)_2$	170–245	27.6	27.2	240	[63]
$PcFe(etpyz)_2$	145–215	27.6	26.6	210	[63]
$PcFe(Clpyz)_2$	145–200	28.7	27.7	195	[63]
$[PcFe(pyz)]_n$	240–310	12.4	12.5	295	[63]
$PcRu(pyz)_2$[b]	255–305/330–560	20.7	20.0	285/540	[64]
$[PcRu(pyz)]_n$	330–560	11.5	10.9	540	[64]

[a] Simultaneous TG/DTA measurement under nitrogen (20 ml min^{-1}), heating rate 2 K min^{-1};
[b] The base molecules are split off in two well-resolved steps

Table 5. ^{1}H-NMR Spectroscopic data of phthalocyaninatometal bisligand complexes $PcML_2$ (M = Fe, Ru and L = pyz, substituted pyrazines, 1,2,4,5-tetrazine and dabco [64,65,66])[a, b]

Compound	H[c]	H[c]	H[c]	R[c]	H^1;H^2 [d]
$PcRu(pyz)_2$	2.35 [4]**m**(3)	6.43 [4]**m**(3)			9.20; 7.90 [8]; [8]
$PcRu(mepyz)_2$	2.15 [2]**d**(3)	6.30 [2]**d**(3)	2.17 [2]**s**	1.09 [6]**s**	9.19; 7.93 [8]; [8]
$PcFe(mepyz)_2$	1.92 [2]**d**(3)	6.01 [2]**d**(3)	1.94 [2]**s**	0.95 [6]**s**	9.35; 8.00 [8]; [8]
$PcRu(etpyz)_2$	2.20 [2]**d**(3)	6.29 [2]**d**(3)	2.17 [2]**s**	1.35 [4]**q**(7.5) 0.13 [6]**t**(7.5)	9.20; 7.93 [8]; [8]
$PcFe(etpyz)_2$	1.96 [2]**d**(3)	6.03 [2]**d**(3)	1.94 [2]**s**	1.23 [4]**q**(7.5) 0.03 [6]**t**(7.5)	9.35; 8.00 [8]; [8]
$PcRu(dabco)_2$	− 2.43 [12]**t**(7.35)	0.68 [12]**t**(7.35)			9.16; 7.91 [8]; [8]
$PcRu(tz)_2$	3.79 [2]**d**(2.64)	7.69 [2]**d**(2.64)			9.29; 8.04 [8]; [8]

[a] Chemical shifts in ppm with $CHCl_3$ (7.24) as internal standard;
[b] Coupling constants (Hz) are in parentheses and the number of protons is given in square brackets
[c] Signals of axial ligand L, where R = me, et
[d] Signals of eqûatorial ligand Pc

pyrazine from $PcFe(pyz)_2$ in solvents like chloroform, benzene or chlorobenzene. The stoichiometric ratio PcFe : pyz = 1 : 1 can be confirmed by thermal analysis and by IR spectroscopy. The combined TG/DTA measurement also shows that $[PcFe(pyz)]_n$ is thermally more stable than the monomeric $PcFe(pyz)_2$ (Table 4).

Table 6. ^{57}Fe-Mößbauer data of phthalocyaninato- and 2,3-naphthalocyaninatoiron(II) complexes with pyrazine, substituted pyrazines, 4,4′-bipyridine, *trans*-1,2-bis(4-pyridyl)-ethylene, 1,2-bis(4-pyridyl)ethane, 4,4′-trimethylene bipyridine and tetrazine as axial ligands (T = 298 K)

Complex	δ (mm s^{-1})[a]	ΔE_Q (mm s^{-1})[a]	Ref.
PcFe	0.634[b]	2.581	[68]
2,3-NcFe	0.36[c]	2.21	[69]
2,3-TNPFe	0.75[c]	1.46	[14a, 14b]
PcFe(py)$_2$	0.26[c]	2.02	[70]
2,3-TNPFe(py)$_2$ × Et$_2$O	0.37[c]	0.90	[14a, 14b]
PcFe(pyz)$_2$	0.500[b]	2.006	[71]
2,3-NcFe(pyz)$_2$	0.26[c]	1.90	[72]
[PcFe(pyz) × 0.5C$_6$H$_6$]$_n$	0.500[b]	2.009	[71]
[PcFe(pyz)]$_n$	0.18[c]	1.98	[73]
[2,3-TNPFe(pyz) × 0.33pyz]$_n$	0.35[c]	0.74	[14a, 14b]
[PcFe(bpe)]$_n$	0.20[c]	2.01	[73]
[PcFe(bpy)]$_n$	0.24[c]	2.00	[73]
[PcFe(bpa)]$_n$	0.28[c]	2.04	[73]
[PcFe(tmbpy)]$_n$	0.28[c]	2.06	[73]
PcFe(mepyz)$_2$	0.498[b]	1.895	[74]
PcFe(me$_2$pyz)$_2$	0.498[b]	1.968	[74]
PcFe(Clpyz)$_2$	0.513[b]	2.149	[74]
PcFe(etpyz)$_2$	0.504[b]	2.016	[74]
PcFe(tz)$_2$	0.15[c]	1.79[d]	[69]
[PcFe(tz)]$_n$	0.13[c]	2.23	[69]
[2,3-NcFe(tz) × 0.5CHCl$_3$]$_n$	0.19[c]	1.97	[69]

[a] Fit to a quadrupole doublet;
[b] Relative to sodium nitroprusside;
[c] Relative to metallic iron;
[d] Additional doublet of PcFe

IR spectroscopy is a useful tool for distinguishing between the mononuclear PcFe(pyz)$_2$ and the bridged compound [PcFe(pyz)]$_n$. Pyrazine shows a characteristic centrosymmetric ring stretch [76] at about 1600 cm^{-1}, which is IR and Raman allowed for complexes containing unidentate pyz {as in PcFe(pyz)$_2$} and, caused by a higher local symmetry, only Raman allowed for bidentate {as in [PcFe(pyz)]$_n$} and for non-coordinated pyrazine [77]. In the spectrum of [PcFe(pyz)]$_n$ there occurs only a weak absorption at 1582 cm^{-1}, whereas a strong intensity at this frequency is observed in mononuclear PcFe(pyz)$_2$. Analysis of the intensities of these absorptions allows to determine the chain length n in [PcFe(pyz)]$_n$ as being greater than 20 [78].

To investigate the influence of the metal atom in the compounds PcML$_2$ and [PcML]$_n$, ruthenium, cobalt and rhodium have also been used in place of iron as the central metal atom. The monomeric PcRuL$_2$ complexes were prepared similarly as the PcFeL$_2$ adducts [64]. Because of their good solubility NMR spectroscopy can be applied for elucidating the molecular structure of these compounds (see Table 5).

Pure [PcRu(pyz)]$_n$ is accessible by heating PcRu(pyz)$_2$ to 300 °C. Only under these conditions one pyrazine molecule is eliminated and the resulting intermediate polymerizes to form [PcRu(pyz)]$_n$ [64].

With the ligands L = py, mepyz, me_2pyz, bpy (see Fig. 7) and *n*-butylamine PcCo prefers to form pentacoordinated complexes PcCoL. Hexacoordinated complexes $PcCoL_2$ are only formed at a high ligand concentration. To distinguish between penta- and hexacoordinated cobalt complexes, the usual spectroscopic methods were applied, including EPR spectroscopy and magnetic measurements [79–81]. Recently complexes $PcRhL_2$ (L = pyz, bpy) have also been synthesized [82].

The influence of peripheral substituents at the phthalocyaninato moiety on the properties of the corresponding compounds was studied with a number of octa-substituted derivatives R_mPcM, R_mPcML_2 and $[R_mPcM(pyz)]_n$ (e.g. R = CH_3, m = 8, M = Fe, L = py) [83]. Substituted mononuclear and bridged phthalocyaninatoiron pyrazine complexes $R_mPcFe(pyz)_2$ and $[R_mPcFe(pyz)]_n$ are accessible according to the procedure for the corresponding unsubstituted complexes [65]. With cobalt as central metal the tetra-substituted macrocycles R_mPcCo (m = 4; R = *t*-bu, NO_2) can be prepared. They coordinate with pyridine and substituted pyridines to form the adducts R_mPcCoL_2 [84]. With pyrazine the binuclear complex $(t\text{-bu})_4PcCo(pyz)CoPc(t\text{-bu})_4$ and the oligonuclear $[(NO_2)PcCo(pyz)]_n$ can be isolated and characterized [84].

Other aromatic and non-aromatic metal macrocycles were employed to prepare the corresponding pyrazine adducts. These include tetraphenylporphyrin (TPPM), tetra(4-nitrophenyl)porphyrin (p-NO_2TPPM), tetrabenzoporphyrin (TBPM), dihydrodibenzotetraaza[14]annulene (taaM), hemiporphyrazine (HpM), 2,3,9,10-tetramethyl-1,4,8,11-tetraazacyclotetradecatetra-1,3,8,10-ene ($MTIM^{2+}$), tetramethyldihydrodibenzotetraaza[14]annulene (tmtaaM), 2,3-naphthalocyanine (2,3-NcM), tetra-2,3-naphthoporphyrin (2,3-TNPM) and octaethylporphyrin (OEPM) (see Fig. 1). The experimental conditions for the preparation of bridged compounds of the general type $[MacM(pyz)]_n$ are given in Scheme 11 [7e, 14, 72, 84–89].

It was possible to grow single crystals of the mononuclear $TPPFe(pyz)_2$. Its structure was solved by X-ray diffraction analysis [85, 90]. Furthermore, the crystal structure [91] of the pyz-bridged (μ-pyrazine)bis(dimethylglyoximato)-cobalt(II) demonstrates, that the pyrazine molecules within a chain are all arranged in a plane perpendicular to the plane of the planar bis(dimethylglyoximato)-cobalt(II) moiety (see Fig. 8).

Other heterocycles containing more nitrogen atoms (see Fig. 7) were also used for the preparation of mononuclear and polynuclear complexes with PcFe, PcRu and 2,3-NcFe as macrocycles [69, 70, 92]. Similar to the synthesis of $[PcFe(pyz)]_n$, $[PcFe(tz)]_n$, $[PcRu(tz)]_n$, and $[2,3\text{-}NcFe(tz)]_n$ can be prepared using 1,2,4,5-tetrazine (tz), as the bridging ligand. The preparation of a mononuclear complex was only possible in the case of $PcRu(tz)_2$, while $PcFe(tz)_2$ could not be isolated in a pure state. 2,3-NcFe does not form a mononuclear complex.

1,4-Diazabicyclo[2.2.2]octane (dabco) (see Fig. 7) was used to synthesize a number of mononuclear $MacM(dabco)_2$ and bridged $[MacM(dabco)]_n$ compounds (MacM = PcFe, PcRu, PcCo, TPPFe, OEPRu and OEPOs) [63, 80,

MacFe $\xrightarrow{\text{molten pyz}}$ $MacFe(pyz)_2$

Mac = TPP, *p*-NO_2TPP, Hp
2,3-NcFe — 2,3-NcFe$(pyz)_2 \times 0.2$ pyz
$[FeTIM(CH_3CN)_2](PF_6)_2$ — $[FeTIM(pyz)_2](PF_6)_2$

OEPM $\xrightarrow{\text{excess pyz}}$ $OEMP(pyz)_2$

M = Fe, Ru, Os

PcM $\xrightarrow{\text{tz}}$ $PcM(tz)_2$

M = Fe — ($CHCl_3$/EtOH/excess tz)

M = Ru — ($CHCl_3$/excess tz)

MacFe $\xrightarrow{\text{molten pyz}}$ $[MacFe(pyz)]_n$

Mac = taa, tmtaa, TPP, *p*-NO, TPP — $[2,3\text{-TNPFe}(pyz) \times 0.33\ pyz]_n$
2,3-TNPFe

MacFe $\xrightarrow[\text{slight excess of pyz}]{\text{heating in chlorobenzene}}$ $[MacFe(pyz)]_n$

Mac = Hp, taa, tmtaa

OEPM $\xrightarrow[\text{toluene}]{\text{slight excess of pyz}}$ $[OEMP(pyz)]_n$

M = Fe, Ru, Os

$[TIMFe(pyz)_2](PF_6)_2$ $\xrightarrow[CHCl_3/H_2O]{\text{extraction with}}$ $[TIMFe(pyz)(H_2O)]_n$

2,3-NcFe$(pyz)_2$ $\xrightarrow{CHCl_3}$ $[2,3\text{-NcFe}(pyz) \times 0.2\,CHCl_3]_n$

Scheme 11. Experimental conditions for the preparation of pyrazine-bridged macrocyclic metal complexes $[MacM(pyz)_n]$

84, 89c]. The ^{1}H-NMR data of the soluble PcRu$(dabco)_2$ are given in Table 5. While pyz, tz and dabco cause nearly the same interring distance of about 680 pm (estimated) between two macrocycles in a polymer chain, other ligands such as 4,4′-bipyridine (bpy) (distance ~1110 pm), 3,3′-dimethyl-4,4′-bipyridine (me_2bpy), 4,4′-bipyridylacetylene (bpyac) (~1320 pm), *trans*-1,2-bis(4-pyridyl)-ethylene (bpe), 1,2-bis(4-pyridyl)ethane (bpa) and 4,4′-trimethylenebipyridine (tmbpy) (see Fig. 7) can be used to enlarge this interring distance.

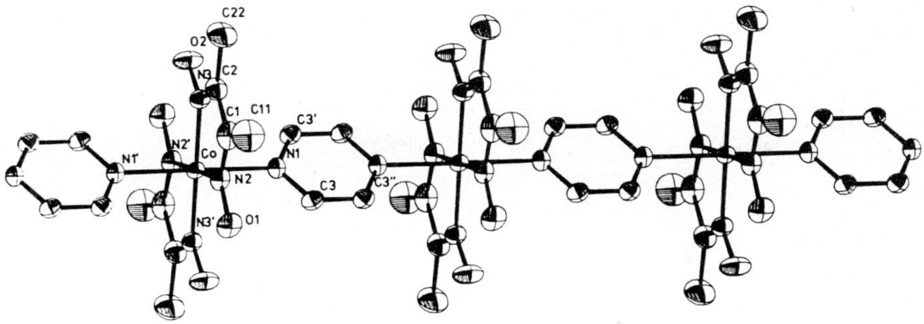

Fig. 8. Crystal structure of (μ-pyrazine)bis(dimethylglyoximato)cobalt(II) (Permission for printing)

A number of mononuclear complexes $MacML_2$ (L = bpy, MacM = PcFe, PcRu, TPPFe, 2,3-NcFe; L = me_2bpy, MacM = PcFe; L = bpyac, MacM = PcFe, PcRu, TPPFe, $Cl_{16}PcFe$), one binuclear complex $\{[PcCo]_2(bpy)\}$ and various polynuclear complexes $[MacML]_n$ (L = bpy, MacM = PcFe, PcRu, 2,3-NcFe, TPPFe, OEPRu, OEPOs; L = me_2bpy, MacM = PcFe; L = bpyac, MacM = PcFe, PcRu, TPPFe, Me_8PcFe, $Cl_{16}PcFe$; L = bpe, bpa, tmbpy, MacM = PcFe) have been reported [42, 64, 66, 72, 73, 85, 89c, 93]. As usual, the metallomacrocycle to ligand ratio is confirmed by thermal analysis.

The room temperature powder conductivities of the compounds described in this section are summarized in Table 7.

Oligomerization of MacM (Mac = Pc, TBP, 2,3-Nc, OEP; M = e.g. Fe, Ru, Co) using bidentate ligands such as pyz, bpy, tz etc. results in a clear increase of the electrical conductivities by a factor of 10^3–10^7 in comparison with the corresponding monomers $MacML_2$. The electronic structure of $[PcFe(pyz)]_n$ has been studied by means of the tight-binding (LCAO) method. As a result a band gap of about 0.7 eV and semiconducting behaviour was predicted [43b]. The band gap according to these calculations is mostly determined by the difference in energies between the LUMO of the bridging ligand and the transition-metal d_{xy}-orbital. The higher conductivity of the tetrazine bridged compounds $[PcFe(tz)]_n$, $[PcRu(tz)]_n$ and $[2,3\text{-}NcFe(tz)]_n$ (about 10^{-2}–10^{-1} S/cm without doping) (see Table 7) is therefore explained by the low lying LUMO of this ligand. Further extended Hückel calculations of the band structure were performed for $[PcFe(pyz)]_n$ and $[PcFe(tz)]_n$ [43d]. As a result of these calculations $[PcFe(pyz)]_n$ should be described as a diamagnetic compound with an energy gap of 1.03 eV. In contrast to the above mentioned compounds no increase in conductivity is observed going from the mononuclears $MacM(dabco)_2$ to the bridged complexes $[MacM(dabco)]_n$ (MacM = PcFe, PcCo, TPPFe). Polymerization with dabco only improves the conductivity (factor 10^2) when PcRu is the base macrocycle.

Peripheral substitution of the phthalocyaninato macrocycle anions by electron donating substituents (CH_3, OCH_3) leads to the same conductivity of the bridged $[R_8PcFe(pyz)]_n$ as in $[PcFe(pyz)]_n$, while substitution with

Table 7. Room temperature electrical conductivity data (powder, 1 kbar) of monomeric and bridged metal complexes with macrocyclic ligands

Compound	Conductivity [S/cm]	Ref.
β-PcFe	4×10^{-11} [a]	[65]
PcRu	2×10^{-5} [c]	[66, 94]
β-PcCo	1×10^{-11} [b]	[84]
(Me)PcFe	2×10^{-9} [a]	[65]
$(MeO)_8$PcFe	3×10^{-8} [a]	[65]
Cl_{16}PcFe	9×10^{-8} [a]	[65]
$(t\text{-bu})_4$PcCo	5×10^{-10} [b]	[84]
$(NO_2)_4$PcCo	1×10^{-11} [b]	[84]
$(MeO)_8$PcCo	3×10^{-9} [b]	[84]
TBPFe	2×10^{-6} [c]	[6c]
TPPFe	1×10^{-13} [b]	[85]
HpFe	1×10^{-14} [a]	[86]
taaFe	1×10^{-12} [a]	[95]
1,2-NcFe	4×10^{-9} [c]	[11]
2,3-NcFe	5×10^{-5} [c]	[10]
2,3-TNPFe	4×10^{-5} [c]	[14]
TBPCo	2×10^{-7} [b]	[96]
2,3-NcCo	3×10^{-6} [b]	[72]
2,3-TNPCo	5×10^{-4} [c]	[14]
$PcFe(pyz)_2$	3×10^{-12} [a]	[63]
$[PcFe(pyz)]_n$	1×10^{-6} [c]	[63]
$(Me)_8PcFe(pyz)_2$	3×10^{-9} [a]	[63]
$[(Me)_8PcFe(pyz)]_n$	9×10^{-6} [c]	[63]
$(MeO)_8PcFe(pyz)_2$	1×10^{-8} [a]	[63]
$[(MeO)_8PcFe(pyz)]_n$	5×10^{-6} [c]	[63]
$Cl_{16}PcFe(pyz)_2$	2×10^{-12} [a]	[63]
$[Cl_{16}PcFe(pyz)]_n$	3×10^{-11} [b]	[63]
$PcRu(pyz)_2$	2×10^{-11} [b]	[64]
$[PcRu(pyz)]_n$	1×10^{-7} [c]	[64]
PcCo(pyz)	5×10^{-12} [b]	[84]
$PcCo(pyz)_2$	1×10^{-10} [b]	[84]
$[PcCo(pyz) \times 0.5C_6H_5Cl]_n$	1×10^{-9} [b]	[84]
$(NO_2)_4PcCo(pyz)_2$	2×10^{-11} [b]	[84]
$[(NO_2)_4PcCo(pyz)]_n$	7×10^{-11} [b]	[84]
$TPPFe(pyz)_2$	3×10^{-12} [b]	[83]
$[TPPFe(pyz)]_n$	2×10^{-8} [b]	[85]
$p\text{-}NO_2TPPFe(pyz)_2$	10^{-13} [b]	[85]
$[p\text{-}NO_2TPPFe(pyz)]_n$	6×10^{-10} [b]	[85]
$HpFe(pyz)_2$	1×10^{-11} [b]	[86]
$[HpFe(pyz) \times 0.9C_6H_5Cl]_n$	2×10^{-9} [b]	[86]
$[taaFe(pyz)]_n$	1×10^{-5} [c]	[97]
$[tmtaaFe(pyz) \times 0.6pyz]_n$	1×10^{-7} [b]	[97]
2,3-$NcFe(pyz)_2 \times 0.2pyz$	2×10^{-5} [c]	[10]
$[2,3\text{-}NcFe(pyz)]_n$	5×10^{-5} [c]	[72]
$[2,3\text{-}TNPFe(pyz) \times 0.33pyz]_n$	2×10^{-4} [c]	[14]
$[TIMFe(pyz)(H_2O)]_n(PF_6)_{2n}$	2×10^{-11} [a]	[98]
$OEPRu(pyz)_2$	1×10^{-11} [a]	[89]
$[OEPRu(pyz)]_n$	1×10^{-8} [a,c]	[89]
$[PcFe(tz)]_n$	2×10^{-2} [c]	[69]
$PcRu(tz)_2$	10^{-11} [b]	[69]
$[PcRu(tz)]_n$	1×10^{-2} [c]	[69]
$[2,3\text{-}NcFe(tz) \times 0.2CHCl_3]_n$	3×10^{-1} [c]	[69]
$PcFe(dabco)_2$	1×10^{-10} [a]	[65]
$[PcFe(dabco) \times 1.4CHCl_3]_n$	1×10^{-9} [a]	[65]

Table 7. (*Contd.*)

Compound	Conductivity [S/cm]	Ref.
$PcRu(dabco)_2$	8×10^{-12} [b]	[66]
$[PcRu(dabco)]_n$	1×10^{-9} [b]	[66]
$PcCo(dabco)_2$	8×10^{-12} [b]	[84]
$[PcCo(dabco) \times 1.1C_6H_4Cl_2]_n$	5×10^{-12} [b]	[84]
$TPPFe(dabco)_2$	1×10^{-12} [b]	[85]
$[TPPFe(dabco)]_n$	2×10^{-12} [b]	[85]
$PcFe(bpy)_2$	5×10^{-13} [a]	[65]
$[PcFe(bpy)]_n$	2×10^{-8} [b]	[65]
$PcRu(bpy)_2$	1×10^{-11} [b]	[64]
$[PcRu(bpy)]_n$	2×10^{-8} [b]	[64]
$[PcCo(bpy)_2$	1×10^{-11} [b]	[84]
$[PcCo(bpy)PcCo] \times 0.5C_6H_5Cl$	1×10^{-11} [b]	[84]
$2,3\text{-}NcFe(bpy)_2$	1×10^{-7} [c]	[10]
$[TIMFe(bpy)]_n(PF_6)_{2n}$	1×10^{-11} [a]	[98]
$TPPFe(bpy)_2$	4×10^{-12} [b]	[85]
$[TPPFe(bpy)]_n$	1×10^{-8} [b]	[85]
$PcFe(bpyac)_2$	3×10^{-11} [b]	[93]
$[PcFe(bpyac)]_n$	1×10^{-7} [b]	[93]
$PcRu(bpyac)_2$	1×10^{-11} [b]	[93]
$Cl_{16}PcFe(bpyac)_2$	3×10^{-12} [b]	[93]
$TPPFe(bpyac)_2$	6×10^{-9} [b]	[85]
$[Cl_{16}PcFe(bpyac)]_n$	9×10^{-11} [b]	[93]
$[(Me)_8PcFe(bpyac)]_n$	8×10^{-8} [b]	[93]
$[TPPFe(bpyac)]_n$	8×10^{-9} [b]	[85]

[a] Two-probe technique, 2×10^8 Pa;
[b] Two-probe technique, 1×10^8 Pa;
[c] Four-probe technique, 1×10^8 Pa

electron withdrawing substituents as in $[Cl_{16}PcFe(pyz)]_n$, $[(NO_2)_4PcCo(pyz)]_n$ or $[p\text{-}NO_2TPPFe(pyz)]_n$ generally cause a decrease in conductivity by a factor of about 10^4.

Pyrazine bridged oligomers containing other macrocyclic anions than Pc^{2-} show a decrease in conductivity with the exception of $[taaFe(pyz)]_n$, $[2,3\text{-}NcFe(pyz)]_n$, $[2,3\text{-}TNPFe(pyz) \times 0.33\ pyz]_n$ and $[OEPM(pyz)]_n$ (M = Fe, Ru, Os). In the case of 2,3-Nc, the macrocycle itself, the monomer $2,3\text{-}NcFe(pyz)_2$ and the oligomer $[2,3\text{-}NcFe(pyz)]_n$ show nearly the same conductivity. A similar observation was made with 2,3-TNP as macrocycle [14].

These results can be explained by oxygen doping of the 2,3-Nc- and 2,3-TNP complexes. As can be seen from the cyclic voltammograms of the metallomacrocycles, 2,3-NcFe and 2,3-TNPFe have significantly lower oxidation potentials as e.g. PcFe (see Table 8). Therefore even a relatively mild oxidant such as air oxygen is able to perform a doping process in these macrocycles.

Many of the bridged compounds $[MacML]_n$ are dopable with iodine. Doped systems $[MacMLI_y]_n$ always have a drastically increased conductivity relative to the undoped species (see Table 9). For example doping of

Table 8. Redox potentials[a] of some iron(II) and cobalt(II) tetrapyrroles in pyridine/Bu_4NClO_4 vs. SCE [V] [5c, 9]

	$E^1_{1/2}$	$E^2_{1/2}$	$E^3_{1/2}$	$E^4_{1/2}$	$E^5_{1/2}$
PcFe	1.10	0.69	− 1.085	− 1.39	− 1.93
1,2-NcFe	1.01	0.68	− 0.95	− 1.21	− 1.80
2,3-NcFe	0.81	0.43	− 1.09	− 1.32	− 1.86
TBPFe	0.82	0.34	− 0.90	− 1.59	− 1.87
2,3-TNPFe[b]	0.61	0.15	− 0.90	− 1.49	− 1.87
assignment[c]	Mac^{-2}/Mac^{-1}	Fe^{II}/Fe^{III}	Fe^{I}/Fe^{II}	Mac^{-3}/Mac^{-2}	Mac^{-4}/Mac^{-3}
PcCo	1.15	0.21	− 0.55	− 0.91	− 1.44
2,3-NcCo	0.77	0.205	− 0.575	− 0.92	− 1.52
TBPCo	0.85	− 0.13	− 0.88	− 1.09	− 1.79
2,3-TNPCo[b]	0.515	− 0.13	− 0.90	—	− 1.86
assignment[c]	Mac^{-2}/Mac^{-1}	Co^{II}/Co^{III}	Co^{I}/Co^{II}	Mac^{-3}/Mac^{-2}	Mac^{-4}/Mac^{-2}

[a] In general, the half wave potentials $E^n_{1/2}$ are reversible (ΔE_p = 58 mV) at lower scan rates (v = 0.02 V/s), but ΔE_p increases with increasing v;
[b] Unstable compound during CV experiments;
[c] By comparison with earlier results

Table 9. Room temperature electrical conductivity data (powder, 1 kbar) of doped chain compounds $[MacML]_n$

Compound	Conductivity[a] [S/cm]	E_a[b] [eV]	Ref.
$[PcFe(pyz)I_{2.54}]_n$	2×10^{-1}	0.045	[71]
$[PcRu(pyz)I_{2.00}]_n$	2×10^{-2}	0.14	[99]
[2,3-TNPFe(pyz) × 0.33pyz$I_{1.25}$]	6×10^{-3}		[14]
$[PcFe(tz)I_{2.04}]_n$	2×10^{-1}		[100]
$[PcFe(bpyac)I_{1.0}]_n$	2×10^{-4}		[93]
$[PcRu(bpyac)I_{1.2}]_n$	3×10^{-3}		[93]
$[(Me)_8PcFe(bpyac)I_{1.8}]_n$	6×10^{-4}		[93]
$[OEPRu(pyz)I_{0.66}]$	1×10^{-2}		[89]
$[PcFe(pyz)(BF_4)_{0.45}]_n$	5×10^{-2}		[101]
$[PcFe(pyz)(PF_6)_{0.5}]_n$	4×10^{-2}		[101]
$[PcFe(pyz)(HSO_4)_{0.4}]_n$	1×10^{-5}		[101]
$[PcFe(pyz)(ClO_4)_{0.3}]_n$	3×10^{-3}		[101]

[a] Four-probe technique;
[b] $\sigma_T = \sigma_0 \exp(-E_a/kT)$

$[PcFe(pyz)]_n$ or $[OEPRu(pyz)]_n$ yields stable compounds with the stoichiometries $[PcFe(pyz)I_y]_n$ (y = 0–2.6) [71] and $[OEPRu(pyz)I_y]_n$ (y = 0.6) respectively [89]. The doped compounds $[PcFe(pyz)I_y]_n$ are obtained either by heterogenous doping or by precipitating the polymer from a solution of $PcFe(pyz)_2$ containing iodine.

The composition of the doped polymers was established by elemental analysis and TG/DTA. The nature of the iodine counterion can be elucidated by resonance Raman spectroscopy. There is a strong scattering at about 170 cm^{-1}, which is invariant with the iodine content y in $[PcFe(pyz)I_y]_n$. This band has been associated with polyiodides having I_2 units coordinated to I_3^- (I_5^-).

$[PcFe(pyz)]_n$ can also be doped electrochemically. With $X = BF_4^-$, PF_6^-, HSO_4^-, SCN^- and ClO_4^- stable compounds $[PcFe(pyz)X_y]_n$ are obtained while with BPh_4^- no noticeable effect is observed (see Table 9) [101].

The results of the ^{57}Fe-Mößbauer spectroscopy prove that doping does not destroy the bridged structure. Isomer shifts and quadrupole splittings of chemically and electrochemically doped compounds show nearly identical values as found for $PcFe(pyz)_2$ and $[PcFe(pyz)]_n$. The oxidation therefore does not take place at orbitals which are centered at the metal atom. Other authors describe an oxidation of the central Fe^{II}-ion [73,102], however their methods of doping $[PcFe(pyz)]_n$ are different from that described above.

An oxidation of metal sites producing mixed-valence polymers is reported for the octaethylporphyrins $[OEPML]_n$ with M = Fe, Ru, Os and L = pyz, bpy, dabco [89]. Partial oxidation of these compounds with various oxidants leads to substantial increases of their electrical conductivities relative to the undoped systems. The conductivities follow the trends Os > Ru > Fe and pyz > bpy > dabco. Both of these trends are readily explained in terms of increased overlap between the metal $d\pi$ and the bridging ligand π^* level and resultant increase in electron delocalization among the metal centers. Electrochemical studies reveal the presence of metal-centered anodic waves at potentials much less positive than is required for the first ring oxidations of the porphyrin. The metal centers are thus implicated in the conduction pathway for these bridged compounds. Optical studies reveal the appearance of a mixed-valence transition which accompanies the doping of these materials. Furthermore, the appearance of antiresonances in the IR spectra of doped samples of $[OEPOs(pyz)]_n$ suggests that the bridging ligand also participates in the conduction process [89].

The temperature dependence of the conductivity can be fit to a model of thermal activation. Undoped materials show typical activation energies between 0.1 and 0.4 eV while the values of doped compounds are significantly lower (see Table 9).

3.1.2 Isocyanides as Bridging Ligand

Another type of bridging ligands L which is used to prepare bridged compounds $[MacML]_n$ is 1,4-diisocyanobenzene (dib), its derivatives tetramethyl- and tetrachlorodiisocyanobenzene (me_4dib, Cl_4dib), 1,3-diisocyanobenzene (*m*-dib) and 4,4′-diisocyanobiphenylene (dibph) (see Fig. 9) [103].

In $[MacML]_n$, dib as a bridging ligand leads to a longer metal–metal distance than, for example, pyrazine (1190 pm vs 680 pm). All the dib-bridged complexes, which have been prepared until now are summarized in Table 10. As macrocyclic anions, Pc^{2-} [63], TPP^{2-} [84], TBP^{2-} [6c], 1,2-Nc^{2-} [11], 2,3-

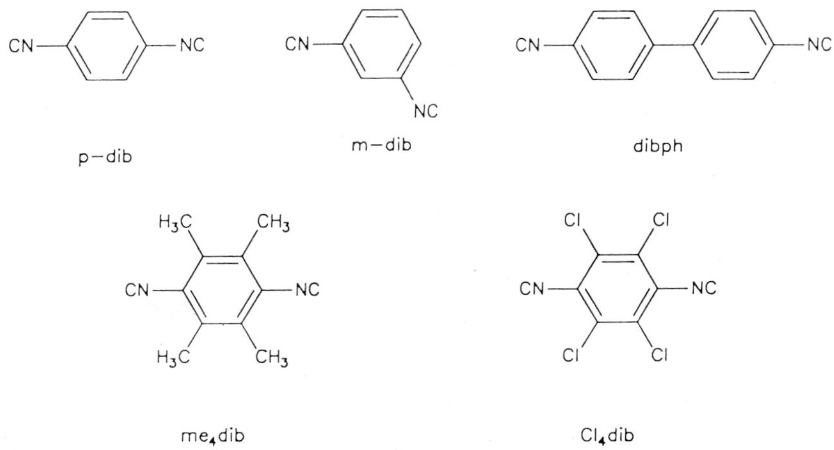

Fig. 9. Bidentate isocyano ligands

Nc^{2-} [104], 2,3-TNP^{2-} [14] and TIM [88] were used with iron and ruthenium as central metal atoms.

With the exception of $[TPPFe(dib)]_n$, which was prepared by a ligand exchange reaction using $TPPFe(py)_2$ as starting material [85], the systems $[MacML]_n$ were synthesized by refluxing MacM with some excess of dib (1.1–1.3 mol) in chloroform, acetone or chlorobenzene [6c, 11, 14, 63, 89, 104].

The corresponding mononuclear compounds $MacML_2$ were obtained only for $Mac = Pc^{2-}$, TBP^{2-}, 2,3-Nc^{2-} and 2,3-TNP^{2-} (M = Fe) and for Mac $= Pc^{2-}$ (M = Ru). Due to the reduced thermal stability of diisocyanobenzene and its derivatives, the synthesis cannot be carried out in a melt of the ligand as it can e.g. in the case of pyrazine monomers, but treatment of MacM with a solution of dib in chloroform, acetone, or methanol leads to the mononuclear complexes $MacML_2$. Alternatively, monodentate ligands such as benzylisocyanide (bzNC) or phenylisocyanide (phNC) [106] are used to form mononuclears of the type $MacML_2$ ($Mac = Pc^{2-}$, TPP^{2-}, TBP^{2-}, 1,2-Nc^{2-}, 2,3-Nc^{2-}, 2,3-TNP^{2-}, $TPyP^{2-}$ see Table 11).

In the case of 1,2-Nc^{2-} and $TPyP^{2-}$, mixtures of four possible isomers are obtained during the synthesis of the macrocycle (Fig. 10) [11, 109]. In the mononuclear complexes 1,2-$NcFe(cHxNC)_2$ and $TPyPFe(me_2phNC)_2$, one of these structural isomers can be separated by column chromatography [11].

The first crystal structure analysis of a 1,2-naphthalocyanine derivative shows it to be the symmetrical isomer (see Fig. 11) [11].

Recently for the first time substituted 1,2-naphthalocyaninatoiron-derivatives R_4-1,2-$NcFe(CNR')_2$ (R = *t*-bu, C_6H_5 methyl, R^3 = *t*-bu, alkyl) have been prepared and, due to their comparatively high solubility, separated by column chromatography. One of the isomers, substituted with four *t*-bu-groups in the ring, was shown to be a symmetrical isomer too by a crystal structure analysis [109a].

Table 10. IR-, TG/DTA- and room temperature conductivity (powder, 1 kbar) data of mononuclear and polynuclear metal complexes with macrocyclic ligands and bisaxially coordinated isocyanides

Compound	IR[a] (ν_{CN}) Free L	IR[a] (ν_{CN}) Coord. L	Dissoc. range of base by TG (°C)[b]	σ_{RT} [S/cm]	Ref.
$[PcFe(dib)]_n$	2130	2100	220[c]	2×10^{-5} [d]	[63]
$PcFe(dib)_2$	2130	2105	—	—	[105]
$[TPPFe(dib)]_n$	2130	2083	290–375	1×10^{-8} [d]	[85]
$[TBPFe(dib)]_n$	2130	2080	230–280	2×10^{-6} [d]	[6c]
$TBPFe(dib)_2$	2130	2098	—	4×10^{-10} [d]	[6c]
$[2,3\text{-}NcFe(dib)]_n$	2130	2110	240[c]	2×10^{-3} [d]	[104]
$2,3\text{-}NcFe(dib)_2$	2130	2124	235[c]	3×10^{-4} [d]	[104]
$[1,2\text{-}NcFe(dib)]_n$	2130	2090	240–310	6×10^{-10} [e]	[11]
$[2,3\text{-}TNPFe(dib)]_n$	2130	2077	—	5×10^{-3} [d]	[14]
$2,3\text{-}TNPFe(dib)_2$	2130	2097	—	2×10^{-3} [e]	[14]
$[TIMFe(dib)]_n(PF_6)_{2n}$	2130	2135	—	9×10^{-9} [d]	[88]
$[PcFe(me_4dib)]_n$	2113	2092	255–350	1×10^{-7} [e]	[94]
$PcFe(me_4dib)_2$	2113	2109	—	—	[94]
$[PcFe(Cl_4dib)]_n$	2128	2058	260–350	4×10^{-6} [d,e]	[94]
$[PcRu(dib)]_n$	2130	2087	210[c]	2×10^{-6} [d]	[64]
$PcRu(dib)_2$	2130	2095	—	—	[64]
$[PcRu(me_4dib)]_n$	2113	2084	255–350	1×10^{-7} [d,e]	[94]
$PcRu(me_4dib)_2$	2113	2092	—	—	[94]
$[PcRu(Cl_4dib)]_n$	2128	2038	255	1×10^{-7} [d]	[94]
$[PcFe(dibph)]_n$	2126	2113	275–500	1×10^{-7} [d]	[94]
$PcFe(dibph)_2$	2126	2130	—	—	[94]
$[PcRu(dibph)]_n$	2126	2101	250–450	1×10^{-7} [d]	[94]
$PcRu(dibph)_2$	2126	2122	—	—	[94]
$[Me_8PcFe(dib)]_n$	2130	2094	235[c]	4×10^{-4} [d]	[65]
$[MeO_8PcFe(dib)]_n$	2130	2092	245[c]	6×10^{-6} [d]	[65]
$[Cl_{16}PcFe(dib)]_n$	2130	2122	290[c]	3×10^{-11} [e]	[65]
$[Me_8PcFe(Cl_4dib)]_n$	2128	2050	260[c]	5×10^{-6} [d,e]	[94]
$[PcFe(m\text{-}dib)]_n$	2135, 2145	2098	230[c]	—	[93]
$PcFe(m\text{-}dib)_2$	2135, 2145	2112s, 2144w	—	2×10^{-6} [d]	[93]
$[PcRu(m\text{-}dib)]_n$	2135, 2145	2083	—	—	[64]
$PcRu(m\text{-}dib)_2$	2135, 2145	2100s, 2143w	—	5×10^{-7} [d]	[64]
$[Me_8PcFe(m\text{-}dib)]_n$	2135, 2145	2082	225[c]	7×10^{-5} [d]	[93]
$[MeO_8PcFe(m\text{-}dib)]_n$	2135, 2145	2078	195[c]	6×10^{-5} [d]	[93]
$[Cl_{16}PcFe(m\text{-}dib)]_n$	2135, 2145	2114	260[c]	4×10^{-10} [d]	[93]

[a] Nujol mull;
[b] Same conditions as in Table 4;
[c] Beginning decomposition;
[d] Four-probe method;
[e] Two-probe method

All isocyanide complexes $[MacML]_n$ and mononuclears $MacML_2$ were characterized by elemental analysis, thermal analysis (TG), differential thermal analysis (DTA), UV/VIS-, IR- and, if sufficiently soluble, by NMR spectroscopy.

The IR spectra of all isocyanide complexes $[MacML]_n$ and $MacML_2$ show the intense stretching frequency of the isocyanide group at about 2080–2150 cm^{-1} (see Tables 10 and 11). The shift of this absorption by changing from free to metal coordinated ligand is attributed to the σ-donor and π-acceptor abilities of the metal ligand bond. The strength of the π-acceptor bond

Table 11. Mononuclear metal complexes with tetrapyrrole ligands and axial unidentate isocyanide ligands, IR-, TG/DTA and room temperature conductivity (powder, 1 kbar)

Compound	IR[a] (ν_{CN}) Free L	IR[a] (ν_{CN}) Coord. L	Dissoc. range of base by TG [°C][b]	σ_{RT} [S/cm]	Ref.
PcFe(*t*-buNC)$_2$	2138	2154	165–250	—	[107]
TBPFe(*t*-buNC)$_2$	2138	2132	—	—	[7e]
2,3-NcFe(*t*-buNC)$_2$	2138	2147	165[c]	—	[10]
1,2-NcFe(*t*-buNC)$_2$	2138	2140	140–230	—	[11]
TPyPFe(*t*-buNC)$_2$	2138	2157	200–225	—	[109]
PcRu(*t*-buNC)$_2$	2138	2145	165–250	—	[107]
TPPRu(*t*-buNC)$_2$	2138	2106[d]	—	—	[108]
PcFe(*c*-hxNC)$_2$	2138	2164	200–290	—	[107]
TBPFe(*c*-hxNC)$_2$	2138	2137	—	—	[7e]
2,3-NcFe(*c*-hxNC)$_2$	2138	2164	210–300	—	[10]
1,2-NcFe(*c*-hxNC)$_2$	2138	2155	170–260	—	[11]
2,3-TNPFe(*c*-hxNC)$_2$	2138	2131	160–255	2×10^{-3} [e]	[14]
TPyPFe(*c*-hxNC)$_2$	2138	2171	210–285	—	[109]
TPyPFe(phNC)$_2$	2138	2141	205–260	—	[109]
PcRu(*c*-hxNC)$_2$	2138	2153	240–350	—	[107]
PcFe(phNC)$_2$	2138	2136	180–265	—	[107]
TBPFe(phNC)$_2$	2126	2105	—	—	[7e]
PcRu(phNC)$_2$	2138	2126	230–310	3×10^{-11} [f]	[107]
PcFe(bzNC)$_2$	2146	2180	200–290	2×10^{-12} [f]	[107]
2,3-NcFe(bzNC)$_2$	2151	2166	130–280	—	[10]
1,2-NcFe(bzNC)$_2$	2151	2153	175–270	—	[11]
PcFe(me$_2$phNC)$_2$	2122	2133	225–295	1×10^{-11} [f]	[107]
TPyPFe(me$_2$phNC)$_2$	2122	2140	200–295	—	[109]
PcRu(me$_2$phNC)$_2$	2122	2122	295–410	1×10^{-11} [f]	[107]
PcRu(me$_2$phNC)	2122	2074	350–410	—	[66]
PcFe(Cl$_4$phNC)$_2$	2133, 2125	2089	235–340	—	[66]
PcRu(Cl$_4$phNC)$_2$	2133, 2125	2075	280–435	—	[66]
PcRu(Cl$_4$phNC)	2133, 2125	2025	370–435	—	[66]
PcFe(*o*-mephNC)$_2$	2122	2130	210–285	—	[109]
TPyPFe(*o*-mephNC)$_2$	2122	2136	205–315	—	[109]
PcFe(*m*-mephNC)$_2$	2122	2143	195–275	—	[109]
TPyPFe(*m*-mphNC)$_2$	2122	2134	205–270	—	[109]
PcFe(*p*-mephNC)$_2$	2125	2145	200–290	—	[109]
TPyPFe(*p*-mephNC)$_2$	2125	2144	210–285	—	[109]
PcFe(*i*-prphNC)$_2$	2120	2131	220–300	—	[109]
TPyPFe(*i*-prphNC)$_2$	2120	2128	230–315	—	[109]

[a] Nujol mull;
[b] Same conditions as in Table 4;
[c] Beginning decomposition;
[d] In benzene;
[e] Four-probe method;
[f] Two-probe method

depends on the central metal atom as well as on the electronic properties of the equatorial macrocycle. In general, all bridged isocyanide compounds exhibit a much stronger π-back-bonding than the monomeric species MacML$_2$. This can be observed in the IR spectra because an increase of the π-back-donation leads to a decrease of the CN-valence frequency since a strong antibonding orbital is available for π-back-bonding. The CN frequency is also influenced by peripheral substituents of the macrocycle in the oligomers [R$_8$PcFeL]$_n$ (R = CH$_3$, OCH$_3$;

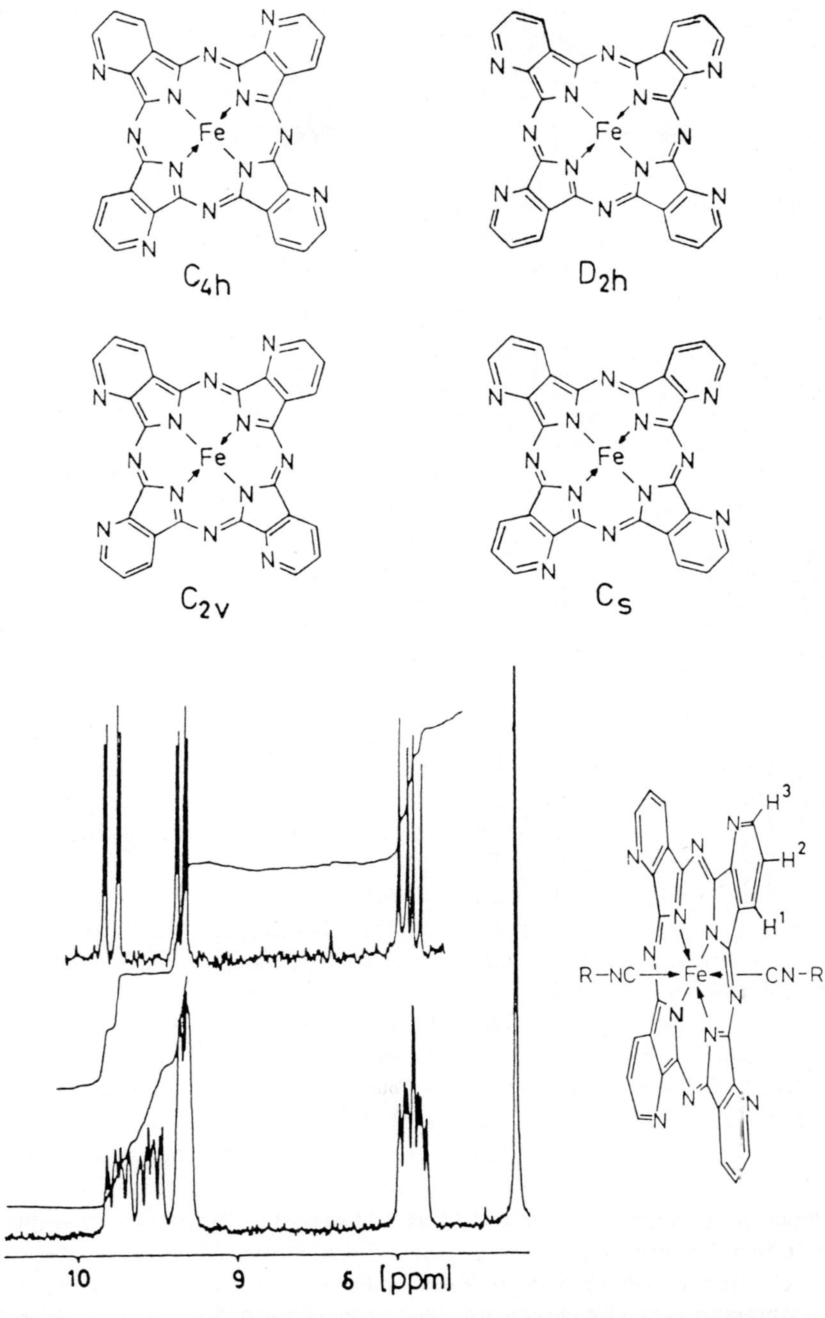

Fig. 10. Possible isomers of tetra(2,3-pyrido)porphyrazinatoiron(II), TPyPFe, and ^{1}H-NMR spectrum of a pure isomer of the bis-isocyanide complex, TPyPFe(Me_2phNC)$_2$ (The proton signals of the macrocycle are depicted.) Upper spectrum: pure isomer. Lower spectrum: original mixture of isomers; 7.9 ppm (H^2), 9.3 ppm (H^1), 9.6 ppm (H^3).

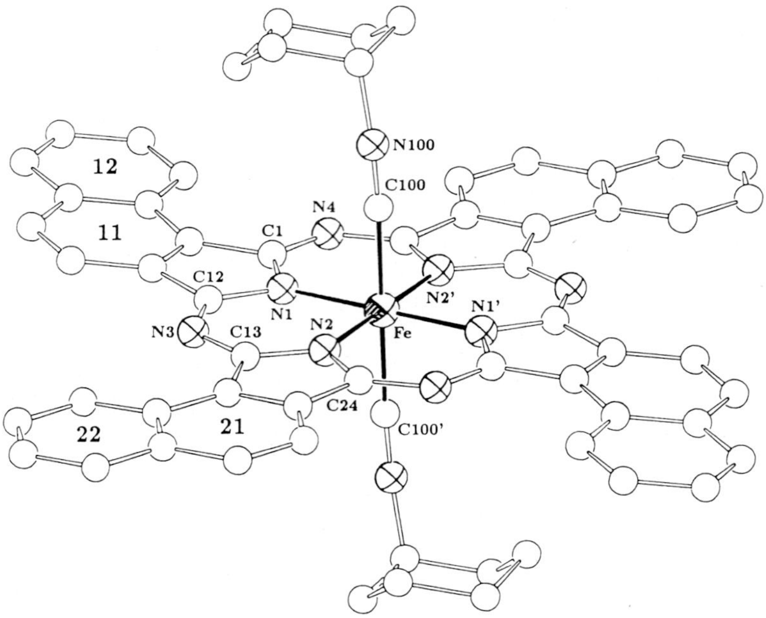

Fig. 11. Crystal structure of bis(cyclohexylisocyano)-1,2-naphthalocyaninatoiron(II)

L = dib, *m*-dib) and $[Cl_{16}PcFeL]_n$ (L = dib, *m*-dib) [65, 93]. Electron donating substituents such as methyl and methoxy shift the CN-stretching frequency to lower energy, while electron withdrawing substituents such as chlorine induce a shift to higher energy (see Table 10).

Like peripheral substitution of the macrocycles, substitution of the bridging ligand also influences the position of the CN frequency in the IR spectra. As expected me_4dib and dibph act only as a weak π-acceptor ligand while Cl_4dib is much stronger (see Table 10).

NMR spectroscopy, which can be used for the identification of soluble mononuclear isocyanides $MacML_2$, proves to be a common and definite method for the structure determination of axially coordinated phthalocyaninatoiron and -ruthenium complexes (for some examples see Table 12). The ratio PcM:RNC = 1:2, which follows from the integration, shows the hexacoordination of the central metal atom according to $PcM(RNC)_2$. In general, the protons of the coordinated ligands are shifted to higher field in comparison with the free ligands [107].

^{13}C-NMR spectroscopy was also applied for further characterization of the mononuclears $PcM(RNC)_2$ with the above-mentioned substituents [107]. The isocyanide C-atom signal is shifted upfield by about 10 ppm for $PcFe(RNC)_2$ complexes and about 20 ppm for the corresponding $PcRu(RNC)_2$ complexes upon coordination to the central metal atom.

Table 12. ^{1}H-NMR data[a] of some bis-isocyanide adducts of iron(II)-tetrapyrrole chelates

Compound	Coordinated L	Free L	Macrocycle	Ref.
$PcFe(bzNC)_2$	2.49s, 5.00d 6.46t, 6.73d	4.57, 7.30	7.98, 9.31	[63]
1,2-$NcFe(bzNC)_2$	2.40s, 5.10d 6.50m	4.57, 7.30	7.85m, 8.1–8.5m, 9.53m, 11.19d	[110]
2,3-$NcFe(bzNC)_2$	2.70s, 5.19d 6.48t, 6.73t	4.57, 7.30	7.78, 8.53, 9.80	[10]
$TBPFe(dib)_2$	4.84, 6.30	7.41s	8.03, 9.38 10.61[b]	[6c]
$PcFe(phNC)_2$	5.15, 6.39 6.59	7.38	8.00, 9.35	[106]
$TPyPFe(phNC)_2$	5.16, 6.40 6.61	7.38	7.91, 9.35, 9.64	[109]
$TBPFe(phNC)_2$	4.83, 6.35	7.38	7.95, 9.37 10.60[b]	[7e]
$PcFe(me_4dib)_2$	0.07s, 1.59s	2.37s	8.00, 9.34	[94]
$PcFe(me_2phNC)_2$	6.07d, 6.35t 0.18s	7.1, 2.40s	7.97, 9.33	[106]
$PcFe(Cl_4phNC)_2$	6.64s	7.65s	7.99, 9.30	[94]
$PcFe(m\text{-}dib)_2$	6.64, 6.49 5.18	7.42m	8.03, 9.36	[93]

[a] Chemical shifts in ppm; $CHCl_3$ (7.24) as internal standard;
[b] Proton of the methine group connecting the 4 isoindole units in tetrabenzoporphyrine

The bidentate ligand me_4dib reacts with PcFe and PcRu yielding either bisaxially coordinated mononuclear complexes $PcM(me_4dib)_2$ (M = Fe, Ru) or the one-dimensional bridged chain structures $[PcM(me_4dib)]_n$ (M = Fe, Ru) depending on the reaction conditions. The synthesis of the bridged complexes is also possible starting with the monomers $PcM(me_4dib)_2$ (M = Fe, Ru) in solution or in the solid state [94]. Cl_4dib forms the corresponding oligomers $[PcM(Cl_4dib)]_n$ (M = Fe, Ru).

For the first time it was possible to follow the formation of $[PcM(me_4dib)]_n$ (M = Fe, Ru) in solution by ^{1}H-NMR spectroscopy and thereby gain some information about the mechanism of formation of the bridged complexes.

The corresponding mononuclears $PcM(me_4dib)_2$ (M = Fe, Ru), which are soluble in $CDCl_3$, were characterized by ^{1}H-NMR spectroscopy [94b]. If the NMR spectra are not recorded directly after preparation of the solutions, additional weaker groups of signals centered at 9.30 and 7.97 ppm are observed. They appear at higher field compared to the signals of the Pc protons of the mononuclears with centers at 9.34 and 8.00 ppm. These new signals result from dissociation of the mononuclears $PcM(me_4dib)_2$ and formation of binuclears $(me_4dib)PcM(me_4dib)PcM(me_4dib)$ and trinuclears $(me_4dib)[PcM(me_4dib)]_2$-$PcM(me_4dib)$ [94b] (see Fig. 12).

The methyl substitution of the dib ligand allows the definite characterization of these oligonuclear complexes. In the binuclear the signals of the terminal me_4dib ligands are shifted to higher field, while the protons of the bridging inner ligand are chemically equivalent and the signal is a singlet (see Table 13). The

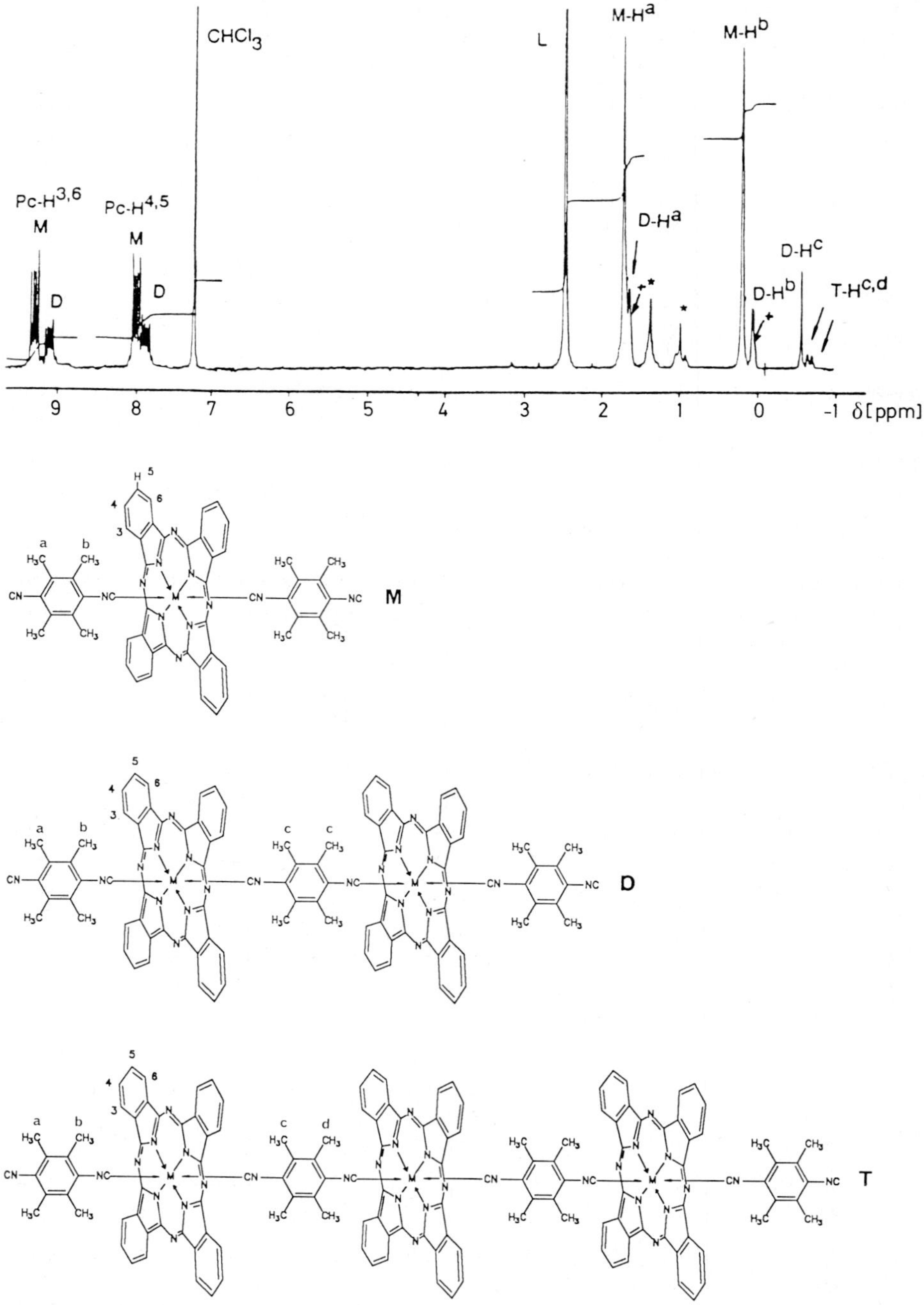

Fig. 12. Mononuclear, dinuclear and trinuclear phthalocyaninatometal complexes with terminal and bridging 1,4-diisocyano-tetramethylbenzene ligands, $PcM(me_4dib)_2$, $[PcM]_2(me_4dib)_3$, and $[PcM]_3(me_4dib)_4$. * denote solvent impurities. L free Ligand. + H^a, H^b of trinuclear species T ($[PcM]_3(Me_4dib)_4$)

multiplets of the Pc ring system of the trinuclear are shifted even further upfield than those of the mononuclear and the binuclear (see Table 14). The phthalocyanine protons in the 1,4-position are shifted more than those in 2,3-position. The reason is that the ring currents of cofacially arranged phthalocyanine rings influence each other. This interaction however is reduced by the bridging ligand me_4dib [94].

Soluble oligomeric phthalocyaninatometal complexes $[t\text{-}bu_4PcRu(L)]_n$ are obtained with L=dib and me_4dib as bridging ligands [111]. Again ^1H-NMR spectroscopy was applied to determine the structure and, additionally the chain lengths n of the compounds. In the spectra two groups of signals show up for the phthalocyanine rings and the bridging ligands: The absorptions of the terminal macrocycles and ligands, and, shifted to higher field, the signals of the corresponding inner protons. The chain length n of $[t\text{-}bu_4PcRu(L)]_n$ (L=dib, me_4dib) is determined from the ratio of the end group signals and the signals of the inner ligand protons. It turns out to be 10–14 phthalocyanine units for $[t\text{-}bu_4PcRu(dib)]_n$ and 15–19 units for $[t\text{-}bu_4PcRu(me_4dib)]_n$. The chain length can be increased by boiling the compounds in $CHCl_3$ [111].

To study the effect of nonlinearity of the bridged compounds the unsymmetrically substituted ligand 1,3-diisocyanobenzene (*m*-dib) has been used for the preparation of phthalocyaninatometal complexes. The polynuclears and

Table 13. ^1H-NMR data of mononuclear, binuclear and trinuclear phthalocyaninatoiron and -ruthenium with me_4dib as terminal and bridging ligand. For the designation of protons H(a) to H(d), see a–d in Fig. 12[a]

Compound	$H^{(a)}$	$H^{(b)}$	$H^{(c)}$	$H^{(d)}$
$PcFe(me_4dib)_2$	1.59	0.07	—	—
$Pc_2Fe_2(me_4dib)_3$	1.51	– 0.07	– 0.71	—
$PcRu(me_4dib)_2$	1.60	0.08	—	—
$Pc_2Ru_2(me_4dib)_3$	[b]	– 0.06	– 0.69	—
$Pc_3Ru_3(me_4dib)_4$	[b]	– 0.05	– 0.76	– 0.82

[a] Chemical shifts in ppm; $CHCl_3$ (7.24) as internal standard[94];
[b] Peak hidden by the signal of H_2O

Table 14. Incremental isoshielding of the ring protons of the complexes $Pc_nRu_n(me_4dib)_{n+1}$ (n = 1, 2, 3) in ppm[94]

	3,6-Protons			4,5-Protons		
n	Outer ring found	Increment. shift	Inner ring calcd.	Outer ring found	Increment. shift	Inner ring calcd.
1	9.30		—	7.97		—
2	9.10	– 0.20	—	7.86	– 0.10	—
3	8.89	– 0.20	8.90	7.73	– 0.13	7.77

mononuclears with *m*-dib, $[R_mPcM(m\text{-dib})]_n$ ($m = 16$, R = H, Cl; $m = 8$, R = CH_3, OCH_3; M = e.g. Fe, Ru) and $PcM(m\text{-dib})_2$ (M = Fe, Ru) as ligands can be synthesized using the same methods as in the case of the dib and me_4dib compounds. The characterization however is more difficult [64, 93]. The IR spectrum of the free ligand *m*-dib shows three CN-frequencies. The mononuclears $PcM(m\text{-dib})_2$ and the polynuclears $[R_mPcM(m\text{-dib})]_n$ show the same behavior concerning the shift of the CN-frequencies as the $PcM(dib)_2$ mononuclears and the $[PcM(dib)]_n$ polynuclears.

The ^{57}Fe-Mößbauer data for mononuclear and bridged complexes with isocyanides as ligands are listed in Table 15. The quadrupole splitting ΔE_Q in these complexes is notably smaller than in other compounds $PcFeL_2$ with L = N-donor ligands, the isomer shift δ is also reduced. The value of ΔE_Q for 2,3-TNPFe$(dib)_2$ is the smallest reported for compounds of this type till now. The reasons for this behaviour are not fully understood; for a discussion see the publications 112, 113.

The conductivity data of the bridged complexes $[MacML]_n$ and of some mononuclear $MacML_2$ are listed in Table 10. In general the conductivities of the bridged complexes $[MacML]_n$ increase in comparison with the corresponding mononuclear $MacML_2$ by several orders of magnitude. In spite of the fact, that the interring distance in the dib-oligomers is larger as compared with the pyz-oligomers, the conductivities are in the same range ($\sim 10^{-5}$ S/cm). Peripheral substitution of the phthalocyanine ring by electron donating substituents has little effect on the conductivities of the corresponding compounds $[R_8PcFe(dib)]_n$ (R = CH_3, OCH_3) in comparison with the non-substituted compound $[PcFe(dib)]_n$. Only substitution of the phthalocyanine with chlorine has a noticeable effect. The conductivity of $[Cl_{16}PcFe(dib)]_n$ decreases to 3×10^{-11} S/cm [65].

Table 15. ^{57}Fe Mößbauer data of phthalocyaninatoiron(II) complexes with isocyanides as axial ligands [14, 66, 72, 94] (T = 293 K)

Complex	δ (mm s^{-1})[a,b]	ΔE_Q (mm s^{-1})[b]
$PcFe(t\text{-buNC})_2$	0.16(3)	0.79(5)
$PcFe(c\text{-hxNC})_2$	0.13(1)	0.69(3)
$PcFe(phNC)_2$	0.11(0)	0.67(8)
$PcFe(me_2phNC)_2$	0.12(2)	0.70(2)
$PcFe(Cl_4phNC)_2$	0.09(5)	0.67(5)
$PcFe(me_4dib)_2$	0.11(7)	0.65(8)
$[PcFe(me_4dib)]_n$	0.14(2)	0.69(7)
$[PcFe(Cl_4dib)]_n$	0.06(6)	0.74(5)
$[me_8PcFe(Cl_4dib)]_n$	0.07(0)	0.58(2)
$[2,3\text{-NcFe(dib)}]_n$	0.12(9)	0.57(9)
$[2,3\text{-TNPFe(c-hxNC)}]_2$	0.26	0.28
$2,3\text{-TNPFe(dib)}_2$	0.23	0.26
$[2,3\text{-TNPFe(dib)}]_n$	0.21	0.33

[a] Relative to metallic iron;
[b] Fit to a quadrupole doublet

Interesting compounds with respect to conductivity are the recently synthesized mononuclear and bridged dib-complexes with 2,3-Nc and 2,3-TNP as macrocycles [10, 14]. 2,3-NcFe(dib)$_2$, 2,3-TNPFe(dib)$_2$, [2,3-NcFe(dib)]$_n$ and [2,3-TNPFe(dib)]$_n$ show powder conductivities of 10^{-3}–10^{-4} S/cm without additional doping. The reason for the high values is, as in the case of the pyz-compounds, an oxygen doping as a consequence of the low oxidation potential of these complexes. In the case of 2,3-TNPFe(dib)$_2$ and [2,3-TNPFe(dib)]$_n$, oxygen contents of 4.4 and 6.4%, respectively, were found in the elemental analyses [14]. Contrary to [2,3-NcFe(dib)]$_n$ [1,2-NcFe(dib)]$_n$ has a much lower conductivity which could be explained by the fact, that 1,2-NcFe is a mixture of isomers [11]. Furthermore, the oxidation potential of 1,2-NcFe is much higher than that of 2,3-NcFe thereby inhibiting doping by air oxygen [14b].

Several of the bridged systems listed in Table 10 were doped with iodine (see Table 16). The doped compounds were characterized by standard spectroscopic methods including resonance Raman spectroscopy (indicating the presence of I_3^- and I_5^- counterions) and ^{57}Fe-Mößbauer spectroscopy. The

Table 16. Room temperature conductivity data (powder, 1 kbar) and activation energies of iodine-doped phthalocyaninatoiron(II) and -ruthenium(II) compounds with diisocyanides as bridging ligands

Compound	σ_{RT} [S/cm]	E_a [eV]	Ref.
[PcFe(dib)]$_n$	2×10^{-5}	0.25	[99, 114]
[PcFe(dib)I$_{1.4}$]$_n$	7×10^{-3}	0.14	[99, 114]
[PcFe(dib)I$_{3.0}$]$_n$	3×10^{-2}	0.10	[99, 114]
[PcRu(dib)]$_n$	2×10^{-6}	—	[64, 99]
[PcRu(dib)I$_{1.0}$]$_n$	1×10^{-3}	0.19	[99, 115]
[PcRu(dib)I$_{1.5}$]$_n$	4×10^{-3}	0.17	[99, 115]
[PcRu(dib)I$_{2.0}$]$_n$	7×10^{-3}	0.15	[99, 115]
[(CH$_3$)$_8$PcFe(dib)]$_n$	4×10^{-4}	0.22	[99, 114]
[(CH$_3$)$_8$PcFe(dib)I$_{2.7}$]$_n$	1×10^{-2}	0.12	[99, 114]
[(CH$_3$)$_8$PcFe(dib)I$_{3.6}$]$_n$	3×10^{-2}	0.11	[99, 114]
[PcFe(me$_4$dib)]$_n$	1×10^{-7}	0.60	[95, 99, 114]
[PcFe(me$_4$dib)I$_{0.5}$]$_n$	1×10^{-4}	0.28	[95, 99, 114]
[PcFe(me$_4$dib)I$_{1.5}$]$_n$	1×10^{-3}	0.17	[99, 114]
[PcFe(me$_4$dib)I$_{3.0}$]$_n$	2×10^{-2}	0.14	[99, 114]
[PcFe(Cl$_4$dib)]$_n$	4×10^{-6}	—	[95, 99, 114]
[PcFe(Cl$_4$dib)I$_{0.5}$]$_n$	6×10^{-4}	0.21	[99, 114]
[PcFe(Cl$_4$dib)I$_{1.5}$]$_n$	9×10^{-3}	0.13	[99]
[PcFe(Cl$_4$dib)I$_{2.6}$]$_n$	6×10^{-2}	—	[99]
[(CH$_3$)$_8$PcFe(Cl$_4$dib)]$_n$	5×10^{-6}	—	[95, 99]
[(CH$_3$)$_8$PcFe(Cl$_4$dib)I$_{2.7}$]$_n$	3×10^{-2}	—	[95, 99]
[PcFe(*m*-dib)]$_n$	2×10^{-6}	0.30	[93, 99]
[PcFe(*m*-dib)I$_{0.6}$]$_n$	1×10^{-3}	0.20	[93, 99]
[PcFe(*m*-dib)I$_{2.3}$]$_n$	2×10^{-2}	0.12	[93, 99]
[(CH$_3$)$_8$PcFe(*m*-dib)]$_n$	7×10^{-5}	0.23	[93, 99]
[(CH$_3$)$_8$PcFe(*m*-dib)I$_{1.0}$]$_n$	2×10^{-2}	0.12	[93, 99]
[(CH$_3$)$_8$PcFe(*m*-dib)I$_{1.6}$]$_n$	1×10^{-1}	0.08	[93, 99]
[PcFe(dibph)]$_n$	1×10^{-7}	—	[95, 99]
[PcFe(dibph)I$_{2.1}$]$_n$	2×10^{-3}	0.17	[99]
[PcFe(dibph)I$_{2.6}$]$_n$	3×10^{-2}	—	[99]

oligomers $[MacML]_n$ are not destroyed during the doping process. Via doping the conductivities can be increased to 10^{-3}–10^{-1} S/cm depending upon the iodine content [93, 94, 99, 114, 115]. In general, the thermal stabilities of all the iodine compounds listed in Table 16 are quite high: they will not loose iodine below 120 °C.

3.2 Complexes with Trivalent Metal Ions

Another type of bridged systems contains the central metal atom in the oxidation state + 3. Appropriate bridging ligands are negatively charged molecules as e.g. cyanide, thiocyanate or azide. The displacement of the axial anion X^- by bidentate CN^-, SCN^- or N_3^- (L^-) in a coordinatively unsaturated compound PcMX (X = Cl, OAc, CCl_3COO) provides a direct path to coordination oligomers $[PcML]_n$. This route has been utilized for the synthesis of cyano complexes $[PcM(CN)]_n$ (M = Fe [116], Mn [117]), thiocyanato complexes $[PcM(SCN)]_n$ (M = Fe [66], Mn [118]), Co [119], and azido complexes $[PcM(N_3)]_n$ (M = Cr [118], Mn [118]).

The starting materials PcFeCl [120] and PcMnCl [121] were prepared from the parent phthalocyanines, PcFe and PcMn, respectively, by treatment with chlorinating agents (see Scheme 12). PcMOAc [122] (M = Cr, Mn) was obtained by air oxidation of PcM (M = Cr, Mn) in acetic acid. A third precursor, $PcCoCCl_3COO \times CCl_3COOH$ [123] was synthesized by reaction of PcCo with CCl_3COOH in CH_2Cl_2. The chlorides and acetates PcMX (X = Cl, OAc, CCl_3COO) were converted into the bridged complexes $[PcML]_n$ in aqueous or ethanolic alkalimetal-cyanide, -thiocyanate and -azide solutions [66, 116–119].

Suitable halogeno precursors for the cobalt and chromium compounds $[PcCoCN]_n$ [124] and $[PcCrCN]_n$ [117] are not known. The reported synthesis of PcCoCl [2b] actually produces impure $PcCoCl_2$ [81]; the oxidation product of PcCo with excess of iodine is reported to lead to a species, formulated as $[Pc^{2-}Co^{3+}I^{1-}]$ [43, 125]. However, in the case of 2,3-TNP as macrocycle chlorination leads to the monomeric pentacoordinated species 2,3-TNPCoCl [14]. This compound exhibits an electrical conductivity of nearly 10^{-1} S/cm which, as in the case of the dib-complexes of 2,3-TNPFe, is caused by an additional oxidative doping of the macrocycle with oxygen.

If 2,3-TNPCoCl is reacted with an alkali metal cyanide, the product is not the bridged compound $[2,3\text{-TNPCo(CN)}]_n$ but the pentacoordinated "monomer" 2,3-TNPCoCN. The same product is obtained by in situ oxidation of 2,3-TNPCo with oxygen in the presence of excess cyanide [14]. Similarly taaCo forms the pentacoordinated compound taaCoCN as shown by its X-ray crystal structure [126].

A convenient method for the introduction of the $Pc^{2-}M^{3+}$-unit into the reaction path, starting from the known dichloroderivatives $PcCoCl_2$ [121] and $PcCrCl_2$ [121], has been developed [117, 124]. Again the educts were converted into the oligomers in an aqueous alkali–metal-cyanide [116, 117, 122]

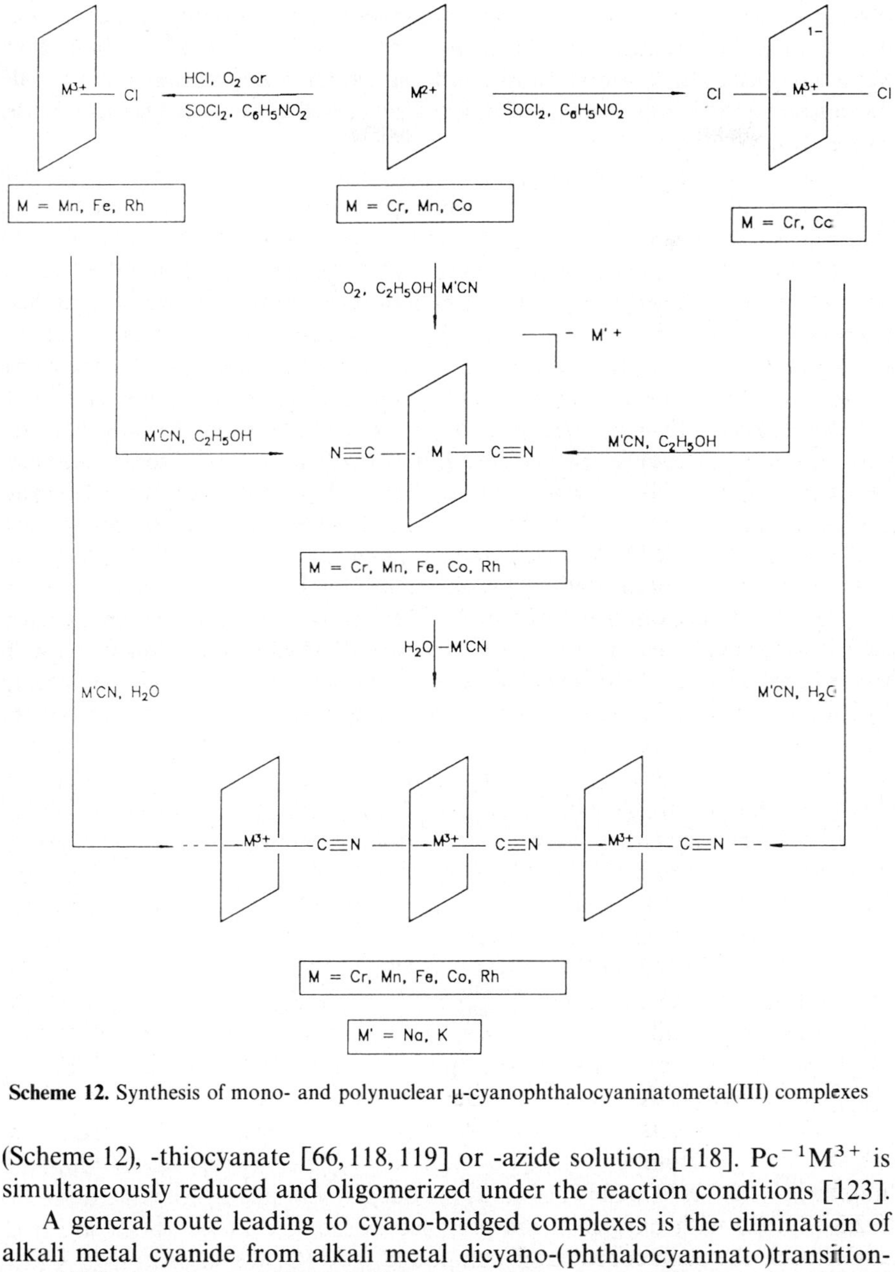

Scheme 12. Synthesis of mono- and polynuclear μ-cyanophthalocyaninatometal(III) complexes

(Scheme 12), -thiocyanate [66, 118, 119] or -azide solution [118]. $Pc^{-1}M^{3+}$ is simultaneously reduced and oligomerized under the reaction conditions [123].

A general route leading to cyano-bridged complexes is the elimination of alkali metal cyanide from alkali metal dicyano-(phthalocyaninato)transition-metal(III) complexes $M'[PcM(CN)_2]$ (see Scheme 12; M' = Na, K; M = Cr [117], Mn [117], Fe [114], Co [124], Rh [127]). The same method can be used to form $[PcCo(SCN)]_n$ from $K[PcCo(NCS)_2]$ [119].

The syntheses of the complexes $M'[PcM(CN)_2]$ and $K[PcCo(NCS)_2]$ were possible either by in situ oxidation of PcM (M = Mn, Co) with oxygen in the presence of excess cyanide or by reaction of the chloro derivatives $PcMCl_2$ (M=Cr, Co) and PcMCl (M=Mn, Fe, Rh) with alkali metal cyanide or of $PcCoCl_2$ with alkali metal thiocyanate in ethanol or acetone [119]. The oligomers $[PcM(CN)]_n$ are formed by treatment of the mononuclear complexes $M'[PcM(CN)_2]$ with water.

According to the described methods, cyano-bridged compounds containing other types of macrocycles e.g. tetrabenzoporphyrin (TBP) [7c] can be synthesized. In the presence of cyanide and oxygen, TBPCo is converted into $H[TBPCo(CN)_2]$, which decomposes in boiling water to $[TBPCo(CN)]_n$ and cyanide [128]. Likewise a cyanobridged Co^{III}-dimethylglyoximato oligomer $[dmgH_2CoCN]_n$ has been synthesized [129]. $[dmgH_2CoCN]_n$ shows a better electrical conductivity than the corresponding mononuclear compounds, but values are low compared to $[PcCo(CN)]_n$ and $[TBPCo(CN)]_n$ (see Table 17).

The mononuclear complexes $M'[PcM(CN)_2]$ (M'=Na, K; M=Cr, Mn, Fe, Co, Rh) were characterized by IR-, FIR-, UV/VIS- and in some cases by ^{1}H-NMR spectroscopy. The IR data (see Table 17) exhibit CN valence frequencies around 2130 cm^{-1}, which are in the anticipated region for terminal Co^{III}, Cr^{III} and Rh^{III} cyano groups [130]. The absorption of the Mn derivative at 2114 cm^{-1} also correlates with reported data [130].

The CN valence frequencies of the bridged compounds shift to higher energy as compared with the mononuclear complexes $M'[PcM(CN)_2]$. This increase in CN valence frequencies is a good indication for the presence of a cyano bridge in $[PcM(CN)]_n$ [129]. Powder X-ray diffraction measurements give evidence

Table 17. IR-, TG/DTA- and room temperature electrical conductivity data (powder, 1 kbar) for mono- and polynuclear cyano metal complexes of macrocyclic ligands

Compound	ν_{CN} [cm^{-1}][a]	Dissociation range for the cyano group [°C] TG/DTA data[b]	Mass loss calc./found [%][c]	Conductivities [S/cm] 10^8 Pa
$M'[PcCo(CN)_2]$[d]	2130	280–310	3.5/4.0 (–CN)	—
$M'[PcRh(CN)_2]$[d]	2130	220–440	7.2/8.4 (–2CN)	3×10^{-9} [e]
$K[PcCr(CN)_2]$	2133	310–455	3.6/2.8 (–CN)	6×10^{-9} [e]
$K[PcMn(CN)_2]$	2114	250–380	3.5/2.7 (–CN)	5×10^{-6} [f]
$K_2[PcFe(CN)_2]$	2065	—	—	—
$H[TBPCo(CN)_2]$	2121	—	—	—
$[PcCo(CN)]_n$	2158	220–300	4.4/4.7 (–CN)	2×10^{-2} [f]
$[PcRh(CN)]_n$	2160	200–350	4.0/3.7 (–CN)	4×10^{-4} [f]
$[PcFe(CN)]_n$	2133	170–230	4.5/5.0 (–CN)	6×10^{-3} [f]
$[PcCr(CN)]_n$	2150	170–300	4.4/3.9 (–CN)	3×10^{-6} [e]
$[PcMn(CN)]_n$	2133	250[g]	—	1×10^{-5} [f]
$[HPcFe(CN)]_n$	2060	170–250	4.4/5.5 (–CN)	8×10^{-4} [f]
$[TBPCo(CN)]_n$	2138	185–285	4.4/4.2 (–CN)	4×10^{-2} [f]
2,3-TNPCoCN	2123	—	—	2×10^{-3} [f]

[a] Nujol mulls;
[b] Heating rate 2 K/min, N_2;
[c] Endothermic mass loss;
[d] M' = Na or K;
[e] Four-probe technique;
[f] Two-probe technique;
[g] Decomposition

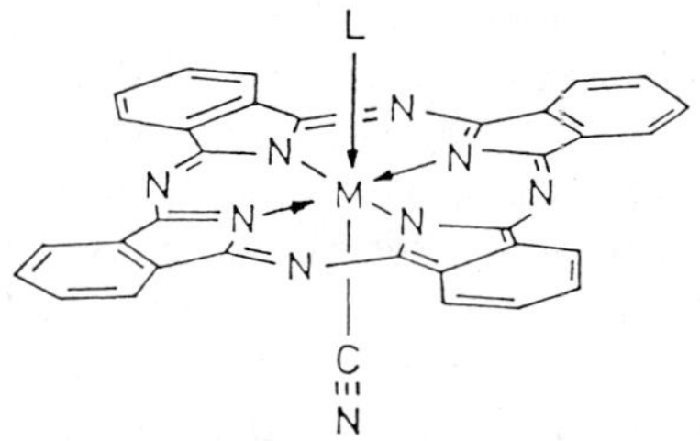

Fig. 13. Mononuclear phthalocyaninatometal complexes with two different axial ligands PcM(L)CN

for an isostructural lattice in the compounds $[PcM(CN)]_n$ (M = Cr, Mn, Fe, Co, Rh).

The oligomers exhibit thermal stabilities up to 200–250 °C and are almost insoluble in non-coordinating solvents. The bridged structure $[PcM(CN)]_n$ is destroyed, when the material is treated with bases L such as pyridine (py) (M = Mn, Fe, Co, Rh), 2-methylpyrazine (mepyz) (M = Co), piperidine (pip) (M = Co) and *n*-butylamine (ba) (M = Co, Rh), yielding mononuclear complexes with the composition PcM(L)CN [124, 127] (see Fig. 13).

The conductivities shown in Table 17 were determined by the usual two- or four-probe manner. The complexes $[PcM(CN)]_n$ exhibit comparatively high electrical conductivities between 10^{-6} and 10^{-2} S/cm without additional doping. When the bridged structure is destroyed by treatment with a competing ligand L to form PcM(L)CN, the conductivities drop 6–10 orders of magnitude down to 10^{-12} S/cm.

The mononuclear and oligonuclear thiocyanate and azide compounds $K[PcCo(NCS)]_2$, $[PcM(SCN)]_n$ (M = Mn, Fe, Co) and $[PcM(N_3)]_n$ (M = Cr, Mn) were characterized by IR- and FIR-spectroscopy, magnetic measurements, thermogravimetrical, microanalytical and powder diffraction analysis [117]. The IR spectrum of $K[PcCo(NCS)_2]$ shows an intense CN valence frequency at 2095 cm^{-1}. In agreement with former investigations on metal-thiocyanate complexes the frequency shifts to higher energy in $[PcCo(SCN)]_n$ [119] compared to the mononuclear $K[PcCo(NCS)_2]$ [131].

The X-ray structure analysis of N_3-bridged $[Mn(acac)_2(N_3)]_n$ (ν_{N3} = 2050 cm^{-1}) [132] and SCN-bridged $[Mn(acac)_2(NCS)]_n$ (ν_{CN} = 2080 cm^{-1}) [133] were reported. Comparing these data with the frequencies of $[PcMn(N_3)]_n$ [118] and $[PcMn(SCN)]_n$ [118] it seems obvious that they are bridged, as is $[PcCo(SCN)]_n$. All SCN-bridged systems show comparable powder diffraction patterns which give evidence for an isostructural lattice [119].

With the exception of $[PcMn(SCN)]_n$, which looses the thiocyanate unit between 350 and 485 °C [118], $[PcM(SCN)]_n$ (M = Fe, Co) and $[PcM(N_3)]_n$ (M = Cr, Mn) compounds are less stable than the cyano-bridged species.

The thiocyanate- and azido-bridged compounds are almost insoluble in all non-coordinating solvents. When treated with N-donor bases (L), either a reaction to mononuclear complexes PcM(L)SCN [117] or a reduction to the

M^{II}-species $PcM(L)_2$ [66] takes place. On the other hand, the very stable $[PcMn(N_3)]_n$ does not react with pyridine even under forcing conditions [118].

The conductivities of the thiocyanato- and azido-complexes are listed in Table 18. As compared with the cyano-bridged complex $[PcM(CN)]_n$ (M = Cr, Mn, Fe, Co, Rh) a longer metal–metal-distance or the angular ligand–metal-bond may be the reason for the lower conductivities. The activation energy of the best conducting thiocyanate compound $[PcCo(SCN)]_n$, which was measured to be 0.22 eV, suggests a larger energy-gap between valence and conduction band than in the cyanide bridged complexes.

Recently penta-coordinated PcCoCN, which differs in its spectral properties from $[PcCo(CN)]_n$, was obtained electrochemically from $K[PcCo(CN)_2]$ [134]. The obtained crystals were investigated by X-ray analysis and a structure was proposed for the compound [134]. These crystals showed conductivities up to 5 S/cm^{-1} [135]. This led to an investigation of the electrochemical behavior of compounds $A[MacMX_2]$ with A = Na, K, *t*-bu_4N, Mac = Pc, TBP, 2,3-Nc, M = Co, Rh, Fe, Ru, Cr, Mn, and X = CNS, CN by cyclic voltammetry in acetone [135b]. It was demonstrated that the first oxidation process occurs on the macrocycle leading to a $(Mac^{\dot{-}})M^{3+}(CN^-)_2$ radical species. Detailed spectroscopic studies concerning the products of galvanostatic and potentiostatic electrocrystallization of e.g. $Na[PcCo(CN)_2]$ or $K[PcRh(CN)_2]$ in acetone clearly demonstrated an oxidation of the macrocycle. This is in accordance with recently reported structures of crystals obtained by electrochemical oxidation of $K[PcCo(CN)_2]$ [135c].

Recent investigations on $[PcCo(CN)]_n$ give evidence that this type of compound also shows good photoconductivity [136].

Solutions of $[PcCo(CN)]_n$ and the aromatic polyamide Kevlar in concentrated H_2SO_4 can be wet-spun to produce flexible darkly colored fibres. Even

Table 18. IR-, TG/DTA- and room temperature electrical conductivity data (powder, 1 kbar) of mono- and polynuclear thiocyanato- and azidophthalocyaninatometal complexes

Compound	ν_{CN} [cm^{-1}][a]	Dissociation range [°C] TG/DTA data[b]	Mass loss calc./found [%][c]	Conductivities [S/cm] 10^8 Pa
$K[PcCo(NCS)_2]\cdot EtOH$	2095	90–500	21.0/10.0 (–2SCN)[d]	—
$[PcCo(SCN)]_n$	2110	140–350	9.2/9.0 (–SCN)	6×10^{-3} [e]
PcCo(py)SCN	2105	160–350	16.9/18.9 (–py, –SCN)	1×10^{-7} [f]
$[PcFe(SCN)]_n$	2118	155–500	9.0/8.6 (–SCN)	9×10^{-5} [e]
$[PcMn(SCN)]_n$	2090	350–495	9.0/8.3 (–SCN)	—
$[PcCr(N_3)]_n$[g]	2050	195–270	6.9/6.4 ($-N_3$)	1×10^{-8} [f]
$[PcMn(N_3)]_n$[g]	2055	260–320	6.9/6.7 ($-N_3$)	3×10^{-10} [f]

[a] Nujol mulls;
[b] Heating rate 2 K/min. N2;
[c] Endothermic mass loss;
[d] Mass loss 21% is calc. for cleavage of crystal solvent EtOH plus that of the ligand: incomplete decomposition;
[e] Four-probe technique;
[f] Two-probe technique;
[g] ν_{NN}

without additional doping the conductivity of a fibre containing 30% of the cyano-polymer is about 10^{-4} S/cm [137].

In addition to $[PcFe(CN)]_n$ and $[PcFe(SCN)]_n$ a new bridging ligand, the imidazolate anion (im^-) was used to prepare $[PcFe(im)]_n$ [93]. The oligomer was characterized by IR-, FIR-, UV/VIS spectra, and thermal analysis. $[PcFe(im)]_n$ exhibits a paramagnetic moment of 2.1 B.M. which is temperature independent in analogy to $[TPPFe(im)]_n$ [138]. The conductivity is about 10^{-5} S/cm; doping with iodine leads to unstable compounds, which completely loose iodine within a short period of time.

Recently the first example of a novel type of a one-dimensional bridged system, consisting of phthalocyanine radical species, was reported [139]. μ-Ethynyl-(phthalocyaninato)-cobalt(III) was synthesized by the reaction of dichlorophthalocyaninato(1-)cobalt(III) with bis(bromomagnesium)acetylide. The one-dimensional structure was confirmed by an IR spectrum and X-ray analysis. The conductivity was found to be 3×10^{-4} S/cm at room temperature without doping. This conductivity was explained by an increase of the density of the charge carriers induced by the radical phthalocyanine rings. Carbanionic complexes $Li_2[PcFe(C{\equiv}CR)_2] \times 7$ THF ($R = C_6H_5$ [140], *t*-bu [141]) having substituted bisaxial alkynyl ligands represent the mononuclear structural features of this new type of polymers. These bisalkynyl complexes were prepared by the anionic organylation of PcFe with the corresponding organolithium compounds.

4 Liquid Crystals

Solid materials which upon heating do not become isotropic liquids are called thermotropic liquid crystals. Within a definite temperature range they exhibit one or more phases between the solid and the liquid state. Thermotropic discotic crystalline liquids, introduced in 1977 by Chandrasekhar [142], are formed from organic compounds possessing mostly a flat aromatic nucleus [143, 144] which is surrounded by long mobile aliphatic chains. The majority of these compounds have hexagonal, tetragonal or trigonal symmetry. The molecules are mainly [145] stacked in columns (see Fig. 14).

The longer the aliphatic chains, the longer is the distance separating the single columns. The columns can for instance form a hexagonal arrangement as determined by X-ray analysis [145b, 146]. Besides this hexagonal lattice it is generally also possible to build rectangular and oblique lattices. These arrangements are schematically depicted in Fig. 15 [146]. Some examples of molecules having liquid crystalline characteristics are given in Fig. 16.

For certain compounds it is of interest that a tilted columnar structure is avoided, so that possibilities open up for manufacturing materials with semiconducting properties which should be useful for electronic and opto-electronic

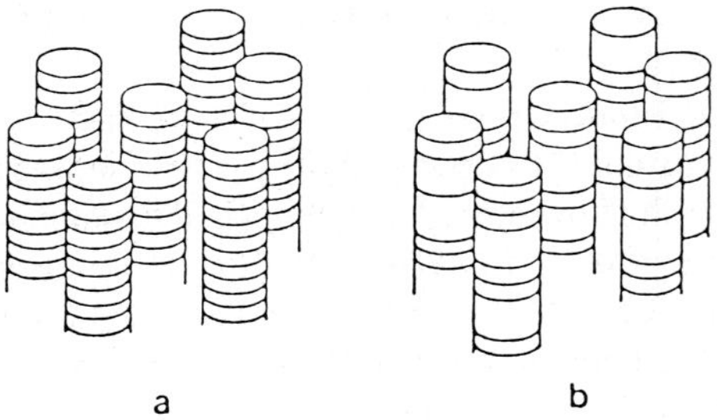

Fig. 14a,b. Columnar arrangement of thermotropic discotics. **a**) ordered: symbol D_o, **b**) disordered: symbol D_d (Permission for printing)

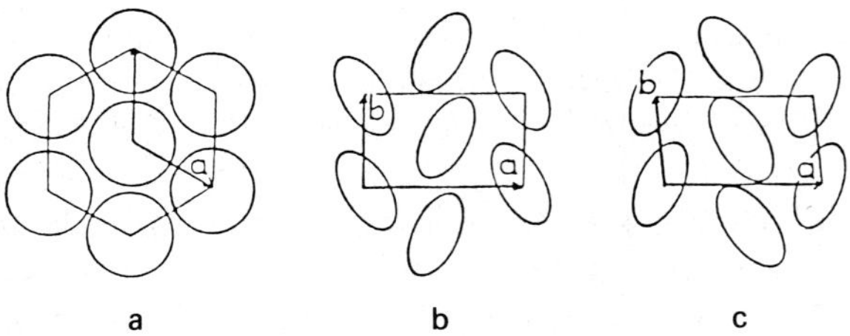

Fig. 15. Modifications of the columnar structure (cross section) **a**) hexagonal, **b**) rectangular, **c**) oblique (Permission for printing)

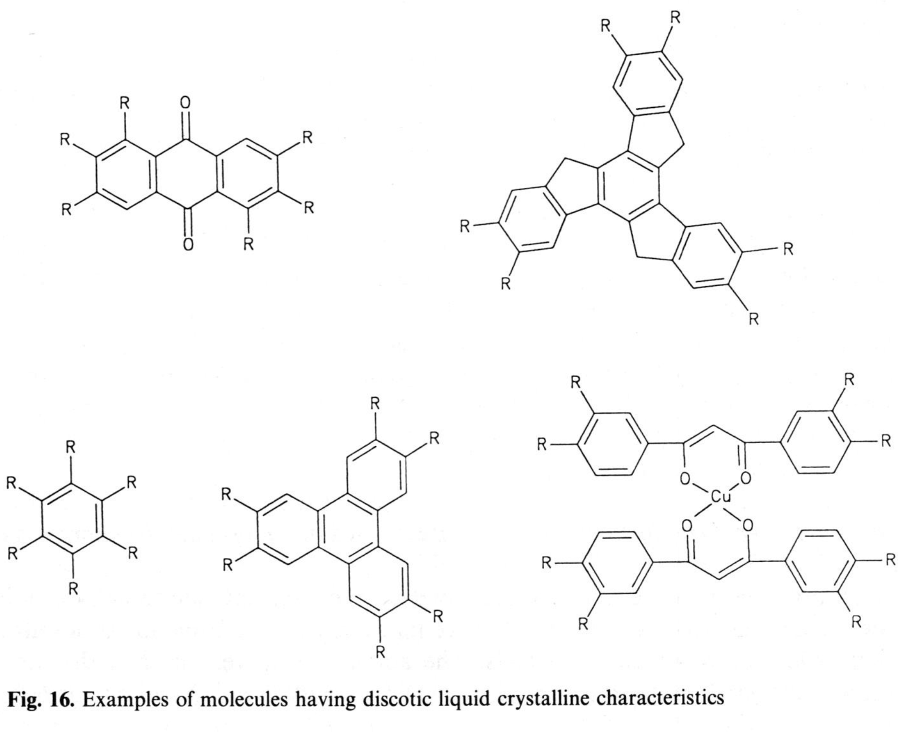

Fig. 16. Examples of molecules having discotic liquid crystalline characteristics

devices. Due to the liquid crystalline behavior of these materials it is difficult to measure their conductivities, as they lack a defined geometry. The electrical properties of liquid crystalline phthalocyanines have been determined for example by complex impedance spectroscopy measurements [147a]. Thus it was possible to observe that liquid crystalline phthalocyanines with a hexagonal ordered columnar (D_{ho}) mesophase show a slight increase in conductivity when going from the solid to the mesophase. The conductivities of these compounds are low (approx. 5×10^{-10} S/cm) [147b]. Higher conductivities are obtained if crown ether phthalocyanines (see Sect. 4.3) are aggregated by adding metal picrate salts (about 10^{-6} to 10^{-7} S/cm) [147c]; other phthalocyaninato-complexes reach conductivities of about 10^{-7} S/cm [147d]. With the help of a special device the reorientation of the liquid crystalline domains could be observed [147e]. Thereby it was evidenced that one-dimensional conduction of stacks of octa-*n*-dodecaoxyphthalocyanine in the liquid crystalline mesophase takes place [147c].

Charge transport along the stacking axis due to interactions between single macrocycles is the basis for semiconducting properties. The arrangement of the single molecules within the columns can hereby be ordered or disordered In an ordered arrangement the particles are separated by the same distances whereas they are separated by different distances in the disordered case. Besides this fact, some compounds show a kind of superposition of the two arrangements which is characterized by a periodic modulation of the electron density within the columnar structures [146c, 146d].

The nomenclature of discotic liquid crystals depends on the arrangement of the compounds (molecules) in columnar or nematic structures. Within a short spatial range and in the temporal and spatial average the longitudinal axes of nematic molecules are oriented parallel to each other.

4.1 Phthalocyanines and Porphyrins as Discotic Liquid Crystals

By introducing long chain substituents in the periphery of phthalocyaninato- and porphyrinatometal complexes it is possible to obtain discotic liquid crystals [148, 149] (see Fig. 17) [150].

4.1.1 Non-polymeric Liquid Crystals Based on Phthalocyanine and Porphyrin

Non-polymeric, liquid crystals are divided into thermotropic and lyotropic liquid crystals. Compounds which have liquid crystalline behavior in solution are called lyotropic liquid crystals. The amount of solvent is then the most important variable. Mainly thermotropic liquid crystals will be discussed here.

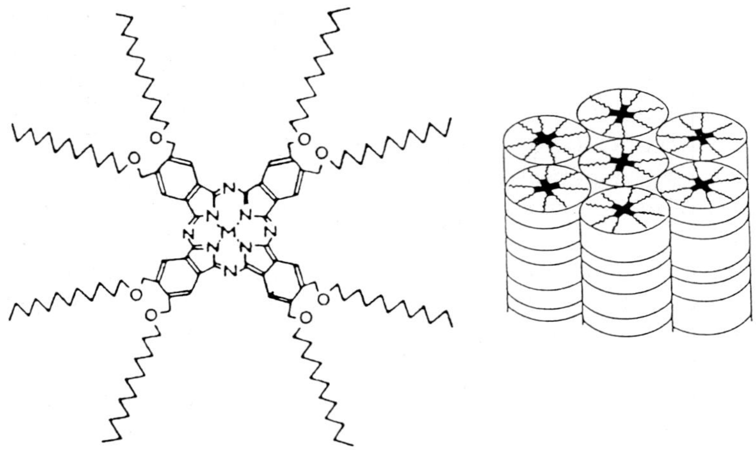

Fig. 17. Phthalocyanine with long peripheral substituents (stacked arrangement)

4.1.1.1 Thermotropic Low Molecular Weight Liquid Crystals

Phthalocyanines and porphyrins with various substituents and central metal atoms have been found to form thermotropic liquid crystals. Examples of phthalocyanines are shown in Fig. 18 [148a–c, 148e–f, 151, 152, 153a].

The desired liquid crystals are generally synthesized from substituted orthodibromobenzene. In a Rosenmund-von-Braun reaction it is converted into the corresponding dicyano compound. Treatment with ammonia leads to the isoindoline from which the substituted phthalocyanine is obtained (Scheme 13).

Scheme 14 summarizes the synthetical routes leading to alkyl-, alkoxy-, alkoxymethyl- and 4-(dodecyloxy)-2-oxa-pentyl-substituted orthodibromobenzenes.

Octaalkyl-substituted phthalocyanine [152] can be synthesized by bromination of dialkylbenzene accessible via a Grignard reaction. The synthesis of the alkoxy-substituted phthalocyanines [153] starts from catechol. The reaction with alkylhalide is followed by a bromination in positions 4 and 5. Alkoxymethyl-substituted phthalocyanines [154] are obtained by substitution of *o*-xylene with bromine and subsequent radical bromination of the two methyl groups of 1,2-dibromo-4,5-dimethylbenzene. The alkoxy groups are introduced by reacting the tetrabromo compound with the corresponding alcoholate.

Up to now, mostly statistical methods have been used for the synthesis of unsymmetrically substituted phthalocyanines. For more details see chapter 5.1. For instance, 1,2,4,5-tetracyanobenzene is reacted with ammonia to the cyano-substituted isoindoline which is then added to the alkoxymethyl substituted isoindoline [148b] (Scheme 15).

1,4,8,11,15,18,22,25-octa-alkyl- (and octa-alkoxy) phthalocyanines are synthesized via 2,5-dialkylfurans [148f], as shown in Scheme 16.

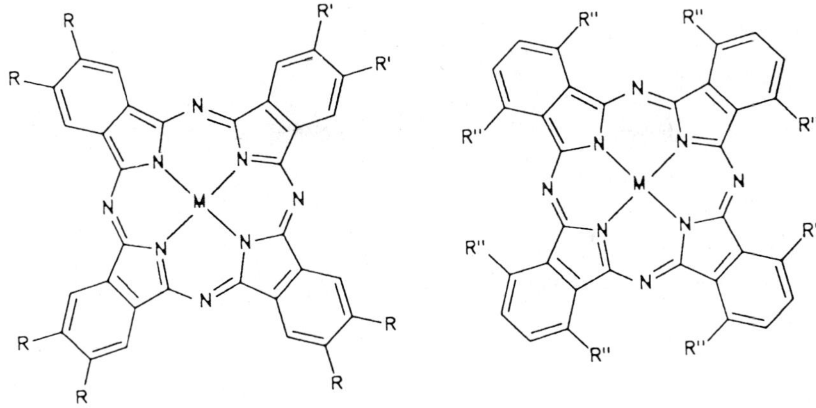

R = R′ = —$CH_2OC_8H_{17}$
= —$CH_2OC_{12}H_{25}$
= —$CH_2OC_{18}H_{37}$
= —$CH_2SC_{12}H_{25}$
= —$OC_{12}H_{25}$
= —$C_{12}H_{25}$
R = —$CH_2OC_{12}H_{25}$
R′ = —CN

R″ = —C_nH_{2n+1}, n = 4, 5, 6, 7, 8, 9, 10

$$R = R' = —CH_2O—CH(CH_2OC_{12}H_{25})_2$$

$$R = R' = —CH_2O—CH_2—CH_2(—OCH_2—CH_2—)_nOCH_3 \quad n = 1, 7, 14$$

M = H_2, Zn, Pb, Sn, Ni, Co, Cu, $SiCl_2$, $Si(OH)_2$

Fig. 18. Substituted phthalocyaninato complexes forming thermotropic liquid crystals

A cholesteric phase represents a special case of a nematic phase. The planes of adjacent molecules are also parallel, but the longitudinal axis of adjacent planes are turned about a definite angle. The result is a screw structure of the system. Cholesteric thermotropic liquid crystalline phthalocyanines are also known. (+)-2,3,9,10,16,17,23,24-octakis[4-(dodecyloxy)-2-oxapentyl]phthalocyanine (preparation see Schemes 13 and 14) shows a texture typical for cholesteric phases [155]. At 160 °C, this compound gives a fluid isotropic phase. Upon cooling an anisotropic phase appears at 153 °C. The texture similar to platelets (blue phase) changes at 66 °C to typical cholesteric fan-shape structure and remains fan-shaped down to room temperature. Except for the discotic

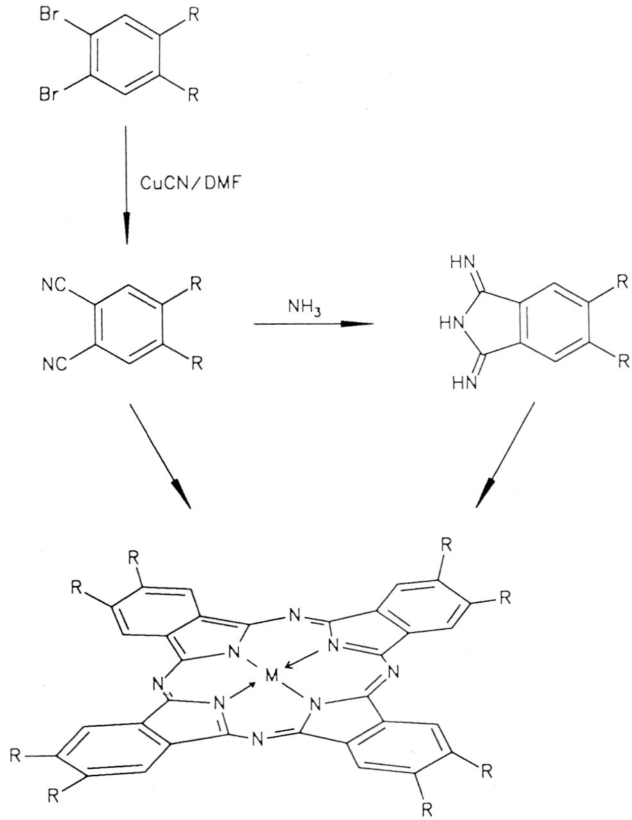

M = H_2, Ni, Pb, Sn, Co, Zn, Cu, $SiCl_2$, $Si(OH)_2$

R = CH_2Oalkyl

= Oalkyl

= alkyl

= crown ether

Scheme 13. Synthesis of substituted phthalocyaninato complexes from corresponding substituted dinitriles and isoindolines.

cholesteric substance, fluid phases have not been observed for liquid crystalline phthalocyanines.

Liquid crystalline porphyrins carrying ester substituents of various chain lengths (see Fig. 19) behave differently [148g]. Some of these compounds show two liquid crystalline phases before they melt yielding isotropic liquids with low viscosity.

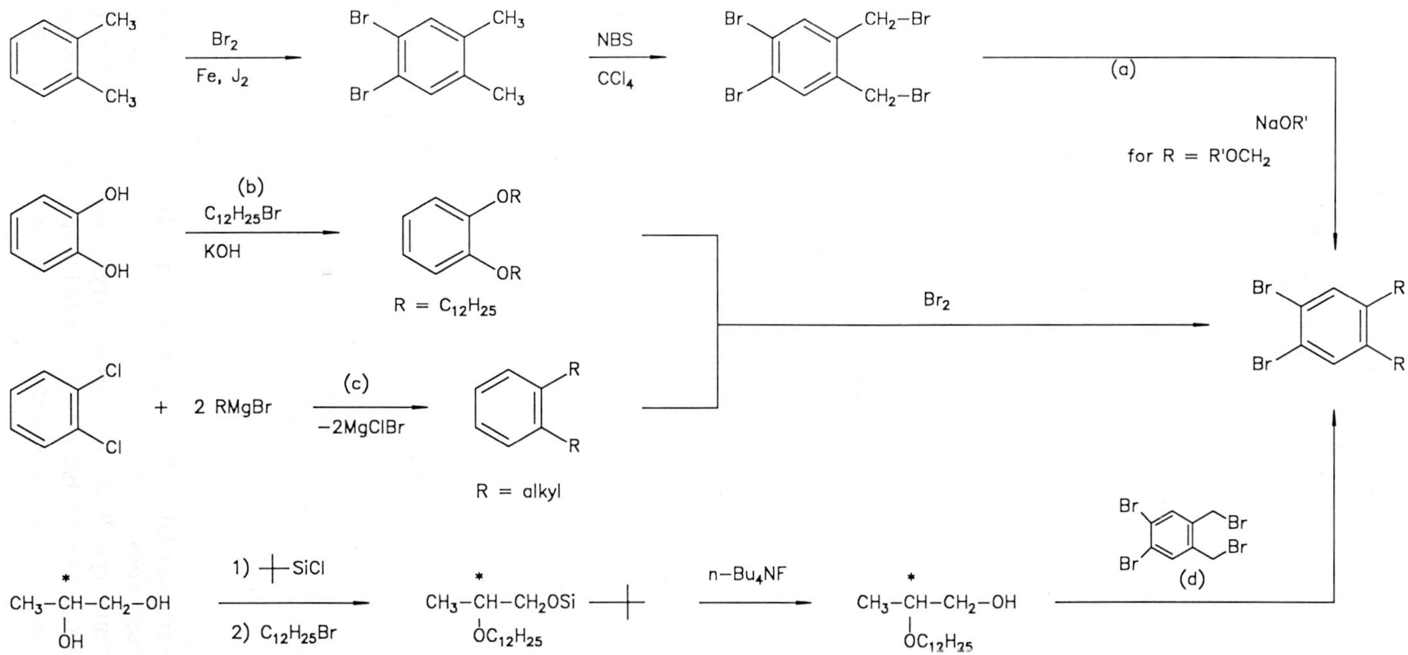

Scheme 14. Syntheses of substituted *o*-dibromobenzenes [R = *n*-alkoxymethyl (a), *n*-alkoxy (b), *n*-alkyl (c) or (2-*n*-alkoxypropyl)oxymethyl (d)]

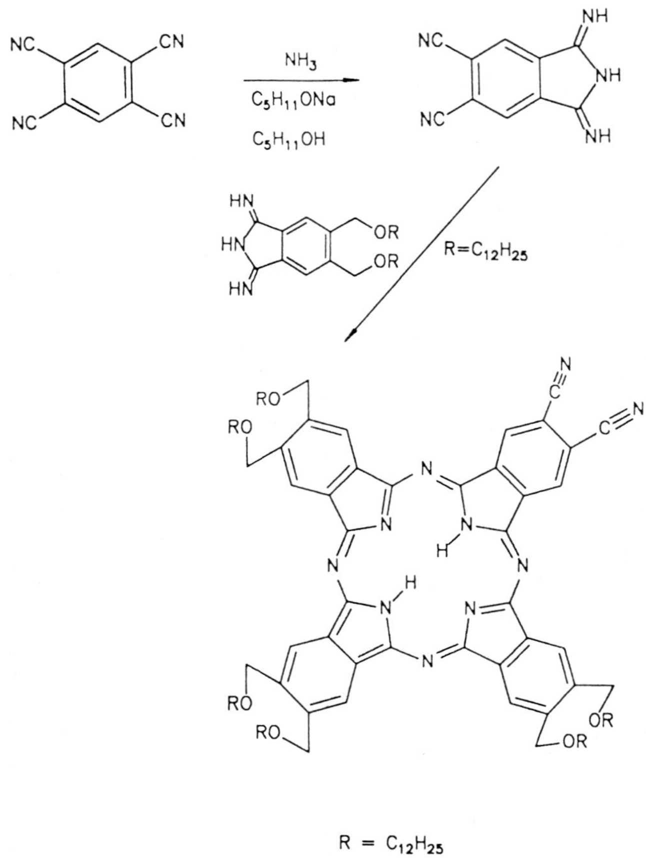

Scheme 15. Synthesis of noncentrosymmetrically substituted phthalocyanines

Some characteristics of non-polymeric, thermotropic, crystallinic liquids based on phthalocyanines and porphyrins are observed via DSC-measurements and UV spectra.

DSC-measurements show endothermic transition changes for liquid crystalline phthalocyanines and porphyrins. An often observed phenomenon is a decrease in phase change temperature when the substances are cooled starting from the liquid crystalline region [156].

It is remarkable that transition temperatures often decrease with increasing chain lengths of the peripheral substituents. Dispersion forces between the molecules are larger for longer chains. The liquid crystalline state in this type of compound is rather similar to the solid state. Therefore contrary to molecules with shorter chains the mesophase is reached at a lower temperature. From the enthalpy values it can be deduced that the transition from the solid to the liquid crystalline domain mainly corresponds to the melting of the flexible chains.

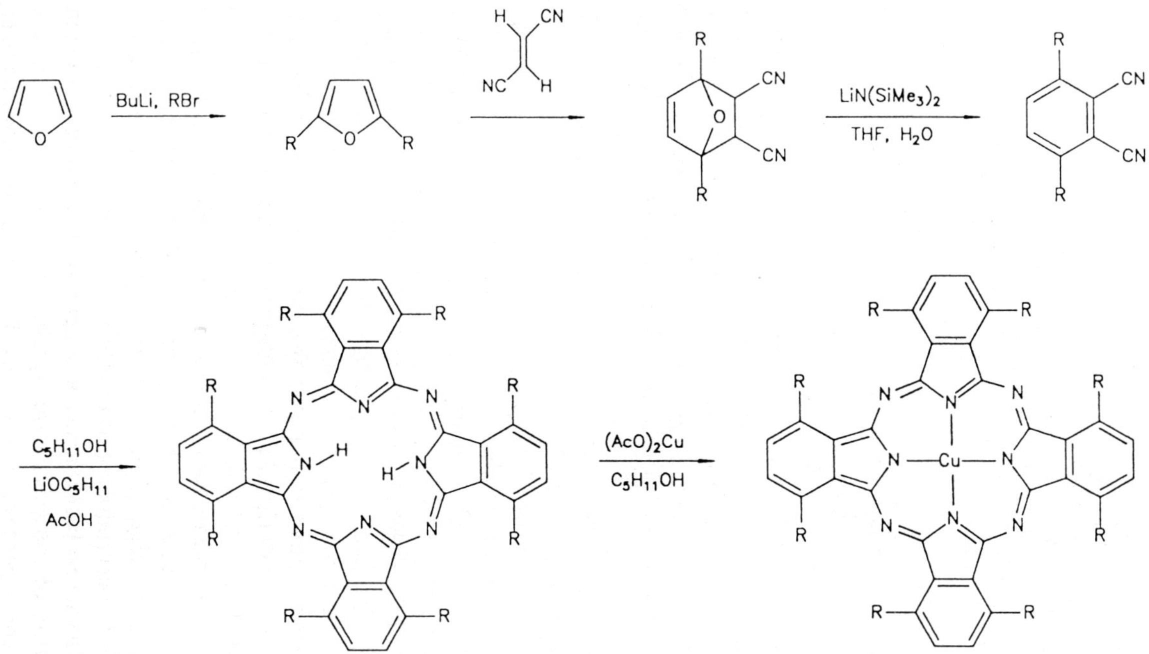

R = C_4H_9, C_5H_{11}, C_6H_{13}, C_7H_{15}, C_8H_{17}, C_9H_{19}, $C_{10}H_{21}$, OC_5H_{11}, OC_8H_{17}

Scheme 16. Synthesis of 1,4,8,11,15,18,22,25-octaalkylphthalocyanines

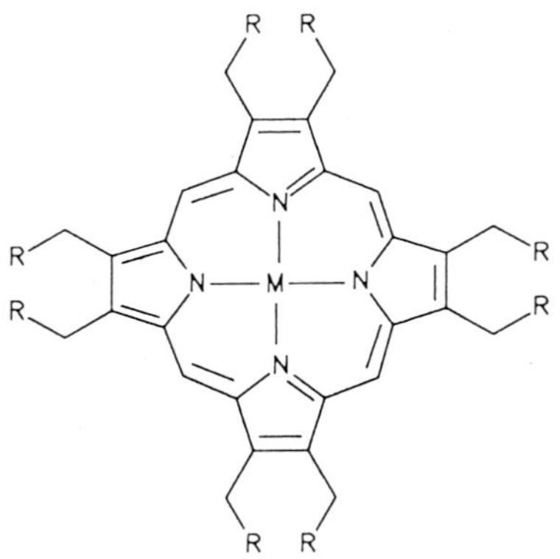

a: M = 2H

b: M = Zn

R = $CO_2H(M{=}H_2$ only)

R = $CO_2[CH_2]_3Me$

R = $CO_2[CH_2]_5Me$

R = $CO_2[CH_2]_7Me$

Fig. 19. Porphyrins forming liquid crystals

The values however are much smaller than for smectic materials [157]. This either implies that the aliphatic chains are not as disordered in the mesophase as in other liquid crystals or that they are not as ordered in the solid state as they usually are in their simple form in the crystal [146c]. The following tables represent transitions of selected liquid crystalline phthalocyanines and porphyrins.

The longer the alkyl chains on the R″-substituted phthalocyanines, the lower become the transition temperatures. The transition D → I even varies linearly. For M = Cu instead of M = H_2 the D domain of the mesophase is enlarged, which means that the D-phase is thermally more stable.

With the help of UV spectroscopy the association of phthalocyanines can be observed (Fig. 20) [158]. Soluble phthalocyanines, but especially liquid crystalline phthalocyanine compounds are susceptible to forming aggregates [148c, 159]. This leads to a significant shift in the maximum of absorption in the visible range as well as to a broadening of the peaks. The degree of aggregation depends on the nature of the central atom as was demonstrated by investigations of tetrakis(cumylphenoxy)-phthalocyanine aggregates [160]. An equilibrium distribution is formed consisting of monomers, dimers and oligomers. It depends on the concentration and the substituents on the phthalocyanine as well as the central atom. Phthalocyanines having Ni, Pd or Pt as central atoms tend to form aggregates in which more than two molecules are associated [148c, 160]. This originates from the d^8-electron configuration of the central metals. When a complex is formed all of the bonding and nonbonding but none of the anti-bonding levels are occupied.

Emission spectra of 2,3,9,10,16,17,23,24-octa(1-dodecyloxymethyl)-29*H*,31*H*-phthalocyanine were also used in order to prove the formation of aggregates [150] (see, however, Ref. 147b). Due to the sensitivity of the emission towards changes in concentration the observation of luminescence is especially suited for this kind of investigation. The measurements indeed reveal a strong

Table 19. Transition temperatures and corresponding enthalpies (kJ/mole) for substituted phthalocyanines (R, R′, and R″ are defined in Fig. 18; R″ = H in every case; see Ref. [148a–c, 148e, 151, 152, 153a]

Compound			Transitions	
R		M	K ⟶ D	⟶ I
$-CH_2OC_{18}H_{37}$		Pb	46 (213. 5)	
$-CH_2OC_{12}H_{25}$		Pb	− 12 (27.2)	
$-CH_2OC_{12}H_{25}$		Co	52 (57.6)	
$-CH_2OC_{12}H_{25}$		Ni	57 (28.6)	
$-CH_2OC_{12}H_{25}$		Cu	53	
$-CH_2OC_{12}H_{25}$		Zn	78	
$-CH_2OC_{12}H_{25}$		Mn	44	280
$-CH_2OC_{12}H_{25}$		H_2	78 (115.1)	260 (4.2)
$-CH_2OC_8H_{17}$		Pb	− 45 (2.1)	155
$-CH_2OC_8H_{17}$		Co	72 (67.7)	
$-CH_2OC_8H_{17}$		Ni	67 (33.6)	
$-OC_{12}H_{25}$		H_2	91 (129.8)	> 300
$-C_{12}H_{25}$		H_2	120 (< 2)	252 (2.1)
$-CH_2OC_{12}H_{25}$	R′ = –CN	H_2	80	

K = solid state; D = discotic mesophase; I = isotropic state.
The temperatures are given in °C, the values in parantheses indicates the enthalpies of transition in kJ/mole

Table 20. Transition temperatures and corresponding enthalpies (kJ/mole) for substituted phthalocyanines (see Fig. 18; R = R′-H in every case). The letters in parentheses indicate the various phase changes, whereby K = solid state, D_{1-4} = discotic mesophases, I = isotropic state. Phthalocyanines with R = R′ = H, R″ = $-OC_5H_{11}$ and R″ = $-OC_8H_{17}$ show no liquid crystalline phases. The mesophases have been provisionally identified by means of their characteristic optical textures (which are observed by cooling from the isotropic liquid) under the polarizing microscope (see Ref. 148f)

R″	M				
$-C_6H_{13}$	H_2	161 (18.4) (K → D_1)			171 (15.9) (D_1 → I)
$-C_6H_{13}$	Cu	184 (18) (K → D_2)	235.5 (1.7) (D_2 → D_1)		242 (11.7) (D_1 → I)
$-C_7H_{15}$	H_2	113 (46) (K → D_2)	145 (1) (D_2 → D_1)		163 (12.6) (D_1 → I)
$-C_7H_{15}$	Cu	144.5 (28.5) (K → D_2)	205 (D_2 → D_1)		235.5 (17.6) (D_1 → I)
$-C_8H_{17}$	H_2	73.5 (D_4 → D_3)	84.5 (41.8) (K → D_1)	101 (0.2) (D_3 → D_1)	152 (14.6) (D_1 → I)
$-C_8H_{17}$	Cu	95.5 (40.6) (K → D_2)	156 (0.8) (D_2 → D_1)		220 (16.7) (D_1 → I)
$-C_9H_{19}$	H_2	73.5 (D_3 → D_1)	103 (49.4) (K → D_1)		142 (8.3) (D_1 → I)
$-C_9H_{19}$	Cu	98.5 (D_3 → D_1)	108 (60.2) (K → D_1)		208 (17.2) (D_1 → I)
$-C_{10}H_{21}$	H_2	77.5 (79.5) (K → D_1)			133 (8.8) (D_1 → I)
$-C_{10}H_{21}$	Cu	69 (D_3 → D_1)	88 (70.3) (K → D_1)		198 (15.5) (D_1 → I)

Table 21. Transition temperatures and corresponding enthalpies (kJ/mole) for substituted porphyrins as depicted in Fig. 19

R	M	Transitions[a]		
		K ⟶ D	⟶ I	
$CO_2C_4H_9$	H_2	178 (1.2)	222 (47.7)	
$CO_2C_4H_9$	Zn	184 (3)	273 (46.9)	
		K ⟶ D_1	⟶ D_2	⟶ I
$CO_2C_6H_{13}$	H_2	59 (15.1)	132 (18)	220 (29.7)
$CO_2C_6H_{13}$	Zn	61 (13.4)	136 (22.2)	232 (44.4)
$CO_2C_8H_{17}$	H_2	96 (18.8)	99 (17.6)	166 (20.5)
$CO_2C_8H_{17}$	Zn	91 (18)	101 (18)	208 (24.7)

[a] K = crystal; D = discotic mesophase; I = isotropic liquid

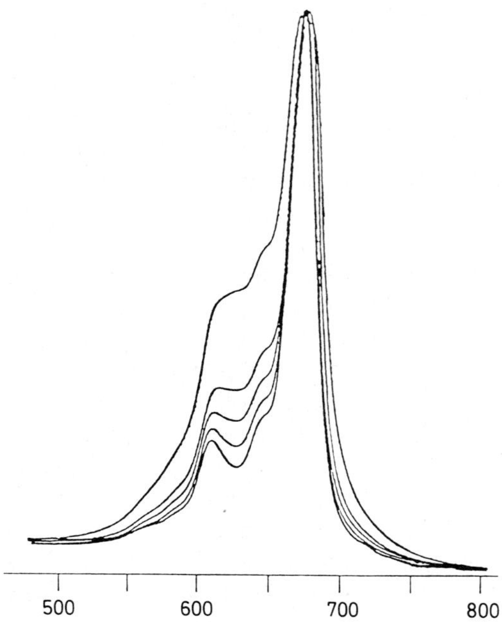

Fig. 20. Absorption spectra of octa-(*n*-octyloxymethyl)-phthalocyaninato-cobalt(II), $(C_8H_{17}OCH_2)_8PcCo$, at various concentrations [158] (λ/nm)

dependence of the emission-characteristics on the concentration. For 2,3,9,10,16,17,23,24-octa(1-dodecyloxymethyl)-29*H*,31*H*-phthalocyanine two luminescence bands are observed at 755 nm and 796 nm at a concentration of 5×10^{-4} mol/L. At further dilution a small red shift occurs. Otherwise, the spectrum resembles the one of the unsubstituted compound. For benzene as solvent, however, a further temperature dependence is observed. Here the overall luminescence intensities increase with rising temperature. From the concentration dependence of the luminescence spectra, in particular, aggregation is assumed to be likely, the bands at 755 nm and at 796 nm being ascribed to the aggregates. With the help of fluorescence spectra of the same compound, but having admixed various amounts of a fluorescence quencher 2,3,9,10,16,17,23,24-octa(1-dodecyloxymethyl)phthalocyaninatocopper, an exciton diffusion length of 100–200 Å was determined [161].

4.1.1.2 Lyotropic Low Molecular Weight Liquid Crystals

4,4′,4″,4‴-Tetracarboxyphthalocyaninatocopper forms lyotropic phases in aqueous solution [162] as long as Li^+ or Na^+ are present as counterions [163]. From the investigated phthalocyanines nevertheless only the copper complex shows this lyotropic behavior. Likewise, the liquid crystalline characteristics disappear by substituting the carboxylate groups with sulfo groups [163].

4.1.2 Oligomeric and Polymeric Phthalocyanines as Liquid Crystals

As has been discussed in Sects. 2 and 3, the synthesis of oligomeric or even polymeric compounds can be carried out by installing ligands at the central atom of the substituted phthalocyanine ring system and then condensing further macrocycles via these bridging ligands [164]. This type of oligomerisation was now applied for the synthesis of oligomeric or polymeric liquid crystalline phthalocyanines [165].

To date Si, Sn and Co have been used as central atoms in polymeric liquid crystalline phthalocyanines. Oxide and cyanide served as bridging ligands.

The synthesis of the μ-oxo-bridged phthalocyanine complexes is similar to that described earlier for $[R_4PcSiO]_n$ (see Sect. 2.1.1). For example: alkoxymethyl substituted isoindoline is treated with $SiCl_4$ in quinoline at 150 °C to give $R_8PcSiCl_2$ which is directly converted to the dihydroxy derivative $R_8PcSi(OH)_2$ by adding water to the reaction mixture. Condensation of $R_8PcSi(OH)_2$ gives the oxo-bridged oligomers [165b, 166]. In case of liquid crystalline polycondensed R_8PcSi where $R = CH_2OC_{12}H_{25}$, different mixtures of oligomers could be separated by gel-chromatography, namely 30% of monomer, 30% dimer, 20% trimer, and 20% higher oligomers [166]. With the help of X-ray spectroscopy a lamellar type order could be determined between room temperature and 60 °C. Two broad and diffuse rings (outer rings) were observed at 4.5 Å (which corresponds to the interalkyl chain spacing) and 3.4 Å (which marks the intermacrocycle distance along the columns). Above 60 °C the isotropic state is reached. The synthesis of alkoxy-substituted μ-oxo-phthalocyaninatosilicon is similar to that of alkoxymethyl-substituted μ-oxo-phthalocyaninatosilicon. For μ-oxo-octa(alkoxy)phthalocyaninatosilicon the degree of polymerization was determined to be about 140 [165c]. This compound is obtained by polymerization of the corresponding alkoxy-substituted phthalocyaninatosilicondihydroxide [153b]. For the condensation reaction either catalysts such as $FeCl_3$ or $AlCl_3$ are used or the monomer is reacted with trifluoroacetic acid anhydride [153b, 165c, 167]. The polymer is also directly accessible starting from the corresponding dichlorosubstituted monomer and using halogenophilic condensation agents such as $AgSO_3CF_3$, $TlSO_3CF_3$ or $[Cu(CH_3CN)_4]SO_3CF_3$.

By employing the general route to cyano bridged systems (see Scheme 12) liquid crystalline μ-cyanophthalocyaninatocobalt oligomers $[R_8PcCo(CN)]_n$ carrying alkoxymethyl substituents (where $R=C_8H_{17}OCH_2$) were prepared [123, 148e, 168]. The oligomer shows a transition from the solid to the liquid crystalline phase at 94 °C. The transition from the liquid crystalline to the solid phase takes place at 2.2 °C. Thus the depression is particularly large for this compound.

4.2 *Bis(octaalkyloxymethyl)phthalocyaninatolutetium*

Sandwich type phthalocyaninato complexes of f-elements as central metals have been known since 1936 [169a]. The first complex of this type, bisphthalocyaninatotin(IV) (Pc_2Sn) was prepared by reacting $PcSnCl_2$ with $PcNa_2$ in chloronaphthalene. Sandwich type complexes Pc_2M (where M = f-element) have been reviewed [169b]. Bisphthalocyaninatolutetium can either be obtained by the reaction of phthalodinitrile and $Lu(OAc)_3$ at 310 °C or by reacting PcH_2 with $Lu(acac)_3$ in trichlorobenzene. In the case of Pc_2Lu, the central metal has the oxidation state + III [32a, 169c] and ESR measurements demonstrate the presence of one spin per Pc_2Lu-molecule. Moreover the measurements indicate, that the radical is mainly localized on the macrocyclic rings rather than on the lutetium ion. The presence of oxygen considerably broadens the linewidths in the ESR spectra. Due to its peculiar electronic nature the HOMO-LUMO difference in Pc_2Lu is much smaller than that of related phthalocyanines (e.g. PcZn, PcNi) [169d]. Pc_2Lu is therefore easily oxidized and reduced:

$$\underset{\text{red}}{Pc_2Lu^+} \underset{+0.03\ V}{\rightleftarrows} \underset{\text{green}}{Pc_2Lu} \underset{-0.45\ V}{\rightleftarrows} \underset{\text{blue}}{Pc_2Lu^-} \underset{-1.5\ V}{\rightleftarrows} \underset{\text{purple}}{Pc_2Lu^{2-}}$$

(The potentials were determined in THF/chloronaphthalene [vs SCE] or in CH_2Cl_2 [vs ferrocene] respectively).

Compared to these values, the differences are large between the first oxidation and reduction potentials of PcM (M = Zn, Ni, Cu) (appr. 1.8–2.0 V) [169d].

The conductivity of thin films [32a] of sublimed Pc_2Lu is approximately equal to that in the presence of air ($2 \times 10^{-6}\ S\,cm^{-1}$ vs $1.8 \times 10^{-6}\ S\,cm^{-1}$). Compared to that of PcZn and PcNi the conductivity is five to six orders of magnitude higher. While the conductivity of Pc_2Lu is hardly influenced by the presence of oxygen, it noticeably increases (factor 100) PcZn. The room temperature conductivity of single crystals of Pc_2Lu are in the same order of magnitude as that of the thin films, demonstrating that structural disorder is of minor importance for the presence of traps. Moreover the interunit interaction in Pc_2Lu must be small. The charge carrier mobility in Pc_2Lu thin films was calculated to be 1.3 $cm^2 V^{-1} S^{-1}$ and is thus much larger than that in other phthalocyaninatometal complexes (10^{-2}–10^{-3} $cm^2 V^{-1} S^{-1}$) [169].

Alkyloxymethyl substituted phthalocyaninatolutetium(III) [169e] were synthesized in order to compare them to the sandwich-like bisphthalocyaninatolutetium(III), $(Pc)_2Lu$, which is considered to be an intrinsic molecular conductor [32, 169]. The substituted sandwich complexes are expected to show intrinsic conductivity properties as well. Their synthesis is analogous to the ones of alkyloxymethyl substituted phthalocyanines mentioned earlier. $(C_nH_{2n}OCH_2)_8PcH_2$, where n = 8, 12 or 18, is then transformed into the dianion using potassium amylate. Subsequently the dianion is reacted with lutetium(III) acetate. The sandwiches, $[(C_nH_{2n}OCH_2)_8Pc]_2Lu$, are obtained after chromatographical purification in 40% yield. The oxidized products $[(C_nH_{2n+1}OCH_2)_8Pc]_2Lu^+SbCl_6^-$, are finally obtained by reaction with phenoxathiinylium hexachloroantimonate.

The absorption spectra of the substituted derivatives resemble that of the unsubstituted Pc_2Lu (λ_{max} = 705 nm for the oxidized form, λ_{max} = 675 nm for the neutral form).

While no liquid crystalline phase exists for the neutral compound for n = 8, a mesophase does exist within a small region for n = 12. At room temperature the compound with a chain length n = 18 is a highly viscous, birefringent substance, which in two subsequent steps turns into a fluid, optically isotropic liquid.

For the oxidized species of $[(C_nH_{2n+1}OCH_2)_8Pc]_2Lu$ (n = 8, 12, 18) the transition temperatures from the solid to the liquid crystalline domain rise with increasing length of the alkyl groups [from − 10 °C (n = 8) to 13 °C (n = 12) and to 56 °C (n = 18)], while the temperatures for the transition from the mesophase to isotropic liquid hardly change with the chain lengths [130 °C (n = 8), 118 °C (n = 12), 132 °C (n = 18)].

To date, X-ray diffraction experiments have only been carried out with the neutral form (n = 18). Reflexes are visible which are consistent with a two-dimensional hexagonal arrangement of the columns. A diffuse band at 0.73 nm is assigned to the average distance between the two Lu atoms. Additionally two relatively sharp bands are obtained at 0.43 and 0.41 nm. These are unexpected for columnar phases. This doublet, which is observed for lyotropic and smectic liquid crystals, is described as a two-dimensional centered rectangular arrangement of the elongated molecules. In this arrangement, the doublet indicates a similar order, initiated by partial crystallization of peripheral aliphatic chains. ESR studies were carried out for all of the three neutral compounds. The ESR signal is inhomogeneous with a g-factor of 2.0021.

4.3 Crown Ether Phthalocyanines

In the course of the past years, phthalocyanines carrying crown ether moieties [170, 171] (Fig. 21) have been synthesized starting from 2,3,5,6,8,9,11,12-octahydrobenzo[1,4,7,10,13]pentaoxacyclopentadeca-2-ene (= benzo-15-crown-5) [172].

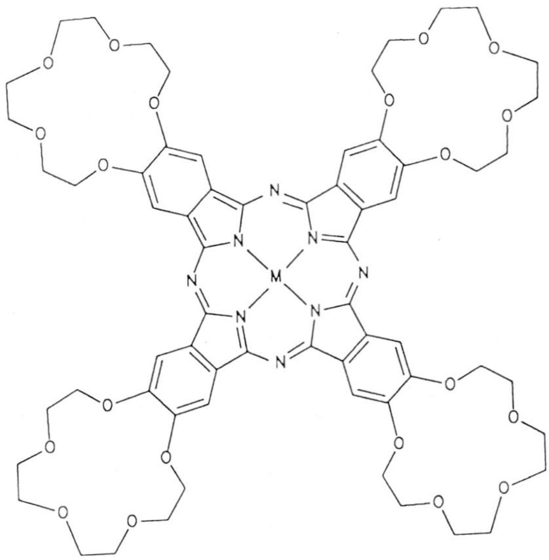

Fig. 21. Metal complex of a crown ether phthalocyanine, CEPcM

The synthesis is performed by bromination of benzo-15-crown-5, and the product, dibromobenzo-15-crown-5 (yield 70%), is reacted with CuCN in DMF (Scheme 13). Subsequently, dicyano-benzo-15-crown-5 (yield 31–70%) is converted to 15-crown-5-phthalocyanine by heating in *N,N*-dimethylaminoethanol (yield 26–41%). The crown ether phthalocyanines CEPcM ($M = H_2$, Zn, Cu, Co, Ni, Fe) are well-soluble in $CHCl_3$ and CH_2Cl_2, but less soluble in acetone, DMF, DMSO, toluene, or benzene, almost insoluble in hexane, dioxane, ethylacetate, and insoluble in water [173, 174].

Sheet polymers containing CEPcM units were synthesized via the corresponding tetrabromodibenzo compounds [175] (see Fig. 22). Due to the insolubility of the polymers it was not yet possible to determine the number of phthalocyanine units. With the help of IR spectra the number of end groups (nitrile groups) per molecule could be estimated by comparing the intensities of the Ar–O–C groups with the end groups. These ratios lie between 0.23 and 0.11 depending on the amount of CuCN used. Therefore only qualitative informations about the number of phthalocyanine units can be gained from this analysis.

In $CHCl_3$ the UV/VIS spectra of the complexes CEPcM show the bands typical for phthalocyanines. By changing the solvents, however, the intensities of the Q bands at 660–700 nm decrease relative to those of the bands at about 625 nm from $CHCl_3$ to CH_2Cl_2, benzene, DMF, DMSO, toluene, THF, ethylacetate, MeOH, etc. [171, 176]. According to these observations associates (dimers) should be formed.

Aggregates form particularly well if cations are admixed such as Na^+, K^+, Rb^+, Cs^+, Ca^{2+} which can be complexed by the crown ether rings. The

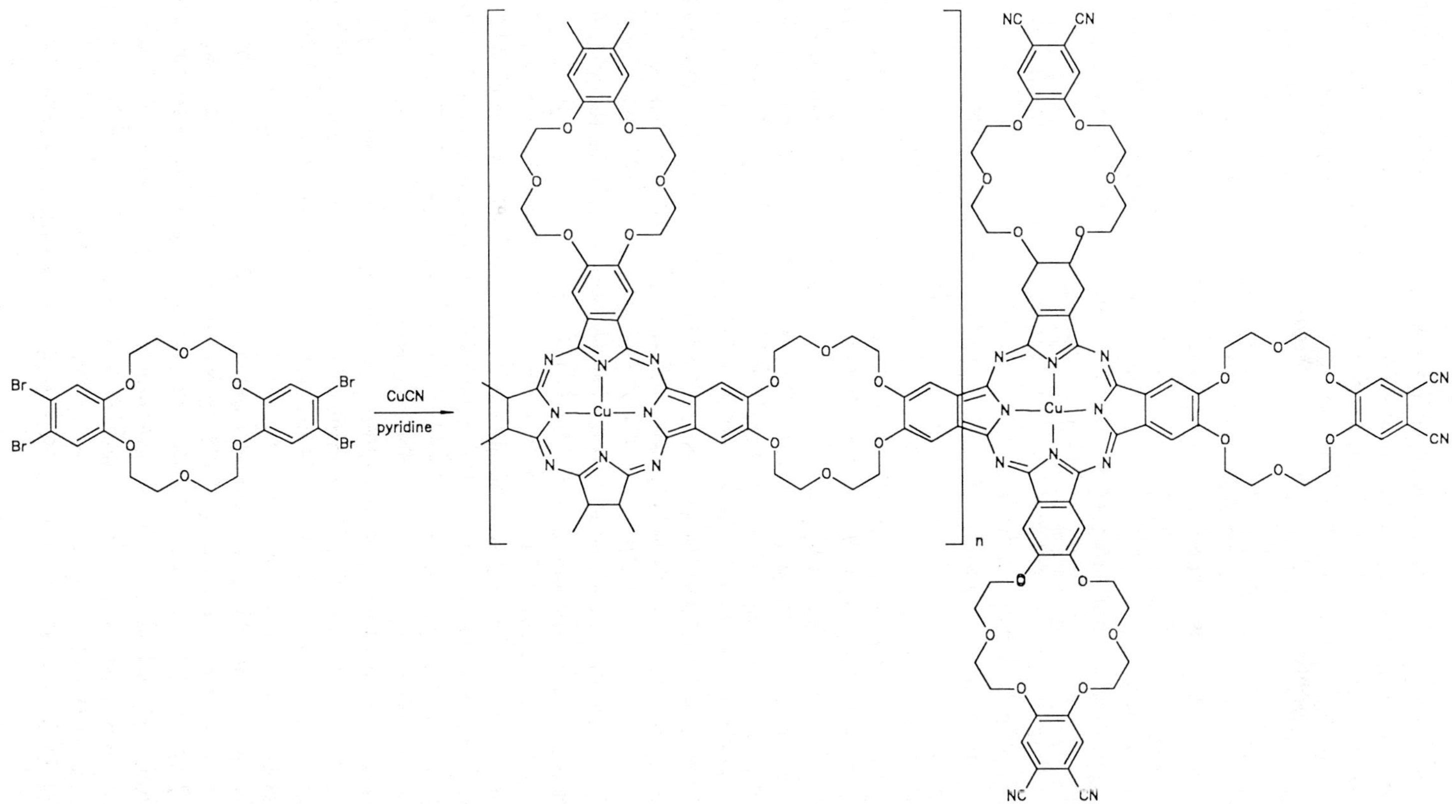

Fig. 22. Synthesis of sheet polymers consisting of crown ether phthalocyanine units (Permission for printing)

comparison of the complexation behavior of Li^+, Na^+, K^+, Rb^+, Cs^+ with a) benzo-15-crown-5 and b) crown ether substituted phthalocyanines show that the free energies (ΔG°) of complexation behave quite differently. While the ΔG°-values for benzo-15-crown-5 become smaller with increasing diameter of the cations, high affinities are detected for Na^+, K^+, Rb^+, and Cs^+, and relatively low affinity for Li^+ in the case of the phthalocyanines. This leads to the assumption that large ions induce dimerization of the phthalocyanine molecules [177], since they are situated somewhat above the plane of the crown ether rings. If the crown ether units are widened, Na^+ and K^+ can be fully encapsulated into the crown ether ring [171]. This can be concluded from the ΔG°-values and the aggregation of the phthalocyanines which is then anion-dependent. In general, the formation of aggregates is especially favored if the cation diameters are larger than the crown ether voids, which is expressed by decreasing ΔG°-values for the phthalocyanine complexes.

Complexation of alkali metal ions in the crown ether rings is clearly indicated by the UV/VIS spectra. Broadening of the absorption as well as a hypsochromic shift is observed in the case of, e.g. sodium and potassium [176, 178]. This broadening is ascribed to dimerization. More accurate investigations reveal that the aggregation takes place in three steps. The finally obtained dimeric species (eclipsed cofacial D_{4h} dimer) is present if the two halves are held together by the alkali metal ions (e.g. K^+) via the crown ether units. A parallel arrangement of the planes of the phthalocyanine rings is assumed to have been ascertained if four alkali metal ions (K^+) are present, which belong to two CEPcM units. This structure is confirmed by the ESR spectra of CEPcCu which show characteristics expected for two equivalent coupled Cu^{II} ions. This structure is also supported by the presence of a single symmetric, rather weak, and rather narrow Q absorption band in the UV spectrum, as well as by the emission spectrum of this compound [176]. The ^{1}H-NMR data from CEPcZn in the absence and presence of Ca^{2+} also indicate a cofacial dimer arrangement. In the presence of Ca^{2+} the signals of the high-field region spread out, especially downfield. In the spectrum of $CEPcH_2$ the pyrrole protons shift from -3.41 to -8.09 ppm. This large upfield shift is indicative for an intense diamagnetic ring current interaction in the dimer. Upper excited state emission (Soret, S_2) was observed for the first time for phthalocyanines in the emission spectra of $CEPcH_2$ and CEPcZn [176]. Addition of K^+ to crown ether phthalocyanines results in quenching of the S_1 and S_2 emission in parallel fashion. The quenching behavior corresponds almost exactly to the absorption studies. The residual emission intensity has an excitation spectrum identical with that of the monomer species and an intensity about 1/700 of the initial intensity. It is due to the small amount of monomer species in equilibrium with the cofacial species, implying that the cofacial dimer does not emit. Addition of Na^+ causes some degree of quenching of the S_1 and S_2 emission, however, at much higher concentration and much less efficiently. With the help of these cofacial dimers the phenomenon of exciton coupling can also be investigated [176].

For solid phases of $CEPcH_2$ and CEPcCu orthorombic structures were found by X-ray determinations at small angles. In these forms two-dimensional rectangular arrays of the substituted phthalocyanines lead to corrugated planes whereby the Pc macrocycles form an angle with the crown ether moieties. The substituents are arranged in an eclipsed conformation and the crown ether macrocycles form channels. Metastable mesophases of the crown ether phthalocyanines are constituted of two-dimensional square lattices superposed in a staggered conformation. The behavior of these mesophases has been compared to that of liquid crystalline phthalocyanines [179].

5 Applications

The observation of conductivity in organic materials has spurred scientific phantasy and interest in their possible applicability. Recent reviews [180, 181] mention the considerable potential of conductive organic materials on many fields, ranging from daily life to the still speculative area of electronic circuits of molecular size.

The uses of phthalocyanines as well as porphyrins and related materials have been summarized in the literature. Phthalocyanines and porphyrins as conductive materials have been covered in the preceding sections in detail. In addition we would like to give an overview over the literature concerning the above-mentioned compounds having appeared in approximately the past five years and dealing with three subjects of particular relevance to our own research work:

— nonlinear optics,
— photoconductivity,
— Langmuir-Blodgett films.

5.1 *Nonlinear Optical Effects*

A number of nonlinear optical (NLO) effects [182] are observed when the highly coherent and very intensive light of a laser interacts with certain anisotropic inorganic or organic materials [183]. The incoming laser light hereby excites the electrons of the constituting atoms or molecules. The change in charge distribution between the positive nuclei and the electrons results in a change in molecular dipole moment. The thus induced polarization $\vec{p}$ depends on the field strength $\vec{E}(\omega)$ of the incoming light in such a fashion that it may be described mathematically by a power series [182, 183]:

$$\vec{P}_i = \Sigma_j \alpha_{ij} \vec{E}_j + \Sigma_{jk} \beta_{ijk} \vec{E}_j \vec{E}_k + \Sigma_{jkl} \gamma_{ijkl} \vec{E}_j \vec{E}_k \vec{E}_l + \dots \quad (1)$$

where the indices i, j, k, l ... refer to the molecular coordinate system and $\vec{E}_j$, $\vec{E}_k$ ... describe the components of the incoming field. The coefficients α, β, γ ... are complex numbers and frequency dependent. The linear polarizability coefficient α is related to the index of refraction. The hyperpolarizability coefficients β, γ ... are responsible for the observable NLO effects. The macroscopic polarization $\vec{P}_I$ of an ensemble of molecules can be expressed as:

$$\vec{P}_I = \Sigma_J \chi_{IJ}{}^{(1)} \vec{E}_J + \Sigma_{JK} \chi_{IJK}{}^{(2)} \vec{E}_J \vec{E}_K + \Sigma_{JKL} \chi_{IJKL}{}^{(3)} \vec{E}_J \vec{E}_K \vec{E}_L \dots \quad (2)$$

where the coefficients χ are the macroscopic polarizability coefficients and the indices denote the crystallographic directions. The macroscopic polarizabilities χ are proportional to the corresponding microscopic polarizabilities, the mathematical expression accounting for the intermolecular interactions, the number of molecules involved, and their spatial arrangement. Consequently the NL response of a material is ultimately limited by the optical characteristics of the constituent molecular units as well as the spatial symmetry of the medium [184, 185].

NLO effects can occur in gases, liquids, solids and in the plasma state [185]. The interaction of the electromagnetical fields with the different media creates new fields having changed their phase, frequency and amplitude or possess new propagation characteristics [183a]. Depending on the order of hyperpolarizability different NLO effects can be observed [185] some of which are listed in Table 22.

Linear effects, e.g. absorption, are described by $\chi^{(1)}$ and are utilized in spectroscopy. The value of $\chi^{(2)}$ is only different from zero for a medium lacking a center of inversion. $\chi^{(2)}$ is responsible for example for the generation of new frequencies (e.g. generation of the second harmonic (SH); hereby the frequency of the laser light is doubled after having passed the medium). $\chi^{(3)}$ which does not require a non-centrosymmetrical medium can generate new frequencies as well (e.g. generation of the third harmonical, TH).

NLO effects have been found to be a powerful tool in spectroscopy and NLO materials may serve as optical devices of various types and in a variety of processes. NLO materials research has thus become a rapidly evolving field. Large polarizabilities and fast responses have been reported for certain organic materials. Even though the structure–property relationships in organic materials have not been fully revealed, their diversity of structure and flexibility make them attractive alternatives to the better studied NLO inorganic materials [186].

To date several papers have appeared presenting the results of theoretical and experimental investigations of the NLO characteristics of phthalocyanine and porphyrin systems [184, 186].

The third order hyperpolarizability coefficients $\chi^{(3)}$ have been determined under double resonance conditions for thin films of PcGaCl and PcAlF [187a]. Depending on the deposition conditions, the films consist, in variable ratios, of cofacially stacked (triclinic) and slipstacked (monoclinic) small crystallites. The samples were irradiated at 1064 nm, a frequency where the compounds are

Table 22. Assignment of characteristic NLO effect to hyperpolarizability[a]

Hyperpolarizability	Effect	Application
$\chi^{(1)}(\omega)$	linear dispersion, absorption induced emission spontaneous Raman-effect (while considering the movements of nuclei)	spectroscopy
$\chi^{(2)}(-2;\omega;\omega)$ $\chi^{(2)}(-\omega_o;\omega_a;\omega_b)$	generation of the second harmonic frequency mixing of 2 waves (generation of sum- and difference-frequencies, parametrical up-conversion parametrical oscillation and amplification)	generation of new frequencies
$\chi^{(2)}(-\omega;\omega,0)$	linear electro-optical effect (Pockels-effect)	Light-modulation
$\chi^{(2)}(0;\omega,-\omega)$	optical rectification measurements	intensity
$\chi^{(3)}(3\omega;\omega,\omega)$ $\chi^{(3)}(-\omega;\omega,\omega,-\omega)$ $\chi^{(3)}(-\omega_o;\omega_a,\omega_b,-\omega_b)$	generation of the third harmonical frequency mixing of 4 waves Raman-scattering, Brilloun-scattering	generation of new frequencies (spectroscopy)

[a] See Refs. 182 and 183 for a more complete list and discussion of the effects

transparent and thus damage thresholds are high. Due to the partially disordered film structure, significant information could be obtained neither by varying the angle of incidence of the laser light nor by changing its angle of rotation about the surface normal. An angle of incidence of 45° and a polarization normal to this angle were chosen for generating the TH signal from the phthalocyanine films. From TH experiments the $\chi^{(3)}$ for the 100 face of a polished silicon crystal was already known. A field correction factor which is a function of the angle of incidence and the complex dielectric constants at the laser frequency ω and TH 3ω had been experimentally validated for a Si single crystal.

This field correction factor was applied to the Pc films. From the ratio of the TH signals from the Pc films and the one from silicon, obtained under the same conditions, the $\chi^{(3)}$ value for Si and by taking the correction factor for Si and Pc into account, the $\chi^{(3)}$ values for PcAlF and PcGaCl were determined. As the PcAlF film was found to have a higher percentage of cofacially stacked crystallites, the higher $\chi^{(3)}$ calculated for this compound is attributed to this symmetry. According to the authors, however a field correction factor is needed which more accurately accounts for the significant scattering loss of the TH signal due to the polycrystallinity of the Pc films.

Polish researchers have developed a liquid nonlinear filter for a ruby laser [187b] consisting of a phthalocyanine dye.

According to theoretical considerations the NLO properties of polymers are mainly determined by polymer moieties, having a length of up to 50 carbon atoms. The degree of polymerization influences the NLO characteristics only indirectly, for instance via a change in conjugation length of the π-electron system with changing polymerization conditions [187c]. Therefore phthalocyanines, having an extended π-electron system as well as a large absorption coefficient, were selected for a systematic investigation of the relationship between the size of χ^3, its relaxation time and the sample preparation. For this purpose various mononuclear as well as bridged phthalocyaninato complexes were examined in solution, as LB-films and in polystyrene [187c,d]. From their studies the authors conclude that the NL signal is caused by an absorption which can be saturated. It thus corresponds to the lifetime of an excited state which in turn corresponds to the fluorescence lifetime of the molecules in question. The time the systems need to relax back into their original state is determined by how fast the energy is transferred via dipole–dipole-interactions. For instance, phthalocyaninato complexes tend to aggregate in concentrated solutions and accordingly the χ^3-signal of a highly concentrated $(C_8H_{17}O)_4(CH_3O)_4PcSiCl_2$ [153c] solution looses its intensity within a few ps. On the other hand the NL-signal was observed to remain constant for up to 70 ps for a solution of $[(t\text{-bu})_4PcRudib]_n$ [187e]. The rigid spacer and the large *t*-bu substituents probably ensure decoupling of the phthalocyaninato-units thus reducing dipole–dipole-interactions.

For NLO applications a short relaxation time is desirable. The relaxation time of a few ps observed in some of the phthalocyaninato systems, however, cannot be exploited since degradation of the systems is observed at high pulse frequency [187c].

Results of computationally obtained hyperpolarizabilities have been compared with experimentally observed values [184]. Optical absorption of chromophores with an extended π-electron system have been shown to be appropriately described by the use of semiempirical model Hamiltonians with SCF ground states and the monoexcited configuration interaction approximation (MECI). As most organic NLO phenomena are related to the π-electron system, the authors employed the π-electron Pariser, Parr, Pople (PPP) formalism, assuming planarity for the molecules. Aniline, nitrobenzene and *p*-nitroaniline are planar molecules possessing a large dipole moment. Therefore the components of β along the dipole direction will be much larger than those in the other directions. To approximate β by these components as required by the PPP formalism is thus valid. The calculated optical excitation energies, oscillator strengths and β values were found to be in excellent agreement with the values obtained from CNDO calculations as well as with experimental data. The frequency dependencies of the β values for the three compounds under consideration could also be modelled successfully. The efficiency of the theoretical method for determining β was demonstrated by the remarkably linear relationship between the β values for a series of para-substituted benzenes and the Hammett electron donor substituent constants σ_p. Moreover a linear relationship was found between ln β and the number of double bonds in disubstituted polyenes. As oscillator strengths and dipole moments of these polyenes are only slightly affected by additional terminal substituents the β values are only slightly enhanced. Having demonstrated the accuracy of the PPP formalism the authors

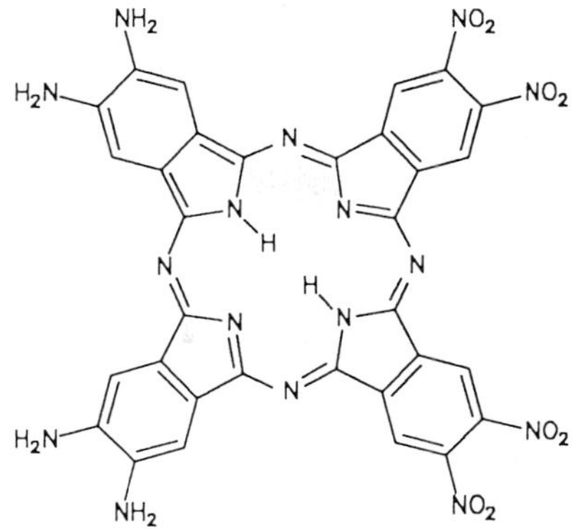

Fig. 23. Hypothetical vicinal tetranitro-tetra-aminophthalocyanine, $(NO_2)_4(NH_2)_4PcH_2$

predict β values, dipole moments and λ_{max} values for several substituted quinodimethanes and stilbenes. Again simple additive substituent effects are not found. The superiority of NO_2 over CN and $-SCH_3$ versus $-N(CH_3)_2$ as β-enhancing substituents becomes evident. The largest β value was calculated for dinitro-dithiomethylquinodimethane to be 307.9×10^{-30} cm^5 esu^{-1}. $\beta = 165 \times 10^{-30}$ cm^5 esu^{-1} has been predicted for the hypothetical, strongly polar noncentrosymmetrically substituted tetraamino-tetranitro-phthalocyanine, $(NO_2)_4(NH_2)_4PcH_2$ (Fig. 23) [184].

Besides their potential applicability as NLO materials noncentrosymmetrical phthalocyanines with different substituents on adjacent pairs of isoindole units promise intriguing new aspects in phthalocyanine chemistry: polymeric phthalocyanines without crosslinking could lead to linear polymers, controlled binding of the phthalocyanine ring to a substrate could improve the synthesis of novel catalysts [188] and the preparation of highly ordered thin films should be possible [189].

For instance the characteristics of Langmuir-Blodgett films using non-centrosymmetrically substituted phthalocyaninato complexes carrying different substituents have been studied (Fig. 24) [189].

The films of the copper complex depicted in Fig. 24A showed good mechanical stability and a preferred orientation over a sample region, much larger than that of other phthalocyanine films [189a]. The films were incorporated into several semiconductor devices. A photovoltaic cell was constructed by depositing about 10–15 monolayers of the noncentrosymmetrically substituted Pc in between a semitransparent Al-electrode and an Ag counterelectrode [189b]. Optimized cells reached a photocurrent output which was about an order of magnitude higher than those of other LB films using merocyanine dyes. Unfortunately the authors do not include the synthesis of the macrocycle composed of the two kinds of subunits or any analytical data. $R_6((CH_2)_3CO_2H)_2PcM$ (where R = *n*-alkyl and M = 2H, Cu; see Fig. 24b) has been prepared by reacting 3,6-di-*n*-alkylphthalonitrile (see also Scheme 16) with 1,2-dicyano-3,6-bis(4,4′,4″-trimethoxybutyl)benzene in a 9:1 ratio [189c]. The

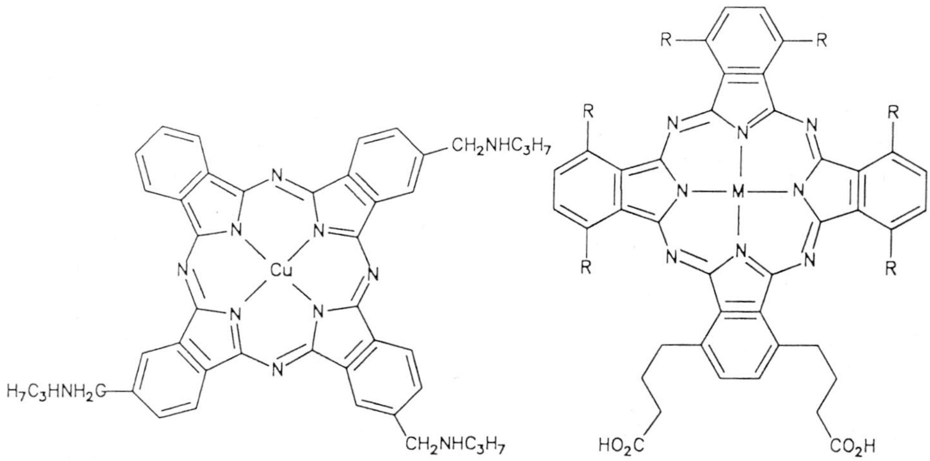

a: R = n−C_8H_{17}, M = 2H

b: R = n−C_9H_{19}, M = 2H, Cu

A **B** c: R = n−$C_{10}H_{21}$, M = 2H

Fig. 24. **A**: 2,9,16-tris(*N*,*N*-isopropylmethyl)phthalocyaninatocopper. **B**: 1,4-bis(carboxypropyl)-8,11,15,18,22,25-hexakis-(*n*-alkyl)phthalocyaninatometal complexes, $R_6[(CH_2)_3COOH]_2PcM$

ring system substituted with six alkyl and two ester groups was separated from the product mixture and the initially formed orthoester hydrolyzed to give the desired product. Highly ordered films of excellent stability could be prepared [189c, 189d].

To date most syntheses reported for noncentrosymmetrically substituted phthalocyanines as well as noncentrosymmetrically substituted tetraarylporphyrin derivatives suffer from relatively low yields and expenditure for separating the statistical mixtures of the various possible isomers, arising from the selfcondensation of the respective precursors. A fairly tedious procedure based on solubility differences in H_2SO_4 (aq) was reported for the separation of pyridoporphyrinatocopper complexes [190]. Pyridoporphyrinatocopper complexes containing four, three, two and one pyridine unit respectively could be isolated. Several positional isomers were detected for dipyridioporphyrinatocopper. As already mentioned [148b] the preparation was reported of $(C_{12}H_{25}OCH_2)_6(CN)_2PcH_2$ in 20% yield after column chromatography from cocondensating a 3:1 mixture of the didodecyloxymethyl substituted and dicyanosubstituted diiminoisoindolines (see Scheme 15). The C_{2v} symmetry and the permanent dipole moment may influence the structure and the degree of orientation of this discotic mesophase which is stable between 80 to $>300\,°C$. The preparations of mononitrophthalocyanine [191] and dicarboxyphthalocyanine [192] have also been published. As no mass spectral data were recorded, the purity of the obtained unsymmetrical material cannot be assessed [193].

The syntheses of mono- and disubstituted phthalocyanines using dithioimide were attempted (Scheme 17) [193]. The high reactivity of the thiocarbonyl group was expected to undermine the selfcondensation of the 1,3-diiminoisoindoline and preferentially crossed condensation should occur. Moreover only the isomer carrying the same substituents on opposite benzene rings should be formed. Exclusive formation of this isomer however did not take place. Besides PcH_2, mono-, di-, tri- and traces of tetrasubstituted phthalocyanine were obtained. Elemental sulfur, produced in small amounts in the course of the reaction, could account for the catalytic selfcondensation of the 1,3-diiminoisoindoline to give PcH_2. The formation of the substituted isomers was attributed to the displacement of the thione functionality by species present in the reaction mixture such as ammonia, amines or imines.

While unsymmetrically substituted tetraaryl (and arylalkyl) porphyrins (for numbering see Fig. 1, Table 23) were prepared by reacting the corresponding aldehydes and separating the mixture via column chromatography [194] a solid phase synthesis was introduced for the preparation of tolylporphyrin [195]. Polystyrene, crosslinked with 2% divinylbenzene, was reacted with 3-hydroxy- or 4-hydroxybenzaldehyde respectively and subsequently was treated with *p*-tolylaldehyde and pyrrole in hot propionic acid. Tetratolylporphyrin, also

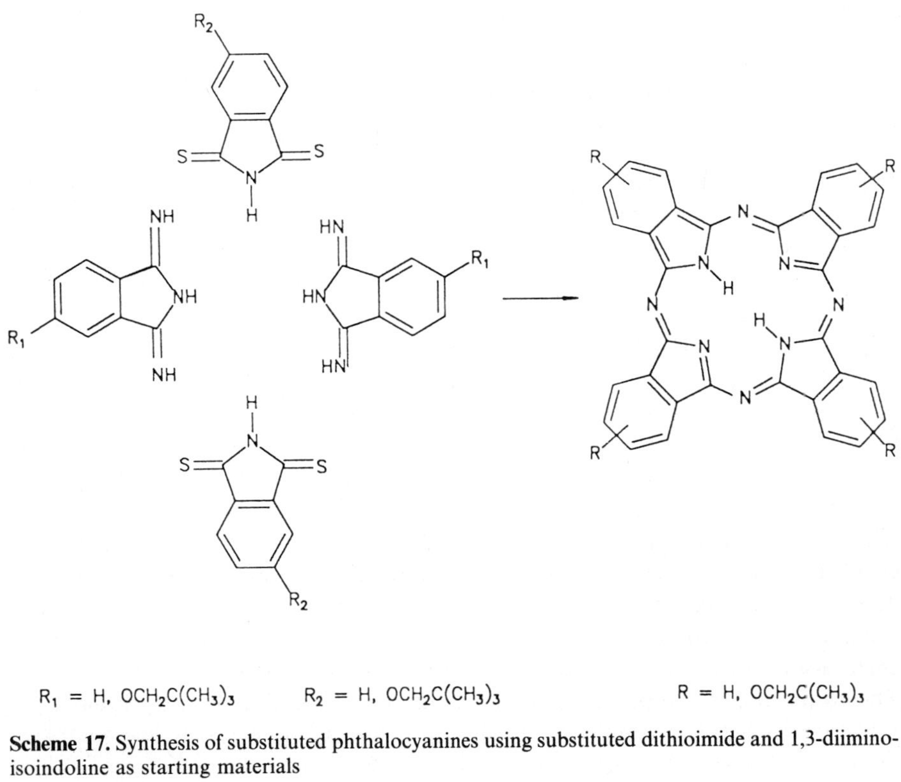

Scheme 17. Synthesis of substituted phthalocyanines using substituted dithioimide and 1,3-diiminoisoindoline as starting materials

Table 23. Unsymmetrically substituted tetraaryl (and arylalkyl) porphyrins (see Ref. 194)

Compound	Yield (%)
5-(4-hydroxy-3-nitrophenyl)-10,15,20-tri-*p*-tolylporphyrin	2.1
5-(5-hydroxy-2-nitrophenyl)-10,15,20-tri-*p*-tolylporphyrin	4.2
5-(4-hydroxy-3-methoxy-5-nitrophenyl)-10,15,20-tri-*p*-tolylporphyrin	1.2
5-(2,6-dinitrophenyl)-10,15,20-tri-*p*-tolylporphyrin	0.4
5-(4-hydroxy-3-ethoxyphenyl)-10,15,20-tri-*p*-tolylporphyrin	10.8
5-(2-nitrophenyl)-10,15,20-tripropylporphyrin	1.1
5-(2-hydroxyphenyl)-10,15,20-tripropylporphyrin	0.4
5-(2-nitrophenyl)-10,15,20-tri-*p*-tolylporphyrin	2.1
5-(2-(1-butoxyphenyl)-15-(2-nitrophenyl)-10,20-di-*p*-tolylporphyrin	0.09
5-(3-hydroxyphenyl)-10,15,20-tri-*p*-tolylporphyrin[a]	2
5-(4-hydroxyphenyl)-10,15,20-tri-*p*-tolylporphyrin[a]	4.5
5-(4-nitrophenyl)-10,15,20-triphenylporphyrin[b]	55
5-(4-formyl)-10,15,20-tri-*p*-tolylporphyrin[c]	24

[a] see Ref. 195; [b] see Ref. 194b; [c] see Ref. 194c

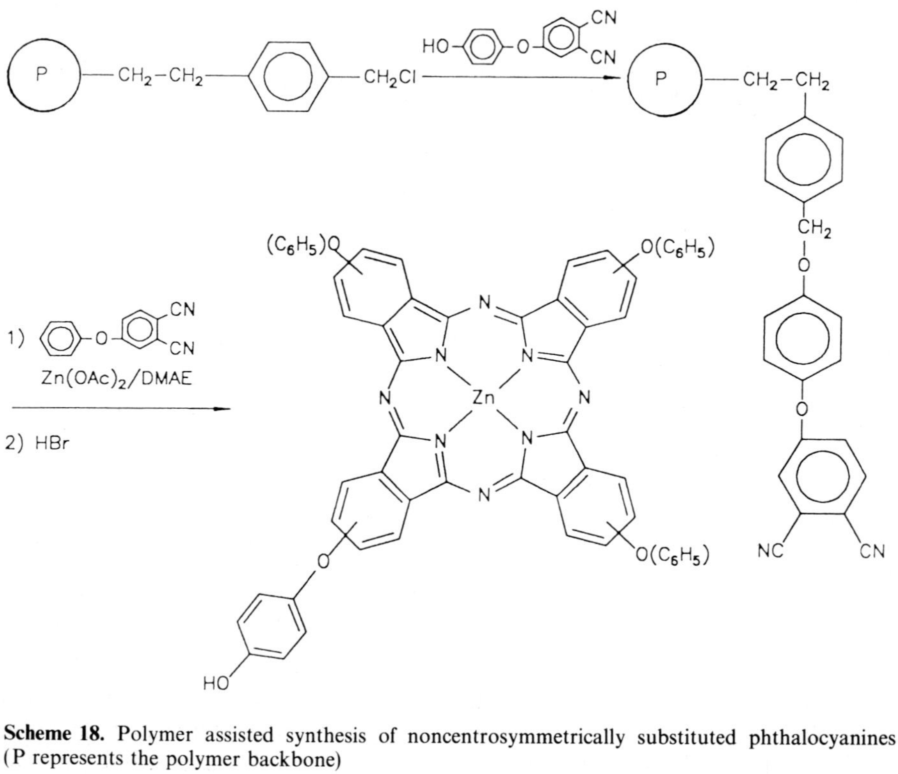

Scheme 18. Polymer assisted synthesis of noncentrosymmetrically substituted phthalocyanines (P represents the polymer backbone)

found during the reaction, was removed by soxhlet extraction. Cleavage from the polymer matrix under basic conditions afforded the unsymmetrically substituted porphyrins. Essentially the same technique was employed for the synthesis of unsymmetrically substituted phthalocyanines [188, 196]. Polymer-bound tritylchloride was reacted with 1,6-hexanediole or 1,4-butanediole to give the corresponding polymer-bound ethers [196a, b]. These were then converted to the dinitriles by reacting them with 4-nitrophthalonitrile in the presence of a phase transfer catalyst. Reaction of the isoindolines with 4-isopropoxydiiminoisoindoline, acid cleavage and chromatographic purification gave the unsymmetrically substituted phthalocyanines as mixtures of positional isomers. Alternatively a divinylbenzenestyrene copolymer with 20% crosslinking can be reacted with 4(4′-hydroxyphenoxy)phthalodinitrile [188] (Scheme 18). Reaction of the resulting polymer-bound dinitrile with 4-phenoxyphthalodinitrile in the presence of zinc acetate, removal of tetraphenoxyphthalocyanine via extraction and acid cleavage yielded the desired unsymmetrically substituted phthalocyaninatometal complex shown in Scheme 18.

Photochemical hole burning denotes a special kind of saturation spectroscopy [197]. With the help of laser light the absorption bands of dyes, imbedded in a matrix, can be changed so that they show small, almost stable dips, “holes”. From their contures information can be gained on the host-guest system. Often NL interactions of the incident light must be taken into account when evaluating hole burning experiments. Phthalocyanines and porphyrins have frequently been used as dyes in hole burning experiments [197].

5.2 *Photoconductivity*

5.2.1 *Introduction*

Photoconductivity is a typical phenomenon for many organic semiconductors. When a photoconductor is illuminated by light, which it is able to absorb, charge carriers are produced and consequently the conductivity of the material increases [198]. Several processes are responsible for the magnitude of a photocurrent within an organic solid [199, 200]:

— For the amount of charge carriers generated, the number of excited charge carriers per absorbed photon (= primary quantum yield η) is decisive. The absorption of photons can cause electronic transitions from occupied states of the valence band to either the conduction band or to free defect levels (e.g. impurities, absorbed gases) within the gap or alternatively from defect levels to the conduction band. Indirect excitation processes (e.g. formation of charge carriers from excitons) can also contribute to the photocurrent. An applied high external voltage may cause injection of electrons or holes from the electrodes into the sample and thus a (so-called space-charge limited) current to flow.

— The transport of these directly or indirectly formed charge carriers can be described by a band model and/or a hopping mechanism. Important parameters controlling the transport are bandwidths, concentration, energetic and spatial distribution of defects and traps.

— The photoelectric behavior of a solid is further determined by deactivation processes and thus the lifetime of the charge carriers. Deactivation can take place via direct recombination of electrons and holes. This process occurs especially when the charge carrier concentration is high and when it is accompanied by the release of a large number of phonons. Electrons or holes can also be trapped by defects (recombination centers) first. Then their recombination with the holes of the valence band or the electrons of the conduction band occurs.

Photoelectrical properties of phthalocyanine powders and their films on a variety of substrates have been the object of numerous investigations. Photoconductivity is affected by the nature of the phthalocyanine substrate as well as its crystal modification, doping agents employed [201], and by the way the substrate is prepared [199b].

Within the scope of this review it is not possible to give a comprehensive overview over the research activities concerning photoconductive phenomena of phthalocyaninato and porphyrinato complexes. Thus studies on phthalocyaninatometal complexes as well as bridged phthalocyaninato systems relating photoconductivity to molecular structure will be summarized.

5.2.2 *Photoconductivity Studies on Phthalocyanine Powders*

5.2.2.1 Introduction

The behavior of several monomeric [199, 200] and polymeric [46, 136, 199, 202] phthalocyanine powders when illuminated has recently been investigated, whereby surface type cells were employed (see Fig. 25). These have the advantage that a) the probe without any additives (e.g. binders) can be directly exposed to the incident light, not weakened by electrodes, b) the total volume of the layer between the electrodes can be studied, c) only several milligrams of substance are needed for each experiment, d) due to the small electrode distance high photocurrents and quantum yields can be achieved at low voltages and interferences from dark current can be mostly kept small [199, 200b]. The samples were measured in vacuo (10^{-5}–10^{-6} torr) in the temperature range of 190–300 K.

Dark conductivities σ_D allow a number of conclusions [199, 200] and are thus measured first. Since $I_D = a\ U^s$, a linear dependence ($s \simeq 1$) of the dark current I_D on the voltage U indicates ohmic behavior, a superlinear dependence ($s \leqq 2$) the presence of space charge limited currents (SCLC). The constant 'a' is directly proportional to the proportion of free to trapped charge carriers, the dielectrical constant of the sample, the electrical field constant and the mobility of the charge carriers. Finally 'a' is also determined by the cell geometry. As 'a' is proportional to the mobility μ of the charge carriers it is in certain cases possible to calculate μ from the slope of the I_D/U curve. The dark conductivity of an ohmic conductor varies with the temperature in an Arrhenius type fashion. The

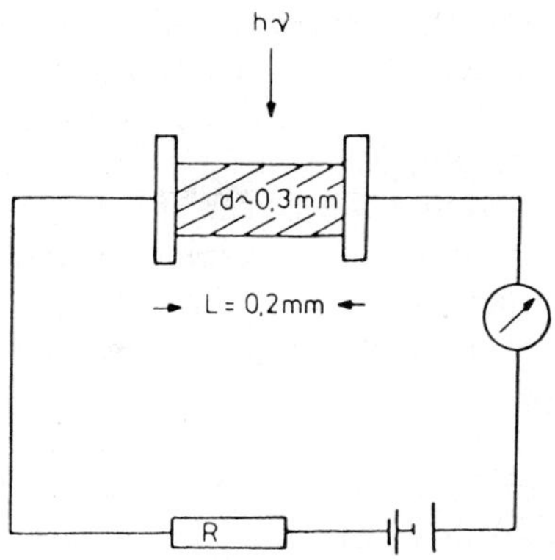

Fig. 25. Schematic representation of the experimental setup using a surface type cell employing copper/zinc contacts; light source: 1000 W xenon lamp

activation energy of a conductor carrying space charges is determined by either the depth of the traps or the energy differences between the Fermi level E_F of the electrode and the valence band or conduction band respectively. The conductivity then fits the following equation.

$$\sigma_D = \sigma_{DO} \exp(-\Delta E/kT)$$

(where σ_{DO} is the preexponential factor, ΔE the activation energy, k Boltzmann's constant, T the temperature). The relationship of σ_D in vacuo and in air indicates whether electrons or holes are the majority carriers if

$$\sigma_{D\,vac} \gg \sigma_{D\,air} \text{ (n-type conductivity)}$$

$$\sigma_{D\,vac} \ll \sigma_{D\,air} \text{ (p-type conductivity).}$$

By analogy to I_D, the photocurrent I_{ph} can be related to applied voltage, temperature and pressure changes.

Thus $I_{ph} = a\ U^s$ and the photocurrent behaves ohmic if $s \simeq 1$. SCLC are expected if $s \simeq 2$. The slope of $\log I_{ph}$ versus $\log U$, indicating SCLC, is influenced by the wavelength of irradiation, the energy distribution and the degree of filling of the traps [200]. The temperature dependence of the photoconductivity is mostly described by [199b]:

$$\sigma_{ph} = \sigma_{ph,o} \exp(-\Delta E_{ph}/kT).$$

As for dark conductivity the activation energy is related to the structure of the material under investigation but could originate from various processes. It could for instance denote the energy difference between the conduction and the valence band (intrinsic conductor) or that of the defect level and the conduction band (extrinsic conductor) or could correspond to the energy necessary to overcome the potential difference between electrode and solid when carriers are injected [199]. The preexponential factor $\sigma_{ph,o}$ is also dependent upon the activation energy and via a linear relationship of $\ln \sigma_{ph,o}$ and ΔE within a class of components (called compensation rule) information on parameters describing defects and traps, for instance carrier mobilities, can be gained. A large change in photoconductivity under vacuum compared to that under air allows the conclusion of n- or p-type conductivity.

As already seen, I_{ph} additionally depends on time, intensity, and wavelength. The photocurrent I_{ph} is proportional to the intensity of the photocurrent I_B according to $I_{ph} \propto I_B \gamma$.

Frequently several γ values are obtained for the same system, according to experimental conditions [199]. Theoretically γ can be calculated by considering the rate of production of charge carriers and the rate of charge carrier recombination. As there is no net change in the number of charge carriers at equilibrium both rates can be equated and γ is deduced. By considering various conditions such as the presence of thermal carriers or the presence of traps sub- as well as superlinear relationships between I_{ph} and I_B can be rationalized. The energetical trap distribution is given by

$$N_z(E) = A \exp\left(-\frac{|E_t - E_{CB}|}{k T_c}\right)$$

where N_z is the number of traps at a certain energy, E_t the depth of a trap, E_{CB} the energy of the lower edge of the conduction band. The temperature T_c characterizes the trap distribution. Small T_c values indicate that the number of traps diminish rapidly as E increases; large T_c values indicate a slow decrease. γ can be expressed in terms of T_c:

$$\gamma = \frac{T_c}{T_c + T}$$

and is therefore indicative for the trap distribution at a known temperature T.

In order to determine the wavelength dependency of a photoconductor a quantity S (photoelectrical sensitivity) is plotted versus the wavelength. This photoelectrical sensitivity is corrected for the dependency of the photocurrent on the light intensity.

$$S = \frac{I_{ph}\,1/\gamma}{N_{q,\lambda}} \quad (\text{in } \%)$$

where $N_{q,\lambda}$ is the number of photons/cm^2 s at the wavelength λ. This procedure ensures that independently of I_B only influences of the wavelengths are recorded [199b].

The relationship between structure and photoelectrical behavior can further be described by the parameters G, quantum yield (or photoconductive gain) and the mean distance of the carrier drift (or "Schubweg"). The quantum yield G is defined as the number of carriers passing through the outer circuit (I_{ph}/e) per number of light quanta absorbed by the photoconductor during the same period of time (gV):

$$G = \frac{\left(\frac{I_{ph}}{e}\right)}{gV}$$

where 'e' is the unit charge, 'g' the number of excitations per time and volume, 'V' the volume of the probe. G can also be expressed in terms of the primary quantum yield η, charge carrier mobility, μ, their lifetime τ and cell parameters (field strength E and electrode distance L).

$$G = \eta \mu \tau \frac{E}{L}$$

Charge carrier mobility and cell parameters determine the transit time of the carriers T_t and thus G can be formulated as:

$$G = \eta \left(\frac{\tau}{T_t} \right)$$

For constant T_t and τ, $\eta(\lambda)$ can be concluded from $G(\lambda)$. The quantum yield G varies with the field strength according to

$$G = \frac{\eta \mu \tau}{L} E^z \quad \text{(where } ^z \text{ is a constant)}$$

if μ and τ remain constant with changing fieldstrength. The following equation then holds:

$$\log(GL) = \log(\eta \mu \tau) + z \log E$$

From a plot of log(GL) versus log E the Schubweg $\omega = \mu \tau E\,[\mathrm{cm}]$ and the drift distance $\omega = \mu \tau [\mathrm{cm}^2/\mathrm{V}]$ can be calculated if the primary quantum yield is assumed to be approximately one.

Table 24 gives an overview over phthalocyaninatometal complexes which were investigated [199, 201]. Table 25 summarizes the results obtained for bridged substrates [46, 136, 199, 201].

5.2.2.2 Phthalocyaninatometal Complexes

Conductivity changes most probably originating from electronical influences of substituents were observed with phthalocyaninatozinc [201] and -copper [199b] complexes. As the dark current I_D shows ohmic behavior for $(CN)_8PcZn$ and $(CH_3O)_8PcZn$ an injection of charge carriers from the electrodes is excluded. The cyano substituted phthalocyaninatozinc is a better dark conductor than the corresponding methoxysubstituted complex. This fact is attributed to a smaller difference between ionization potential and electron affinity in the complex carrying the electron-withdrawing groups.

The photocurrents of both octacyano- and octamethoxyphthalocyaninatozinc show a similar dependency on the incident light intensity and invariance of the γ-values on the wavelength of the incoming light. These results point to ohmic photocurrents and the presence of exponentially distributed traps. The ohmic character of the photocurrent for the two zinc complexes is further confirmed by their current-voltage characteristics. The photoconductivities of

Table 24. Photoconductivities and related parameters of mononuclear phthalocyaninatometal complexes of the type PcM

Compound	Photocurrent I_{ph} dependency on:						Quantum yield G	Schubweg w/cm²V	T/K	Type of conductor	Ref.
	Light intensity			Voltage	Temperature						
	γ	at λ/nm	at T/K	s	σ_{ph}/S cm^{-1}	λ/nm					
$(CH_3O)_8PcZn$	0.72	498	293	1.29–1.32	3.1×10^{-11}	900[a]	$\simeq 1.5 \times 10^{-8}$ [b]	8.5×10^{-15}	293	p	[201]
	0.63	498	181				7.5×19^{-9} [c]	—	—	—	[199b]
	0.74	1000	293								
	0.59	1000	181								
$(CN)_8PcZn$	0.79	900	—	—	5.8×10^{-9}	496[d]	$\simeq 1.4 \times 10^{-5}$ [e]	3.7×10^{-12}	293	p	[201]
							7.0×10^{-6} [c]	—	—	—	[199b]
$(CH_3O)_8PcCu$	—	—	—	—	1.5×10^{-8}		3.5×10^{-7} [c]	—	—	—	[199b]
$(CH_3O)_8PcCu$	—	—	—	—	5.0×10^{-7}		4.1×10^{-8} [c]	—	—	—	[199b]
PcCu	—	—	—	—	2.5×10^{-6}		4.8×10^{-8} [c]	—	—	—	[199b]
$(CN)_8PcCu$	—	—	—	—	1.3×10^{-1}		1.4×10^{-3} [c]	—	—	—	[199b]

[a] at U = 150 V;
[b] at $\lambda = 900$ nm and E = 5000 V cm^{-2};
[c] at λ_{max} and E = 2500 V cm^{-2};
[d] at U = 120 V;
[e] at $\lambda = 498$ nm and E = 5000 V cm^{-2}

Table 25. Photoconductivities and related parameters of metallomacrocycles polymerized via bridging ligands, $[MacML]_n$

Compound $[MacML]_n$	Photocurrent I_{ph} dependency on:							Quantum yield G at λ_{max} and $E = 2500\ V\,cm^{-1}$	T/K	Type of Conductor	Ref.
	Light intensity			Voltage	Temperature						
	γ (U/V)	at λ/nm	at T/K	s (U/V) at T = 293 K	$\sigma_{ph}/S\,cm^{-1}$ at $\beta = 10^5\,cm^{-1}$	ΔE_{ph}/eV	λ/nm				
$[PcGeO]_n$				1.2 (20–60)	2.0×10^{-8}			6.7×10^{-7} [a]		p	[199b]
				1.8 (80–165)	2.8×10^{-8} [b]			9.6×10^{-7}			
$[(t\text{-}Bu)_4PcGeO]_n$				1.3	6×10^{-10}			7.5×10^{-8}		p	[199b]
$[(Me_3Si)_4PcGeO]_n$				1.0	1.9×10^{-10}			2.2×10^{-8}		p	[199b]
$[PcGeS]_n$	0.63	498	195	1.3 $(1\text{–}6 \times 10^3)$	6.7×10^{-8}	0.11	< 223	$\simeq 4 \times 10^{-6}$ [c]	293		[46]
	0.50	498	367	2[d] (3×10^3)	1.28×10^{-5}	0.21	< 283	5×10^{-6} [c]	365		[46]
					0.83	0.52	308 < T < 352	1.6×10^{-7}			[199b]
$[PcCrCN]_n$	0.88	696.7			1.2×10^{-8} [b]			5.6×10^{-6} [a]			[199b]
	(50)				2.6×10^{-7}						
$[PcMnCN]_n$	0.81	696.7			1.3×10^{-8}			1.3×10^{-6} [a]			[199b]
	(50)										
					2.2×10^{-4} [e]						
$[PcCoCN]_n$	0.93		187	$\simeq 1.2$	4.5×10^{-3}	0.04	< 273	$\simeq 7 \times 10^{-4}$ [f]	300		[136]
	0.83		357		0.14	0.13	303 < T < 323	7×10^{-2} [a]			[199b]
					10.17	0.25	> 323				
$[PcFe(tz)]_n$	0.63	696			5×10^{-4}			4.4×10^{-2} [a]		n	
	(0.40)										

[a] at λ_{max} and $E = 2000\ V\,cm^{-1}$;
[b] from Ref. 199b;
[c] $E = 6000\ V\,cm^{-1}$;
[d] T = 295 K;
[e] at T = 193 K;
[f] at $\lambda = 496$ and $E = 25\ V\,cm^{-1}$

Table 25. (*Contd.*)

Compound $[MacML]_n$	Photocurrent I_{ph} dependency on:							Quantum yield G at λ_{max} and $E = 2500\ V\,cm^{-1}$	T/K	Type of Conductor	Ref.
	Light intensity			Voltage	Temperature						
	γ (U/V)	at λ/nm	at T/K	s (U/V) at T = 293 K	$\sigma_{ph}/S\,cm^{-1}$ at $\beta = 10^5\,cm^{-1}$	$\Delta E_{ph}/eV$	λ/nm				
$[Me_8PcFe(dib)]_n$	0.97 (5)	696.7		2.9	3.4×10^{-5}			1.6×10^{-3}	a	n	[199b]
$[Me_8PcFe(Cl_4dib)]_n$				1.8							
$[PcFe(pyz)]_n$					3.2×10^{-7}			4.2×10^{-6}	a	n	[199b]
$[Cl_{16}PcFe(pyz)]_n$	1.10 (165)	696		1.59							
$[PcFe(bpy)]_n$					9.4×10^{-9}			6.5×10^{-7}	a	n	[199b]
$[PcRu(dib)]_n$	1.02 (60)	696.7			6.5×10^{-7}			2.3×10^{-5}	a		[199b]
$[PcRu(pyz)]_n$					1.6×10^{-9}			4.7×10^{-8}	a		[199b]
$[HpFeO]_n$					$< 10^{10}$			$< 10^{-9}$	a		[199b]
$[taaFe(pyz)]_n$	0.89	647	298	1.43	6.6×10^{-7}			8.7×10^{-6}	a		
								5×10^{-5}			[202b]
$[TPPFe(bpy)]_n$					2.8×10^{-9}			1.4×10^{-8}	a		

the zinc compounds are higher when O_2 is present. Holes are therefore the majority charge carriers.

From the photoconductive gain values G, listed in Table 24, the carrier ranges were calculated to be $\mu\tau = 3.7 \times 10^{-12}\,cm^2\,V^{-1}$ for $(CN)_8PcZn$ and $\mu\tau = 8.5 \times 10^{-15}\,cm^2\,V^{-1}$ for $(CH_3O)_8PcZn$. As the carrier transport through both substrates is of comparable efficiency it is postulated that the carrier generation efficiency η of the octacyanosubstituted compound is larger than that of the octamethoxysubstituted one by a factor of 400. The following sequence of photoelectrical sensitivity for the substituted macrocyclic complexes can be derived from the G and σ_{ph} values [199b]:

$$CN \gg H > OCH_3 > CH_3$$

One restriction however has to be made: octacyanosubstituted phthalocyanines most probably always contain a certain amount of sheet polymerized material, which might contribute to the observed photoconductivity [199b]. Tetracyanophthalocyaninatometal complexes are unable to form sheet polymers and are therefore presently under investigation [203]. The central metal atom also influences the photoconductivities whereby generally larger G and σ_{ph} values were observed for the copper compounds.

Two major observations can be made from the photoaction spectra (Fig. 26) of the listed macrocyclic substances [199b].

- Despite the differences in σ_{ph}, electron withdrawing and electron donating substituents on the macrocyclic rings hardly change the photoaction spectra.
- Unsubstituted PcCu shows a high sensitivity in the near IR region compared to substituted phthalocyaninatocopper complexes. This is explained by a derangement of the slipped stacked arrangement characteristic for PcCu by substituents [199b].

5.2.2.3 Bridged Phthalocyaninatoelement-14 Complexes

The photoaction spectra of the macrocyclic copper compounds can be compared to the ones of substituted and unsubstituted μ-oxo-phthalocyaninatogermanium $[PcGeO]_n$ (Fig. 27). The oxo bridge maintains a stacked arrangement even if the compound is substituted by bulky groups. Thus the infrared absorption of the photoconduction is not diminished [199b].

Except for electronic influences of substituents on the macrocycle on the photoconductivity parameters, electronic influences of substituents on the bridging ligands have to be taken into account when bridged phthalocyaninato complexes are investigated [199b]. Bulky groups however reduce the size of the photocurrent. The σ_{ph} values of $[R_4PcGeO]_n$ (where R = *t*-bu, tms) are approximately two orders of magnitude smaller than that of $[PcGeO]_n$ (see Table 25). Aside from the size of the photocurrent the trap distribution is also influenced by the bulky substituents as the different slopes in the I_{ph}/U plot demonstrates (Fig. 28). The three polyphthalocyaninato germoxanes are p-type conductors [199b].

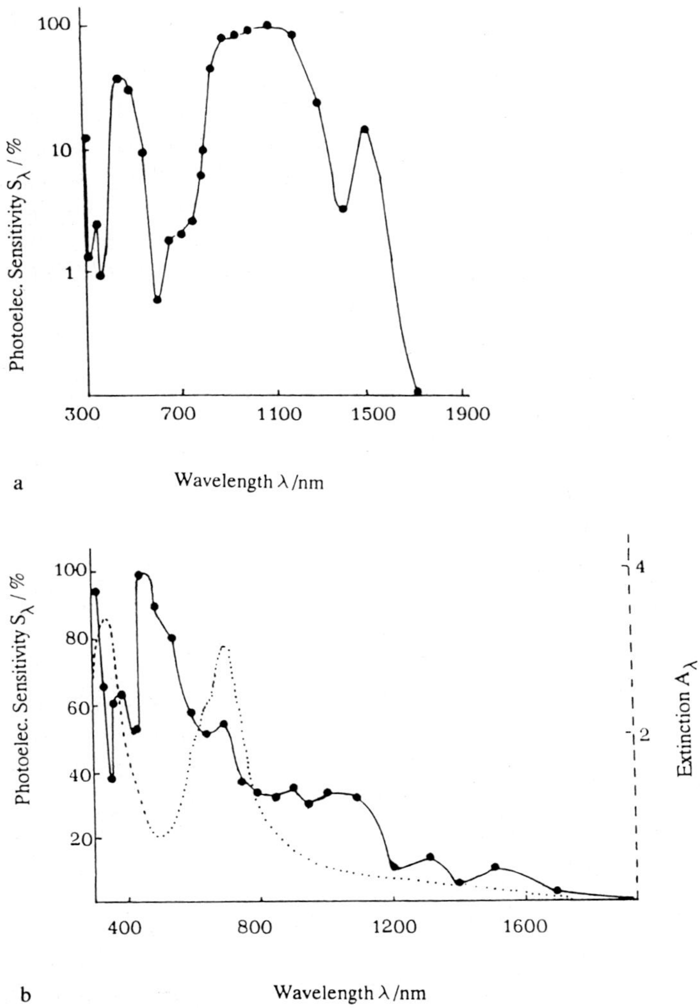

Fig. 26 a, b. Photoaction spectra of unsubstituted and substituted copper(II) phthalocyanines: **a)** PcCu, **b)** Me_8PcCu (the *dotted line* represents the UV/VIS absorption spectrum)

Changing the bridging ligand from oxygen to sulfur leads to a reduction in photoconductivity [199b], which can be inferred from the data given in Table 25. Upon heating the photocurrent of $[PcGeS]_n$ shows an abnormal drop. This is attributed to a phase change in the crystal structure of the compound [46].

5.2.2.4 Metallomacrocycles Bridged via Ligands

Unsubstituted μ-pyrazine phthalocyaninatoiron(II) $[PcFe(pyz)]_n$ can be compared with the corresponding perchlorosubstituted complex [199b]. σ_{ph} is

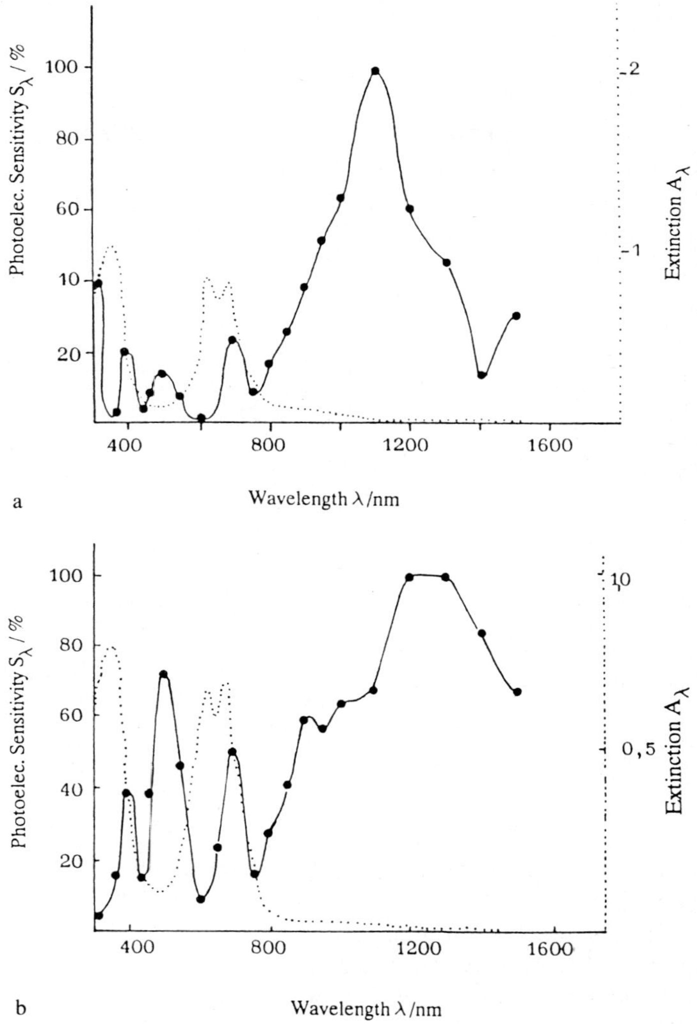

Fig. 27 a, b. Photoaction spectra of unsubstituted and substituted μ-oxo-phthalocyaninatogermanium complexes **a**) $[PcGeO]_n$, **b**) $[(t\text{-bu})_4PcGeO]_n$ (the *dotted line* represents the UV/VIS absorption spectrum)

found to be two orders of magnitude larger for $[PcFe(pyz)]_n$ than for $[Cl_{16}PcFe(pyz)]_n$. Substitution of the bridging ligand, diisocyanobenzene, with chlorine also decreases the photoconductivity as becomes evident when comparing the G and σ_{ph} values of $[Me_8PcFe(dib)]_n$ and $[Me_8PcFe(Cl_4dib)]_n$ (see Table 25).

The bridging ligand can also influence the photoresponse via its size. For this purpose tz, dib, pyz and bpy linked iron and ruthenium complexes were

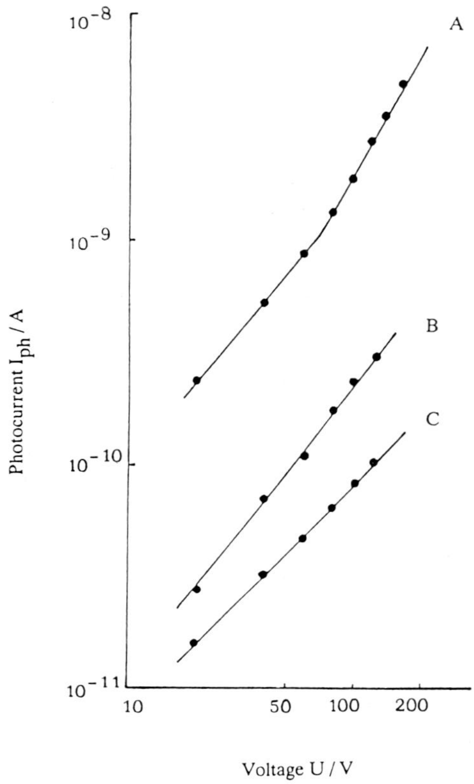

Fig. 28. Photocurrent-voltage characteristics of μ-oxo-phthalocyaninatogermanium complexes:
A) $[PcGeO]_n$: 696.7 nm, 293 K; s (20–60 V) = 1.2, s (80–165 V) 1.8
B) $[(t\text{-bu})_4PcGeO]_n$: 1201 nm, 293 K; s = 1.3
C) $[(tms)_4PcGeO]_n$: 1201 nm, 293 K; s = 1.0

investigated, and a decrease in photoconductivity from tz to bpy was noticed [199b].

The G and σ_{ph} values of iron and ruthenium pyz and dib oligomers (Table 25) further demonstrate the influence of the central metal atom. The iron oligomers were found to be the better photoconductors [199b]. The photoelectrical sensitivity of cyanobridged phthalocyaninato complexes decreases when replacing cobalt with chromium and manganese: $[PcCoCN]_n \gg [PcCrCN]_n > [PcMnCN]_n$. The influence of the macrocyclic ligand on σ_{ph} and G values was tested by comparing $[taaFepyz]_n$ and $[TPPFebpy]_n$ with the respective phthalocyaninato complex ($[PcFepyz]_n$ and $[PcFebpy]_n$). The taa complexes seem to be the most and the TPP complexes the least efficient photoconductors. For several iron complexes, e.g. $[PcFetz]_n$ (see Table 25), electrons were found to be the majority charge carriers in the illuminated materials.

The dependency of the photocurrent on the light intensity seems to be similar for the three $[PcMCN]_n$ compounds. The intensity parameter γ for the cobalt complex was measured to be 0.83 (357 K) [136] and those of the chromium and manganese complexes are 0.88 and 0.81 [204] respectively

[199b], pointing to exponentially distributed traps which control the carrier recombination. In this context it is interesting to note that for $[PcCoCN]_n$ a solid–solid phase transition at 289 K, documented by DSC measurements, coincides with an anomaloüs drop in its photoconductivity between 273 and 303 K. This decrease also coincides with a transition region observed in the dark current density temperature graph as depicted in Figs. 29 and 30 [136].

The anomalous behavior of the photoconductivity may therefore originate from this phase change; its mechanism on an electronical level, however, has so far not been clarified. By comparing absorption- and photoaction spectra of bridged phthalocyaninato transition metal complexes the characteristic bands in the photoaction spectra (see for instance Fig. 31) were assigned to various π–π* transitions. The possible π–π* transitions, involving macrocycle, metal-*d* and ligand orbitals are depicted in Scheme 19.

5.2.2.5 Photoconductivity Mechanisms

A two-step process (Onsager mechanism) seems to be responsible for the photoconductivity observed in monomeric phthalocyaninatometal complexes as well as in polyphthalocyaninatogermoxanes [199b]. Electronic excitation

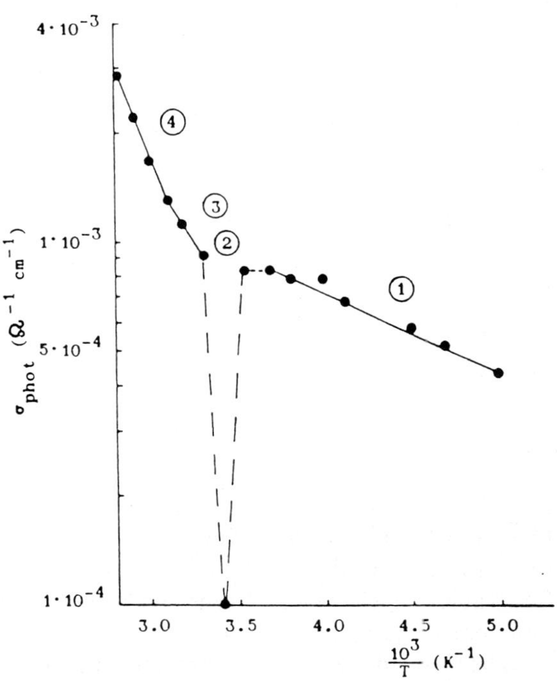

Fig. 29. Temperature dependence of the photoconductivity of μ-(s-tetrazine)-phthalocyaninatocobalt(III), $[PcCoCN]_n$; I_B (unfiltered ≃ 20 mW/sample; region *1*) T ≥ 273 K; *2*) 273 ≤ T ≤ 303 K; *3*) 303 ≤ T ≤ 323 K; *4*) T ≥ 323 K.

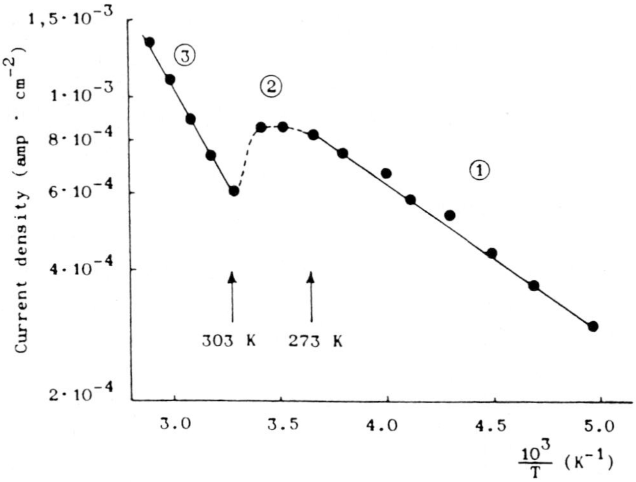

Fig. 30. Temperature dependence of dark current density of μ-cyano-phthalocyaninatocobalt(III), $[PcCoCN]_n$ measured in surface type cells (E = 25 V/cm); region *1)* T ≤ 273 K; *2)* 273 ≤ T ≤ 303 K; *3)* T ≤ 303 K

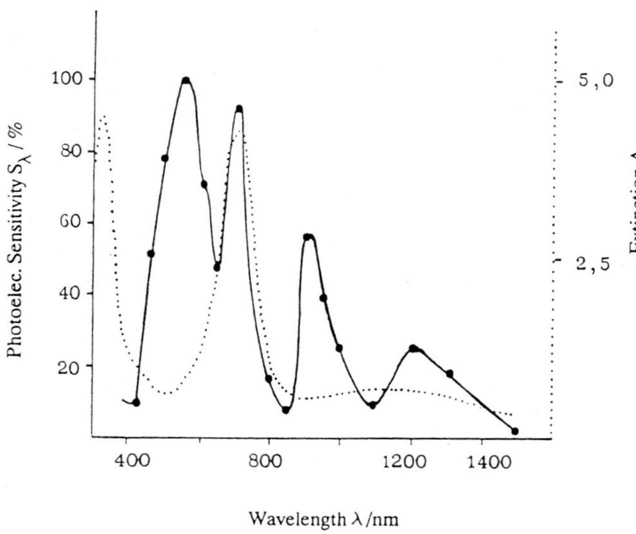

Fig. 31. Photoaction spectrum of μ-(s-tetrazine)-phthalocyaninatoiron(II), $[PcFetz]_n$ (the *dotted line* represents the UV/VIS absorption spectrum)

first produces electron-hole pairs separated by an average distance calculated to be 20–40 Å. The electron-hole pairs then separate into mobile charge carriers. Their transport takes place in small energy bands originating from π-orbital overlap of the stacked molecules [199b, 200b].

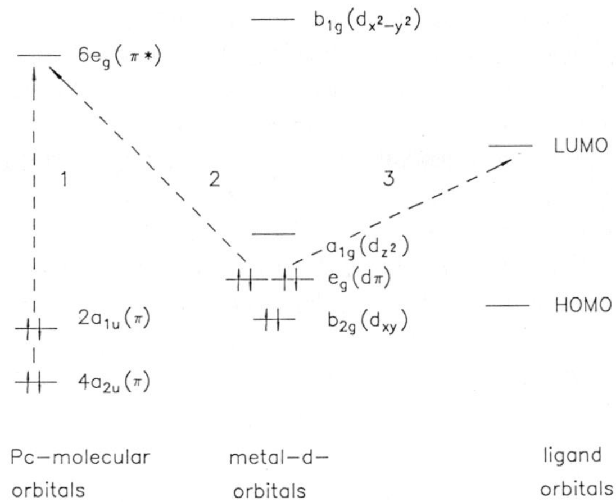

Scheme 19. Schematic representation of possible π–π* transitions for bridged phthalocyaninatoiron(II) complexes $[PcFeL]_n$ (e.g. L = tz, dib) as deduced from photoaction spectra
1) π → f* (transitions within the macrocycle; bands at about 320 nm)
2) d → Pc (π*) (charge-transfer transition between the metal and the macrocycle)
3) d → L (π*) (charge-transfer transition between the metal and the bridging ligand)

The photoelectrical behavior of bridged transition metal complexes can be explained by a one-step mechanism where optical excitation directly produces the mobile charge carriers [199b]. Electronic transitions from the metal to the π* orbital of the bridging ligand are assumed to be decisive for this mechanism. From the bridging ligand the electron more probably reaches a neighboring unexcited PcM center than that it returns. The energy bands formed from orbitals of the phthalocyanine moieties, the central metals and the π-electron-system of the bridging ligands take care of the carrier transport and ensure a high probability of charge separation. Thus larger photosensitivity can be obtained for this class of compounds as compared to the sulfur or oxygen bridged complexes [199b].

5.3 Langmuir-Blodgett Films

5.3.1 Introduction

Molecular films, ordered thin organic films in a thickness range from a few nanometers (a monolayer) to several hundred nanometers, show considerable technological promise [205, 206]. Phthalocyanine thin films have been of particular interest because of their photo and electrical responses [207–210]. However, unsubstituted phthalocyanines generally have some limitations as far as arranging and organizing phthalocyanine moieties into a desired crystal structure and thickness onto solid substrates is concerned as they usually exhibit polymorphisms in the solid state and poor solubility in common organic solvents. Thin films of phthalocyanines can be prepared by vacuum evaporation, spin-casting and dispersion in a polymer binder.

Recently, the Langmuir-Blodgett (LB) technique has been recognized as a useful way of tailoring thin films of molecular thickness. Interest in the LB technique has led to a number of investigations of different types of materials. For example, the classic long-chain fatty acids and alcohols as well as polymerizable molecules, e.g. diacetylenic acids [211–213], aromatic hydrocarbons, e.g. substituted anthracenes [214, 215], TCNQ radical anion salts [216, 217] and charge transfer complexes [218–220] and dye substances can now all be produced as monomolecular layers.

5.3.2 Preparation of LB Films

The preparation of LB films of phthalocyanine and its derivatives was reported by Roberts et al. [221]. A related patent describes a range of phthalocyanine compounds which can be successfully deposited using the Langmuir trough [221]. Several groups have studied the preparation, structure and electrical properties of LB films based on substituted phthalocyanines including cyano, isopropyl, *tert*-butyl, isopropylaminomethyl and amylphenoxy groups [160, 189b, 221–230]. Other researchers have studied the LB films of Pc's involving long alkyl chains such as dodecaoxymethyl, octadecoxy and octadecylamide [227, 231–233].

Detailed descriptions of the principles and techniques of preparing Langmuir monolayers and Langmuir-Blodgett monolayers, bilayers and multilayers are given in a number of recent sources [234–238]. In order to deposit thin films by the LB technique, a few drops of a dilute solution of the organic material in a volatile solvent are placed on the surface of the sub-phase liquid. When spread upon the surface, appropriate molecules may be compressed with the aid of a moveable teflon barrier. The relationship between the surface pressure and the occupied area (at constant temperature) indicates when all of the molecules are all aligned into a compact floating solid locked together by van der Waals forces. The pressure–area isotherm gives information about the molecular arrangement on the surface. Phthalocyanines were found to align both mainly edge-on [189b, 224, 228, 230] and in an end-on [231] fashion. It should be emphasized, that molecular orientations cannot be established unequivocally from surface pressure–area measurements alone, and further evidence to support the stacking hypothesis is necessary.

Once the layer is compressed into a two-dimensional solid, a suitable substrate is repeatedly dipped through the floating layer. For one dipping cycle (down and up) it is possible to deposit two layers (Y-type deposition), one layer on the down-stroke only (X-type deposition) or one layer on the up-stroke only

(Z-type deposition) [238]. In the case of certain substituted monomeric phthalocyanines a Z-type deposition is reported [189b, 224, 228] while polymeric liquid crystalline polysiloxanes are transferred both on the down- and up-stroke (Y-type deposition) [239]. For the dipping process the pH of the subphase and the surface pressure at which the dipping occurs are important variables which must be optimized in order to achieve high quality films.

5.3.3 Characterization of LB Films

Many different experimental techniques have been used to study LB films. To assess the reproducibility of film deposition, both optical and electrical measurements are convenient. If the optical absorption at a distinct wavelength is plotted as a function of the number of deposited layers, a linear relationship is indicative of a constant transfer ratio during sequential dippings of the substrate ($(t\text{-bu})_4PcSiCl_2$) through the floating film [224, 228]. The same information is obtained if there is a linear dependence of the inverse capacitance from the number of deposited layers [224, 228]. Characterization experiments involving electrical DC measurements [224, 230], ESR spectroscopy [226] ($(t\text{-bu})_4PcM$, M = 2H, Cu), electron microscopy [239, 240] and electron diffraction [239] ($(CH_3O)_4(C_8H_{17}O)_4PcSi(OH)_2$, $[(CH_3O)_4(C_8H_{17}O)_4PcSiO]_n$) are also reported. For example tetra-*tert*-butyl phthalocyaninatocopper has been deposited, by LB techniques, upon an electron microscope grid [240]. Minimum dose conditions were used to avoid rapid destruction of the film by the electron beam. The image showed that the lines of the molecules are well ordered. Small and highly disordered domains were present, although there was a high degree of crystallographic order within the domains. These films could be regarded as consisting of an amorphous matrix containing embedded crystallites [240].

5.3.4 Potential Applications of Langmuir-Blodgett Films

Besides the value of LB-films as model systems in fundamental research there are a number of potential applications for these layers. The incorporation of LB monolayers and multilayers into both metal/LB-film/metal and metal/LB-film/semiconductor (MIS) devices has recently been attracting considerable attention [237]. Structures in the first category may find application as the basis for simple photovoltaic cells or switches. When deposited onto semiconducting substrates, the fine control of the LB layer thickness permits the optimization of the efficiency of both photovoltaic and electroluminescent structures. Thicker films can be used to control the surface conductivity of a variety of semiconductors and as the basis for a field effect transistor. The three particular examples presented in this section should serve to indicate the usefulness of monomolecular insulating films in the field of microelectronics.

5.3.4.1 Photovoltaic Cell

The photovoltaic properties between a conductor and an organic film can be investigated using the sandwich configuration. In this configuration the organic film is sandwiched between rectifying and ohmic contacts. One advantage of the Langmuir trough technique is the fine control over the thickness of these organic films. There are several reasons for incorporating layers of tunnelling dimensions in certain electronic devices. For example, the Schottky barrier height as well as the conversion efficiency of a photovoltaic cell based on a metal–semiconductor contact can be influenced by the presence of a thin insulating layer. Both the work by Loutfy et al. [241] using ITO (indium–tin-oxide)/metal free Pc/metal structures and by Roberts et al. [225] using ITO/(*t*-bu)$_4$PcSiCl$_2$/aluminium or In-5wt%Sn structures has revealed the presence of a Schottky barrier at the metal–organic layer interface. LB-films of a substituted phthalocyanatocopper and of (*t*-bu)$_4$PcSiCl$_2$ were investigated for their conversion efficiency [189b, 225]. However, the low short-circuit photocurrent density obtained for the photoelectric devices preclude the immediate use as a high efficiency solar cell. Nevertheless, by suitably modifying the molecular structure, or even by doping the material, it may well be possible to affect the conductivity of the LB layers so that practical photovoltaic devices may be realized.

5.3.4.2 Electroluminescent Diode

It is also possible to capitalize on the thinness and perfection of LB-films in improving the efficiency of MIS electroluminescent cells. The insulating layers of the organic film have to adhere well to the semiconductor, be thermally and mechanically stable and, in particular, they must be able to withstand the operating current densities required for electroluminescence. The best results have been obtained using substituted phthalocyanine LB-films, the incorporation of which results in a yellow–green [242] or blue–white [243] light emission. The role of the organic film is to enhance the injection of holes into an n-type semiconductor and thereby create more luminescence due to electron-hole recombination.

5.3.4.3 Gas Detector

It has long been known that the electrical conductivity of phthalocyanines is very sensitive to the presence of certain gases. The increased conductivity is confined to the surface of the crystal, therefore phthalocyanines have been studied as gas sensors in the form of vacuum-sublimed films [244, 245]. Unfortunately, because phthalocyanines exhibit polymorphism (see however Ref. 189d), the exact structure of such films can be complicated, making interpretation of results and subsequent device optimisation difficult.

Langmuir-Blodgett films of substituted phthalocyanines have been used for the detection of N_2O_4 [228, 246], NH_3 [246–248], SO_2 [247, 248] and carbon monoxide [246] as pristine films or as composite films with stearic acid [247].

The response and recovery times were found to be faster than those previously found for vacuum-sublimed phthalocyanine devices. It is suggested that this is due to the more ordered structure of the LB-film, which enables the gas to adsorb on, and desorb from the molecular sites more readily.

6 Abbreviations

acac	acetylacetonate
aq	aqueous
ba	*n*-butylamine
bpa	1,2-bis(4-pyridyl)ethane
bpe	*trans*-1,2-bis(4-pyridyl)ethylene
bpy	4,4′-bipyridine
bpyac	4,4′-bipyridylacetylene
bzNC	benzylisocyanide
chxNC	cyclohexylisocyanide
$CEPcH_2$	crown ether phthalocyanine
Cl_4dib	2,3,5,6-tetrachloro-1,4-diisocyanobenzene
Cl_4phNC	tetrachloroisocyanobenzene
$Cl_{16}PcH_2$	1,2,3,4,8,9,10,11,15,16,17,18,22,23,24-hexadecachloro-phthalocyanine
Clpyz	2-chloropyrazine
CNDO	complete neglect of differential overlap
CPMAS	cross-polarisation and magic-angle spinning
CV	cyclic voltammetry
dabco	1,4-diazabicyclo[2.2.2]octane
dib	1,4-diisocyanobenzene
dibph	4,4′-diisocyanobiphenylene
$dmgH_2$	dimethylglyoxime
D	discotic mesophase
DC	dark current
DMF	dimethylformamide
DMSO	dimethylsulfoxide
DSC	differential scanning calometry
DTA	differential thermal analysis
etpyz	2-ethylpyrazine
EPR	electron paramagnetic resonance
E_Q	quadrupole splitting
FIR	far infra-red
HOMO	highest occupied molecular orbital
HpH_2	hemiporphyrazine
i-prphNC	isopropylphenylisocyanide

imH	imidazole
I	isotropic state
IR	infra-red
ITO	indium tin oxide
K	crystal phase
L	ligand
LB	Langmuir-Blodgett
LUMO	lowest occupied molecular orbital
Mac	macrocycle
m-dib	1,3-diisocyanobenzene
m-mephNC	3-methyl-isocyanobenzene
me_2bpy	3,3′-dimethyl-4,4′-bipyridine
me_2phNC	2,6-dimethylphenylisocyanide
me_2pyz	2,6-dimethylpyrazine
me_4dib	2,3,5,6-tetramethyldiisocyanobenzene
Me_8PcH_2	2,3,9,10,16,17,23,24-octamethylphthalocyanine
$(MeO)_8PcH_2$	2,3,9,10,16,17,23,24-octamethoxyphthalocyanine
mepyz	2-methylpyrazine
MeOH	methanol
MECI	monoexcited configuration interaction approximation
MIS	metal insulator semiconductor device
MO	molecular orbital
$MTIMH_2$	2,3,9,10-tetramethyl-1,4,8,11-tetracyclotetradeca-tetra-1,3,8,10-ene
NcH_2	naphthalocyanine
NL	nonlinear
NLO	nonlinear optics
$(NO_2)_4PcH_2$	tetranitrophthalocyanine
$(NO_2)_4(NH_2)_4PcH_2$	tetranitro-tetraaminophthalocyanine
NMR	nuclear magnetic resonance
o-mephNC	2-methyl-isocyanobenzene
OAc^-	acetate
$OEPH_2$	octaethylporphyrin
$OMPH_2$	octamethylporphyrin
$OMTBPH_2$	octamethyltetrabenzoporphyrin
p-dib, dib	diisocyanobenzene
p-mephNC	4-methyl-isocyanobenzene
p-NO_2-$TPPH_2$	5,10,15,20-(4-nitrophenyl)porphyrin
phNC	phenylisocyanide
pip	piperidine
py	pyridine
pyz	pyrazine
PcH_2	phthalocyanine
R_mPcH_2	peripherally substituted phthalocyanine
S	Siemens

SCE	saturated calomel electrode
SCF	self consistent field
SH	second harmonic
t-bu	tertiary butyl
$taaH_2$	dihydrodibenzotetraaza[14]annulene
tmbpy	4,4′-trimethylenebipyridine
tms	trimethylsilyl
$tmtaaH_2$	tetramethyldihydrodibenzotetraaza[14]-annulene
tz	*s*-tetrazine
$TAPH_2$	tetraazaporphyrin
$TBPH_2$	tetrabenzoporphyrin
TCNQ	tetracyanoquinodimethane
TG	thermal gravimetry
TH	third harmonic
THF	tetrahydrofurane
$TIMH_2$	1,4,8,11-tetracyclo-decatetra-1,3,8,10-ene
$TMPH_2$	5,10,15,20-tetramethylporphyrin
$TNPH_2$	tetranaphthoporphyrin
$TPPH_2$	tetraphenylporphyrin
$TPyPH_2$	tetra(2,3-pyrido)porphyrazin
UV/VIS	ultraviolet/visible
wt	weight

Acknowledgement: We want to thank Professor H. Meier, Bamberg, for helpful discussions, for looking over part of the manuscript and especially for his kind permission to use results from his research work prior to publication.

For helpful discussions the authors also thank Professor G. Gauglitz, Tübingen.

We are grateful to Frau Erika Schmid, Tübingen, for patiently typing and retyping the manuscript.

7 References

1. Moser FH, Thomas AL (1983) The phthalocyanines, vols I, II. CRC Press, Boca Raton, FL
2a. Ullmanns Enzycl Tech Chem (1979) 4th edn, vol 18, p 501
2b. Moser FH, Thomas AL (1963) Phthalocyanine compounds, Reinhold, New York; Chapman and Hall, London
2c. Lever ABP (1965) Adv Inorg Radiochem 7: 27
2d. Boucher LJ (1979) In: Melson GA (ed) Coordination chemistry of macrocyclic compounds, Plenum, New York, chap 7
2e. Kasuga K, Tsutsui M (1980) Coord Chem Rev 32: 67
2f. Sayer P, Goutermann M, Connell CR (1982) Acc Chem Res 15: 73
2g. Leznoff CC, Lever ABP (1989) Phthalocyanines, VCH Publishers, New York
3. Hamann C, Lehmann G, Starke M, Tantscher C, Wagner H (1978) Organische Festkörper und dünne Schichten (Görlich P, ed.) Akademische Verlagsgesellschaft, Leipzig, chap 2, p 90
4a. Bennet WE, Broberg DE, Baenziger NC (1973) Inorg Chem 12: 930
4b. Gieren A, Hoppe W (1971) J Chem Soc Chem Commun 413

4c. Kasuga K, Tsutsui M, Pettersen RC, Pepe G, van Opdenbosch N, Meyer EF (1980) J Am Chem Soc 102: 4835
5a. Lever ABP, Licoccia S, Magnell K, Minor PC, Ramarwany BS (1982) Adv Chem Ser 201: 237
5b. Behnisch R, Hanack M, Kellog G, Marks TJ, Inorg Chem (in press)
5c. Behnisch R (1989) Doctoral Thesis, University of Tübingen
6a. Hoffman BM, Ibers JA (1983) Acc Chem Res 16: 15
6b. Fischer K, Hanack M (1983) Angew Chem 95: 741
6c. Lau PW, Lin WC (1975) J Inorg Nucl Chem 37: 2389
6d. Vogler A, Kunkely H, Rethwish B (1980) Inorg Chim Acta 46: 101
6e. Aartsma TJ, Gouterman M, Jochum C, Kwiram AL, Pepich BV, Williams LD (1982) J Am Chem Soc 104: 6278
6f. Kobayashi N, Koshiyama M, Osa T (1983) Chem Lett 163
6g. Kobayashi N, Koshiyama M, Osa T (1985) Inorg Chem 24: 2502
6h. Hellberger JH, von Rebay A, Hever DB (1938) Ann Chem 533: 197
6i. Solov'ev KN, Tsvirko MP, Kachura TF (1976) Optics and Spectroscopy 40: 391
7a. Remy DE (1983) Tetrahedron Lett 24: 1451
7b. Edwards L, Gouterman M, Rose CB (1976) J Am Chem Soc 98: 7638
7c. Kopranenkov VN, Makarova EA, Luk'yanets EA (1981) J Gen Chem USSR 51: 2353
7d. Vogler A, Kunkely H (1978) Angew Chem 90: 808
7e. Fischer K (1984) Doctoral Thesis, Universität Tübingen
7f. Kopranenkov VN, Makarova EA, Dashkavich SN, Luk'yanets EA (1982) Khim Geterotsikl Soedin 11: 1563
8. Koehurst RB, Kleibenker JF, Schaafsma TJ, de Bie DA, Geurtsen B, Henric RN, van der Plas HC (1981) J Chem Soc Perk Trans II 1005
9. Hanack M, Lange A, Behnisch R, Renz G, Leverenz A (1989) Synth Met F1
10. Deger S, Hanack M (1986) Isr J Chem 27: 347
11. Hanack M, Renz G, Strähle J, Schmid S (1988) Chem Ber 121: 1479
12. Bradbrook EF, Linstead RP (1936) J Chem Soc 1744
13. Kopranenkov VN, Vorotnikov AM, Luk'yanets EA (1979) J Gen Chem USSR 49: 2467
14a. Rein M, Hanack M (1988) Chem Ber 121: 1601
14b. Hanack M, Lange A, Rein M, Behnisch R, Renz G, Leverenz A (1989) Synth Met 29: F1
15a. Whitlock HW, Hanauer R (1968) J Org Chem 33: (5) 2169
15b. Inhoffen HH, Fuhrhop J-H, Voigt H, Brockmann H Jr (1966) Ann 695: 133
15c. Chamberlin KS, LeGoff E (1979) Heterocycles 12: 1567
15d. LeGoff E, Cheng DO (1979) Porphyrin Chem Adv [Pap Porphyrin Symp] 1977: 153
15e. Callot HJ, Louati A, Gross M (1983) Bull Chim Soc Fr 11–12 (II): 317
16. Elvidge JA, Linstead RP (1952) J Chem Soc 5008
17a. Campell JP (1956) US Patent 2:765, 308
17b. Esposito JN (1966) Ph.D. Thesis, Case Inst Techn, Cleveland, Ohio
18. Meyer G (1974) Doctoral Thesis, Freie Universität Berlin
19. Speakman JC (1953) Acta Cryst 6: 784
20. Hiller W, Strähle J, Mitulla K, Hanack M (1980) Liebigs Ann Chem 1946
21a. Dirk CW, Schoch KF, Jr, Marks TJ (1981) In: Conductive polymers (Seymour RB, ed) Plenum, New York, p 209
21b. Marks TJ, Kalina DW (1982) In: Extended linear chain compounds (Miller JS, ed) Plenum, New York, vol 1, p 197
22a. Hanack M (1983) Chimia 37: 238
22b. Hanack M (1985) Isr J Chem 25: 205
22c. Hanack M, Datz A, Fay R, Fischer K, Keppeler U, Koch J, Metz J, Mezger M, Schneider O, Schulze H-J (1986) Handbook of conducting polymers (Skotheim TA, ed) M Dekker, New York, p 133
22d. Zipplies T, Hanack M (1987) Houben-Weyl (Bartl H, Falbe J, ed), Georg Thieme, Stuttgart, 4th ed, vol E-20, p 2237
22e. Hanack M, Deger S, Keppeler U, Lange A, Leverenz A, Rein M (1987) Conducting polymers (Alcácer L, ed), Reidel, Dordrecht, Holland, p 173
22f. Hanack M, Deger S, Keppeler U, Lange A, Leverenz A, Rein M (1987) Synth Met 19: 787
22g. Hanack M (1987) GIT Fachzeitschrift für das Laboratorium 31: 75
22h. Hanack M, Deger S, Lange A (1988) Coord Chem Rev 83: 115
23. Berlin AA (1979) Russ Chem Rev 48: 1125

24. Wöhrle D (1983) Adv Polym Sci 50: 45
25. Epstein A, Wildi BS (1960) J Chem Phys 32: 324
26a. Ukei K (1973) Acta Cryst B29: 2290
26b. Ukei K, Takamoto K, Kanda E (1973) Phys Lett A, 45: 345
27. Iyechika Y, Yakushi K, Ikemoto I, Kuroda H (1982) Acta Cryst B38: 766
28a. Schramm CJ, Scaringe RP, Stojakovic DR, Hoffmann BM, Ibers JA, Marks TJ (1980) J Am Chem Soc 102: 6702
28b. Palmer SM, Stanton JM, Hoffmann BM, Ibers JA (1986) Inorg Chem 25: 2296
28c. Almeida M, Kanatzidis MG, Tonge LM, Marks TJ, Marcy HO, McCarthy WJ, Kannewurf CR (1987) Solid State Commun 63: 457
29. Pace LJ, Martinsen J, Ulman A, Hoffman BM, Ibers JA (1983) J Am Chem Soc 105: 2612
30. Martin J, Pace LJ, Philips TE, Hoffman BM, Ibers JA (1982) J Am Chem Soc 104: 83
31. Ibers JA, Pace LC, Martinsen J, Hoffman BM (1982) Structure and Bonding 50: 1
32a. André JJ, Holczer K, Petit P, Riou M-T, Clarisse C, Even R, Fourmigue M, Simon J (1985) Chem Phys Lett 115: 463
32b. Even R, Simon J, Markovitsi D (1989) Chem Phys Lett 156: 609
32c. Aroca R, Clavijo RE, Jennings CA, Kovacs GJ, Duff JM, Loutfy RO (1989) Spectrochim Acta Part A, 45A (9), 957
33a. Joyner RD, Kenney ME (1960) J Am Chem Soc 82: 5790
33b. Joyner RD, Kenney ME (1962) Inorg Chem 1: 717
33c. Joyner RD, Kenney ME (1962) Inorg Chem 1: 236
34a. Marks TJ, Schoch KF, Kundalkar BR (1979/80) Synth Met 1: 337
34b. Dirk CA, Inabe T, Schoch KF, Jr, Marks TJ (1983) J Am Chem Soc 105: 1539
34c. Diel BN, Inabe T, Lyding JW, Schoch KF, Jr, Kannewurf CR, Marks TJ (1983) J Am Chem Soc 105: 1551
34d. Ciliberto E, Doris KA, Pietro WJ, Reisner GM, Ellis DE, Frigala I, Herbstein FH, Ratner MA, Marks TJ (1984) J Am Chem Soc 106: 7748
34e. Pietro WJ, Marks TJ, Ratner MA (1985) J Am Chem Soc 107: 5387
34f. Marks TJ (1985) Science 227: 881
34g. Zhou X, Marks TJ, Carr SH (1984) Polym Mat Sci Eng 51: 651
34h. DeWulf DW, Leland JK, Wheeler BL, Bard AJ, Batzel DA, Dininny DR, Kenney M (1987) Inorg Chem 26: 266
35a. Orthmann E, Enkelmann V, Wegner G (1983) Macromol Chem Rapid Commun 4: 687
35b. Orthmann E (1983) Diplomarbeit, Universität Freiburg
36. Nohr RS, Kuznesof PM, Wynne KJ, Kenney ME, Siebermann PG (1981) J Am Chem Soc 103: 4371
37a. Toscano PJ, Marks TJ (1985) Mol Cryst Liq Cryst 118: 337
37b. Toscano PJ, Marks TJ (1986) J Am Chem Soc 108: 437
37c. Wehrle B, Limbach H-H, Zipplies T, Hanack M (1989) Angew Chem Adv Mater 101: 1783
38. Zhou X, Marks TJ, Carr SH (1985) J Polym Sci 23: 305
39. Zhou X, Marks TJ, Carr SH (1985) Mol Cryst Liq Cryst 118: 357
40. Ibers JA, Pace LJ, Martinsen J, Hoffmann BM (1982) Struct Bond 50: 47
41a. Martinsen J, Stanton JL, Greene RL, Tanaka J, Hoffman BM, Ibers JA (1985) J Am Chem Soc 107: 6915
41b. Dirk CW, Mintz EA, Schoch KF, Jr, Marks TJ (1981) J Macromol Sci Chem A16: 275
41c. Inabe T, Moguel MK, Kannewurf CR, Marks TJ (1983) Mol Cryst Liq Cryst 93: 355
41d. Inabe T, Moguel MK, Marks TJ, Burton R, Lyding JW, Kannewurf CR (1985) Mol Cryst Liq Cryst 118: 349
41e. Gaudiello JG, Almeida M, Marks TJ, McCarthy WJ, Butler JC, Kannewurf CR (1986) J Phys Chem 90: 4917
42. Schneider O, Metz J, Hanack M (1982) Mol Cryst Liq Cryst 81: 273
43a. Whangbo MH, Stewart KR (1983) Isr J Chem 23: 133
43b. Canadell E, Alvarez S (1984) Inorg Chem 23: 573
43c. Sheng P (1980) Phys Rev B 21: 2180
43d. Koch W (1986) Dissertation, University of Tübingen
44. Inabe T, Lyding JW, Marks TJ (1983) J Chem Soc Chem Commun 1084
45. Hanack M, Fischer K (1983) Chem Ber 116: 1860
46. Meier H, Albrecht W, Zimmerhackl E, Hanack M, Fischer K (1985) J Mol Electron 1: 47
47a. Meyer G, Wöhrle D (1974) Makromol Chem 175: 714

47b. Hartmann M, Meyer G, Wöhrle D (1975) Makromol Chem 176: 831
48. Metz J, Pawlowski G, Hanack M (1983) Z Naturforsch 38B: 378
49. Hanack M, Marks TJ (unpublished)
50a. Dirk CW, Marks TJ (1984) Inorg Chem 23: 4325
50b. Sutton LE, Kenney ME (1967) Inorg Chem 6: 1869
50c. Meyer G, Hartmann D, Wöhrle D (1975) Makromol Chem 176: 1919
50d. Meyer G, Wöhrle D (1981) Materials Science 7: 265
50e. Dirk CW, Montz EA, Schoch KF, Marks TJ (1981) J Macromol Sci Chem A16: 45
51. Moyer TJ, Schechtmann LA, Kenney ME (1984) Polym Prep 25: 234
52a. Honeybourne CL (1982) J Chem Soc Chem Commun 744
52b. Hanack M, Zipplies T (1985) J Am Chem Soc 107: 6127
53. Hanack M, Zipplies T (1988) Synth Met 25: 341
54a. Hiller W, Strähle J, Datz A, Hanack M, Ter Haar LW, Hatfield WE, Gütlich P (1984) J Am Chem Soc 106: 329
54b. Hiller W, Strähle J, Datz A, Hanack M (1984) Mol Cryst Liq Cryst 107 (1–2): 151
55a. Linsky JP, Paul TR, Nohr RS, Kenney ME (1980) Inorg Chem 19: 3131
55b. Kuznesof PM, Nohr RS, Wynne KJ, Kenney ME (1981) J Macromol Sci Chem A16: 299
55c. Wynne KJ, Nohr RS (1983) Mol Cryst Liq Cryst 81: 243
55d. Nohr RS, Wynne KJ (1981) J Chem Soc Chem Commun 1210
55e. Wynne KJ (1985) Inorg Chem 24: 1339
55f. Brant P, Nohr RS, Wynne KJ, Weber DC (1982) Mol Cryst Liq Cryst 81: 255
56a. Berthet G, Djurado D, Fabre L, Faury F, Maleysson C, Robert H (1985) Mol Cryst Liq Cryst 118: 345
56b. Djurado D, Hamwi A, Cousseins JC, Bidar H, Fabre C, Berthet G (1985) Synth Met 11: 109
57a. Schechtmann LA, Kenney ME (1983) Proc Electrochem Soc 83: 340
57b. Shimura Y, Hoshi M, Shimura M (1986) J Electrochem Soc 133: 239
58a. Goulon J, Friaut P, Goulon-Ginet C, Coutsolelos A, Guilard R (1984) Chem Phys 83: 367
58b. Guilard R, Barbe J-M, Richard P, Petit P, André JJ, Lecomte C, Kadish KM (1989) J Am Chem Soc 111: 4684
59. Maskasky JE, Kenney ME (1973) J Am Chem Soc 95: 1443
60a. Hanack M, Mitulla K, Pawlowski G, Subramanian LR (1979) Angew Chem 91: 343 (1979), Int Ed Engl 18: 322
60b. Mitulla K, Hanack M (1980) Z Naturforsch 35b: 1111
60c. Hanack M, Mitulla K, Pawlowski G, Subramanian LR (1981) J Organomet Chem 204: 315
60d. Hanack M, Kobel W, Metz J, Mezger M, Pawlowski G, Schneider O, Schulze H-J, Subramanian LR (1981) Mat Science 185
60e. Hanack M, Mitulla K, Schneider O (1981) Chem Scripta 17
61. Hanack M, Fischer K (1985) Synth Met 10: 347
62. Hanack M, Seelig FF, Strähle J (1979) Z Naturforsch 34a: 983
63a. Schneider O, Hanack M (1980) Angew Chem 92: 391
63b. Schneider O, Hanack M (1980) Angew Chem Supp 41: (1982), Int Ed Engl 19: 392
63c. Schneider O, Hanack M (1983) Chem Ber 116: 2088
63d. Hanack M, Datz A, Kobel W, Koch J, Metz J, Mezger M, Schneider O, Schulze H-J (1983) J de Physique C3: 633
64. Kobel W, Hanack M (1986) Inorg Chem 25: 103
65. Schneider O (1983) Doctoral Thesis, University of Tübingen
66. Keppeler U (1985) Doctoral Thesis, University of Tübingen
67. Marks TJ, Stojakovic OR (1978) J Am Chem Soc 100: 1695
68. Taube R, Drews H, Fluck E, Kuhn P, Brauch KF (1969) Z Anorg Allg Chem 364: 297
69. Keppeler U, Deger S, Lange A, Hanack M (1987) Angew Chem 99: 349 (1987) Int Ed Engl 26: 344
70. Dale BW, Williams RJP, Edwards PR, Johnson CE (1968) Trans Faraday Soc 64: 620
71. Diel BN, Inabe T, Jaggi NK, Lyding JW, Schneider O, Hanack M, Kannewurf CR, Marks TJ, Schwartz LH (1984) J Am Chem Soc 106: 3207
72. Deger S (1986) Doctoral Thesis, University of Tübingen
73. Wei H-H, Shyu H-L (1985) Polyhedron 4: 979
74. Jaggi NK, Schwartz LH, Schneider O (unpublished data)
75. Quedraogo GV, More C, Richard Y, Benlian D (1981) Inorg Chem 20: 4387
76a. Lord RC, Marston AL, Miller FA (1957) Spectrochim Acta 9: 113

76b. Perkampus HH, Baumgarten E (1963) Spectrochim Acta 19: 1473
76c. Simmons JD, Innes KK (1964) J Mol Spectrosc 14: 190
77. Zarembowitsch J, Bokobza-Sebagh L (1976) Spectrochim Acta 32A: 605
78. Metz J, Schneider O, Hanack M (1982) Spectrochim Acta 38A: 1265
79. Metz J, Hanack, M (1981) Nouv J Chem 5: 541
80. Hanack M, Metz J (1987) Chem Ber 120: 1307
81. Metz J, Hanack M (1988) Chem Ber 121: 231
82. Münz X, Hanack M (1988) Chem Ber 121: 235
83. Metz J, Schneider O, Hanack M (1984) Inorg Chem 23: 1065
84. Metz J (1983) Doctoral Thesis, University of Tübingen; Mezger M, Hanack M, Chem Ber in print
85. Mezger M (1983) Doctoral Thesis, University of Tübingen
86. Datz A (1981) Diplomarbeit, University of Tübingen
87. Koch J, Hanack M (1983) Chem Ber 116: 2109
88. Koch JW, Hanack M (1987) Chem Ber 120: 1853
89a. Collman JP, McDevitt JT, Yee GT, Leidner CR, McCullough LG, Little WA, Torrance JB (1986) Proc Natl Acad Sci USA 83: 4581
89b. Collman JP, McDevitt JT, Yee GT, Zisk MB, Torrance JB, Little WA (1986) Synth Met 15: 129
89c. Collman JP, McDevitt JT, Leidner CR, Yee GT, Torrance JB, Little WA (1987) J Am Chem Soc 109: 4606
90. Hanack M, Mezger M, Hiller W (1987) Act Crystallogr Sect C 43: 1264
91. Kubel F, Strähle J (1981) Z Naturforsch Teil B 36: 441
92. Schneider O, Hanack M (1983) Angew Chem 95: 804
93. Schulze HJ (1985) Doctoral Thesis, University of Tübingen
94a. Hedtmann-Rein C, Keppeler U, Münz X, Hanack M (1985) Mol Cryst Liq Cryst 118: 361
94b. Keppeler U, Hanack M (1986) Chem Ber 119: 3363
95. Müller R, Wöhrle D (1978) Makromol Chem 179: 2161
96. Hedtmann-Rein C (1986) Thesis, University of Tübingen
97. Koch J (1981) Diplomarbeit, University of Tübingen
98. Koch J (1984) Thesis, University of Tübingen
99. Hanack M, Keppeler U, Schulze H-J (1987) Synth Met 20: 347
100. Lange A (1985) Diplomarbeit, University of Tübingen
101a. Hanack M, Leverenz A (1987) Synth Met 22: 9
101b. Hanack M, Leverenz A (1987) In: Kuzmany H, Mehring M, Roth S (eds) Solid-State Sciences 76, Springer, Berlin Heidelberg New York
102. Molins E, Labarta A, Tejada J, Caubet A, Alvarez S (1983) Transition Met Chem 8: 377
103. For preparation of isocyanides see:
103a. Ugi I (1962) DAS 1 158 500, April 6th
103b. Ugi I, Fetzer U, Eholzer U, Knupfer H, Offermann K (1965) Angew Chem 77: 492
103c. Obrecht LR, Herrmann R, Ugi I, Synthesis 1985: 400
104a. Deger S, Hanack M (1985) Electronic properties of polymers and related compounds; Springer Series in Solid-State Sciences 63. In: Kuzmany H, Mehring M, Roth S (eds) Springer-Verlag, Heidelberg, p 327
104b. Deger S, Hanack M, (1986) Synth Met 13: 319
105. Schneider O, Hanack M, unpublished results
106. Appel R, Kleinstück R, Ziehn K-D (1971) Angew Chem 83: 143
107. Keppeler U, Kobel W, Siehl H-U, Hanack M (1985) Chem Ber 118: 2095
108. Boschi T, Bontempelli G, Mazzocchin GA (1979) Inorg Chem Acta 37: 155
109. Hanack M, Thies R (1988) Chem Ber 121: 1225
109a. Hanack M, Renz G, Strähle J, Schmid S, J Org Chem Soc, in press
110. Renz G (1989) Doctoral Thesis, University of Tübingen
111. Hanack M, Vermehren P (1989) Synth Met 32: 257
112. Calderazzo F, Frediani S, James BR, Pampaloni G, Reimer KJ, Sams JR, Serra AM, Vitali O (1982) Inorg Chem 21: 2302
113. Kennedy BJ, Murray KS, Zwack PR, Homborg H, Kalz W (1986) Inorg Chem 25: 2539
114. Keppeler U, Schneider O, Stöffler W, Hanack M, Tetrahedron Lett 1984: 3579
115. Vermehren P (1985) Diplomarbeit, University of Tübingen
116. Schneider O, Hanack M (1984) Z Naturforsch 39b: 265

117. Datz A, Metz J, Schneider O, Hanack M (1984) Synth Met 9: 31
118. Datz A (1985) Doctoral Thesis, University of Tübingen
119. Hedtmann-Rein C, Hanack M, Peters K, Peters E-M, Schnering HG (1987) Inorg Chem 26: 2647
120. Barrett PA, Frye DA, Linstead RP, J Chem Soc 1938: 1157
121. Myers JF, Canham GWR, Lever ABP (1975) Inorg Chem 14: 461
122. Khidekel ML, Zhilyaeva EL (1981) Synth Met 4: 1
123. Kalz W (1984) Doctoral Thesis, University of Kiel
124. Metz J, Hanack M (1983) J Am Chem Soc 105: 828
125. Taube R (1974) Pure Appl Chem 38: 427
126. Deger S, Hanack M, Hiller W, Strähle J (1984) Liebigs Ann Chem 1791
127a. Hanack M, Münz X (1985) Synth Met 10: 357
127b. Münz X, Hanack M (1988) Chem Ber 121: 239
128. Hanack M, Hedtmann-Rein C (1985) Z Naturforsch 40b: 1087
129. Alvarez S, Lopez C (1982) Inorg Chim Acta 63: 57
130. Nakamoto K (1983): In: Infrared spectra of inorganic coordination compounds, Wiley, New York
131a. Bailey RA, Kozak SL, Michelsen TW, Mills WN (1971) Coord Chem Rev 6: 407
131b. Norbury AH (1975) Adv Inorg Chem Radiochem 17: 231
132. Stults BR, Marianelli RS, Day VW (1975) Inorg Chem 14: 722
133. Stults BR, Day OR, Marianelli RS, Day VW (1979) Inorg Chem 18: 1847
134a. Orihashi Y, Kobayashi N, Tsuchida E, Matsuda H, Nakanishi H, Kato M, Chem Lett 1985: 1617
134b. Orihashi Y, Kobayashi N, Ohno H, Tsuchida E, Mabuda H, Nakanishi H, Kato M (1987) Synth Met 19: 751
135a. Orti E, Brédas JL, Synth Met (in press)
135b. Behnisch R, Hanack M (1990) Synth Met 36: 387
135c. Inabe T, Maruyama Y (1989) Chem Lett 55: Inabe T, Maruyama Y, Bull Chem Soc Jpn (in press)
136. Meier H, Albrecht W, Zimmerhackl E, Hanack M, Metz J (1985) Synth Met 11: 333
137. Rein M (1984) Diplomarbeit, University of Tübingen
138. Cohen FA, Ostfeld D (1974) ACS Symp Ser 5: 221
139. Orihashi Y, Kobayashi N, Tsuchida E, Matsuda H, Nakanishi H, Kato M, Nippon Kagaku Kaishi 1986: 410
140. Taube R, Drews H (1977) Z Anorg Allg Chem 429: 5
141. Schulze H-J (1981) Diplomarbeit, University of Tübingen
142. Chandrasekhar S, Sadashiva BK, Suresh KA (1977) Pramana, 9: 471 (CA 88:30 566 y)
143. Simon J, André JJ, Skoulios A (1986) Nouv J Chim 10: 295
144. see however:
144a. Kohne B, Praefcke K (1985) Chemiker-Ztg 109: 121
144b. Kohne B, Marquard P, Praefcke K, Psaras P, Stephan W (1987) Z Naturforsch 42b: 628
144c. Giroud-Godquin AM, Marchon JC, Guillon D, Skoulios A (1986) J Phys Chem 90: 5502
145. The other possibility is the nematic arrangement of the disk-like molecules, which shows up as the typical nematic "Schlieren-texture", see:
145a. Malthete J, Jaques J, Tinh NH, Destrade C (1982) Nature 298: 46
145b. Destrade C, Tinh NH, Gasparoux H (1981) Mol Cryst Liq Cryst 71: 111
145c. Tinh NH, Destrade C, Gasparoux H (1979) Phys Lett 72A: 251
146a. Levelut AM (1979) J Phys Lett 40: L81
146b. Levelut AM (1983) J Chim Phys 80: 138
146c. Guillon D, Skoulios A, Piechocki C, Simon J, Weber P (1983) Mol Cryst Liq Cryst 100: 275
146d. Guillon D, Skoulios A, Piechocki C, Simon J, Weber P (1985) Mol Cryst Liq Cryst 130: 223
147a. Van der Linden JH, Schoonman J, Nolte RJM, Drenth W (1984) Recl Trav Chim Pays-Bas 103: 260
147b. Van der Pol JF, Neeleman E, Zwikker JW, Nolte RJM, Drenth W, Aerts J, Visser R, Picken SJ (1989) Liq Cryst 6: 577
147c. Silcken OE, Van Lindert HCA, Drenth W, Schoonman J, Schram J, Nolte RJM (1989) Ber Bunsenges Phys Chem 93: 702
147d. Van der Pol JF, Neeleman E, Van Miltenburg JC, Zwikker JW, Nolte RJM, Drenth W (1990) Macromol 23: 155

147e. Sluyters JH, Baars A, Van der Pool JF, Drenth W (1989) J Electroanal Chem 271: 41
148a. Piechocki C, Simon J, Skoulios A, Guillon D, Weber P (1982) J Am Chem Soc 104: 5245
148b. Piechocki C, Simon J (1985) J Chem Soc Chem Comm 259
148c. Piechocki C, Simon J (1985) Nouv J Chim 9: 159
148d. Fay R (1985) Doctoral Thesis, University of Tübingen
148e. Hanack M, Beck A, Lehmann H (1987) Synthesis 703
148f. Cook MJ, Daniel MF, Harrison J, McKnoewn NB, Thomson AJ (1987) J Chem Soc Chem Comm 1086
148g. Gregg BA, Fox MA, Bard AJ (1987) J Chem Soc Chem Comm 1134
148h. Cook MJ, Dunn AJ, Howe SD, Thompson AJ, Harrison KJ (1988) J Chem Soc Perkin Trans I, 2453
149. Gregg BA, Fox MA, Bard AJ (1989) J Am Chem Soc 111: 3024
150. Knoesel R, Piechocki C, Simon J (1985) J Photochemistry 29: 445
151. Cho I, Lim Y (1988) Mol Cryst Liq Cryst 154: 9
152a. Kumada M, Tamao K, Sunitani K (1978) Org Synth 58: 127
152b. Cuellar EA, Marks TJ (1981) Inorg Chem 20: 3766
152c. Ohta K, Jacquenin L, Sirlin C, Bosio L, Simon J (1988) New J Chem 12: 751
152d. The Grignard reaction for the synthesis of dialkylbenzene as substrate was also used for the synthesis of liquid crystalline octasubstituted disk-like bis(β-diketonato)-copper(II) complexes, see: Ohta K, Ema H, Muroki H, Yamamoto I, Matsuzaki K (1987) Mol Cryst Liq Cryst 147: 61
153a. Masurel D, Sirlin C, Simon J (1987) New J Chem 11: 455
153b. Sauer T, Wegner G (1988) Mol Cryst Liq Cryst 162B: 97
153c. Sauer T (1989) Doctoral Thesis, Mainz
154. Pawlowski G, Hanack M (1980) Synthesis 287
155. Cho I, Lim Y (1987) Chem Lett 2107
156a. Vauchier C, Zann A, LeBarny P, Dubois JC, Billard J (1981) Mol Cryst Liq Cryst 66: 103
156b. Destrade C, Foucher P, Gasparoux H, Tinh NH, Levelut AM, Malthete J (1984) Mol Cryst Liq Cryst 106: 121
157. Seurin P, Guillon D, Skoulios A (1981) Mol Cryst Liq Cryst 65: 85
158. Beck A (1986) Diplomarbeit, University Tübingen
159. Nevin WA, Liu W, Melnik M, Lever ABP (1986) J Electroanal Chem 213: 217
160. Snow AW, Jarvis NL (1984) J Am Chem Soc 106: 4706
161. Blanzat B, Barthou C, Terrier N, André JJ, Simon J (1987) J Am Chem Soc 109: 6193
162. Gaspard S, Hochapfel A, Viovy R (1979) CR Hebd Seances Acad Sc, Ser C 289 (15): 387
163. Gaspard S, Hochapfel A, Viovy R (1980) Springer Ser Chem Phys 11: 298
164. Joyner RD, Kenney ME (1963) Inorg Chem 2: 1064
165a. Sirlin C, Bosio L, Simon J (1987) J Chem Soc Chem Comm 379
165b. Sirlin C, Bosio L, Simon J (1988) Mol Cryst Liq Cryst 155: 231
165c. Caseri W, Sauer T, Wegner G (1988) Macromol Chem Rapid Commun 9: 651
166. Sirlin C, Bosio L, Simon J (1988) J Chem Soc Chem Comm 236
167. Orthmann E, Wegner G (1986) Makromol Chem Rapid Commun 7: 243
168. Fay R, Hanack M (1986) Recl Trav Chim Pays-Bas 105: 427
169a. Barrett PA, Dent CE, Linstead RP (1936) J Chem Soc 1719
169b. Kasuga K, Tsutsui M (1980) Coord Chem Rev 32: 67
169c. L'Her M, Cozien Y, Courtout-Coupez J (1983) J Electroanal Chem 157: 183
169d. Turek P, Petit P, André JJ, Simon J, Even R, Boudjona B, Guillard G, Maitrot M (1987) J Am Chem Soc 109: 5119
169e. Piechocki C, Simon J, André JJ, Guillon D, Petit P, Skoulios A, Weber P (1985) Chem Phys Lett 122: 124
169f. Chang AT, Marchon JC (1981) Inorgan Chim Acta 53: L241
169g. De Cian A, Moussavi M, Fischev J, Weiss R (1985) Inorg Chem 24: 3162
170. For crown ether porphyrins (not mentioned here) see:
170a. Thanabel V, Krishna V (1982) Inorg Chem 21: 3606
170b. Maiya G, Krishna V (1985) Inorg Chem 24: 3253
170c. Chandrasekhar TK, Willigen H, Ebersole MH (1985) J Phys Chem 89: 3453
170d. Willigen H, Chandrasekhar TK (1986) J Am Chem Soc 108: 709
171. Sielcken OE, Tilborg MM, Roks MFM, Hendriks R, Drenth W, Nolte RJM (1987) J Am Chem Soc 109: 4261

172. Pedersen CJ (1967) J Am Chem Soc 89: 7017
173. Bekaroglu Ö, Ahsen V, Koray AR (1986) J Chem Soc Chem Commun 932
174. Kobayashi N, Nishiyama Y (1986) J Chem Soc Chem Commun 1462
175. Gül A, Bekaroglu Ö, Ahsen V, Yilmazer E (1987) Makromol Chem Rapid Commun 8: 243
176. Kobayashi N, Lever ABP (1987) J Am Chem Soc 109: 7433
177. Hendriks R, Sielcken OE, Drenth W, Nolte RJM (1986) J Chem Soc Chem Commun 1464
178. Ahsen V, Yilmazer E, Ertas M, Bekaroglu Ö (1988) J Chem Soc, Dalton Trans 401
179. Sirlin C, Bosio L, Simon J, Ahsen V, Yilmazer E, Bekaroglu Ö (1987) Chem Phys Lett 139: 362
180. Alcácer L (1987) Conducting polymers special applications, Reidel D, Dordrecht, Holland
181. A selection: 181a–181f
181a. Epstein AJ, Conwell EM (ed) (1981–1982) In: Proceedings of the international conference on low-dimensional conductors, Boulder, Colorado, Aug. 9th–14th, 1981, Mol Cryst Liq Cryst 77: 79: 81: 83: 86
181b. Pecile C, Zerbi G, Bogio R, Girlando A (ed) (1985) In: Proceedings of the international conference on the physics and chemistry of low-dimensional synthetic metals, Mol Cryst Liq Cryst 117: 118
181c. Proceedings of the international conference on science and technology of synthetic metals (ICSM'88), Santa Fe, NM, USA, June 26–July 2, 1988, Aldissi M (ed) Polyheterocycles, Polysilanes, Applications and Processing, Volume C (reprinted from Synth Met 28: 1–2 (1988), Elsevier, London (1989)
181d. Miller JS (ed) (1982) Extended linear chain compounds, Plenum, New York, vol 1–3
181e. Skotheim TS (ed) (1985) Handbook on conducting polymers, Marcel Dekker, New York
181f. Dolphin D (ed) (1979) The porphyrins, vol VI, Academic, New York
182. For an introduction into the field of NLO see for instance: 182a–182e
182a. Weber H, Herziger G (ed) (1972) Laser-Grundlagen und Anwendungen, Physik Verlag, Weinheim
182b. Demtröder W (1973) Physik iu Zeit 4 (5): 137
182c. Demtröder W (1981) Yoldqanskii VI, Gomer R, Schäfer FP, Toennies JP Editors: Laser spectroscopy, basic concepts and instrumentation, Springer Series in Chemical Physics 5: Springer, Berlin Heidelberg New York
182d. Shen YR (1984) The principles of nonlinear optics, Wiley, New York
182e. Zernike F, Midwinter JE (1973) Applied nonlinear optics, Wiley, New York
183a. Williams DJ (1984) Angew Chem 96: 637
183b. Williams DJ (ed) (1983) Nonlinear optical properties of organic and polymeric materials, ACS Symposium Series 233: Am Chem Soc, Washington, Chem Abstr 99 B: 166769b
183c. Chemla DS, Zyss J (eds) (1987) Nonlinear optical properties of organic molecules and crystals, Academic, New York, vol 1–2
184. Li DQ, Ratner MA, Marks TJ (1988) J Am Chem Soc 110: 1707
185. Brunner W, Jung K (1987) Lasertechnik, Hüthig Verlag, Heidelberg
186. Auston DH (1987) Applied Optics 26 (2): 211
187a. Ho ZZ, Ju CY, Hetherington III WH (1987) J Appl Phys 62 (2): 716
187b. Graczyk A, Andrzejewska T, Wodnicki R, Pol Pat PL 112414 B 1, 15.1.1982; CA 96(24): 208187f
187c. Kaltbeitzel A (1989) Dissertation, University Mainz
187d. Bubeck C, Neher D, Kaltbeitzel A, Duda G, Arndt T, Sauer T, Wegner G (1989) in "Nonlinear optical effects in organic Polymers"; Messier J, Kajzer F, Prasad PN, Ulrich DR (eds) Kluwer Acad Publ
187e. Bubeck C, Kaltbeitzel A, Vermehren P, Hanack M unpublished results
188. Wöhrle D, Krawczyk G (1986) Polymer Bull 15: 193
189a. Roberts GG, Petty MC, Baker S, Fowler MT, Thomas NJ (1985) Thin Solid Films 132: 113
189b. Yoneyama M, Sugi M, Saito M, Ikegami K, Kuroda S, Iizima S (1986) Jpn J Appl Phys, Part 1 25: 961
189c. Cook JM, Daniel MF, Harrison KJ, McKeown NB, Thomson AJ (1987) J Chem Soc Chem Commun 1148
189d. McKeown NB, Cook JM, Thomson AJ, Harrison KJ, Daniel MF, Richardson RM, Roser SJ (1988) Thin Solid Films 159: 469
190. Sakamoto K, Yoshioka M, Shibamiya F (1985) Shikizai Kyokaishi 58 (3): 121; CA 103 (6): 38688p
191. Hedayatullah M (1983) CR Seances Acad Sci Ser 2 296: 621

192a. Shirai H, Hanabusa K, Kitamura M, Masuda E (1984) Macromol Chem 185: 2537
192b. Idelson EM (1978) US Patent No. 4061654 (1977) CA 88: 171797m
193. Leznoff CC, Greenberg S, Khouw B, Lever ABP (1987) Can J Chem 65: 1705
194a. Little RG (1981) J Heterocyclic Chem 18: 129
194b. Kruper WS Jr, Chamberlin TA, Kochanny M (1989) J Org Chem 54: 2753
194c. Cosmo R, Kantz C, Meerholz K, Heinze J, Müllen K (1989) Angew Chem 101: 638 (1989), Angew Chem Int Ed Engl 28: 604
195. Leznoff CC, Svirskaya PI (1978) Angew Chem 90 (12): 1001
196a. Hall TW, Greenberg S, McArthur CR, Khouw B, Leznoff CC (1982) Nouv J Chimie 6 (12): 653
196b. Leznoff CC, Hall TW (1982) Tetrahedron Lett 23 (30): 3023
197. Friedrich J, Haarer D (1984) Angew Chem 96: 96
198. Hamann C, Heim J, Burghardt H (1981) Organische Leiter, Halbleiter und Photoleiter, Vieweg (Reihe Wissenschaften), Braunschweig, Wiesbaden
199a. Meier H (1.8.1986–31.10.1987) Zwischenbericht über die Forschungsarbeit I/61 635 (Stiftung Volkswagenwerk) mit dem Thema: Untersuchungen über Zusammenhänge zwischen Molekülstruktur und Photoleitfähigkeit organischer Verbindungen
199b. Meier H, Albrecht W (1.8.1986–31.12.1988) Abschlußbericht über die Forschungsarbeit I/61 635 (Stiftung Volkswagenwerk) mit dem Thema: Untersuchungen über Zusammenhänge zwischen Molekülstruktur und Photoleitfähigkeit organischer Verbindungen
200a. Meier H, Albrecht W, Tschirwitz U (1972) Angew Chem 84 (22): 1077
200b. Meier H (1974) Organic Semiconductors: Dark and Photoconductivity of Organic Solids; Verlag Chemie, Weinheim
201. Meier H, Albrecht W, Wöhrle D, Jahn A (1986) J Phys Chem 90 (23): 6349
202a. Meier H, Albrecht W, Zimmerhackl E (1985) Polymer Bull 13: 43
202b. Meier H, Albrecht W, Hanack M, Koch J (1986) Polymer Bull 16: 75
203. Meier H, personal communication
204. No temperature given in Ref. 197b
205. Swalen JD, Allara DL, Andrade JD, Chandross EA, Garoff S, Israelachvili J, McCarthy TJ, Murray R, Pease RF, Rabolt JF, Wynne KJ, Yu H (1987) Langmuir 3: 932
206. Honeybourne CL (1987) J Phys Chem Solids 48: 109
207. Loutfy RO, Sharp JH (1979) J Chem Phys 71: 1211
208. Tang CW (1982) Appl Phys Lett 40: 183
209. Arishima K, Hiratsuka H, Tate A, Okada T (1985) Appl Phys Lett 46: 279
210. Honeybourne CL, Ewen RJ, Hill CAS (1984) J Chem Soc Faraday Trans 1, 80: 851
211. Tieke B, Wegner G, Naegele D, Ringsdorf H (1976) Angew Chem Int Ed Engl 15: 764
212. Bubeck C, Tieke B, Wegner G (1982) Ber Bunsenges Phys Chem 86: 499
213. Bässler H (1984) Adv Poly Sci 63: 1
214. Roberts GG, McGinnity TM, Barlow WA, Vincett PS (1980) Thin Solid Films 68: 223
215. Vincett PS, Barlow WA (1980) Thin Solid Films 71: 305
216. Barraud A, Lequan M, Lequan RM, Lesieur P, Richard J, Ruandel-Teixier A, Vandevyver M (1987) J Chem Soc Chem Commun 797
217. Vandevyver M, Richard J, Barraud A, Ruandel-Teixier A, Lequan M, Lequan RM (1987) J Chem Phys 87: 6754
218. Nakamura T, Takei F, Tanaka M, Matsumoto M, Sekiguchi T, Kawabata Y, Saito G (1986) Chem Lett 323
219. Kawabata Y, Nakamura T, Matsumoto M, Tanaka M, Sekiguchi T, Konizu H, Manda E, Saito G (1987) Synth Met 19: 663
220. Richard J, Vandevyver M, Barraud A, Morand JP, Lapouyade R, Delhaes P, Jacquinot JF, Roulliay M (1988) J Chem Soc Chem Commun 754
221. Baker S, Petty MC, Roberts GG, Twigg MV (1982) Thin Solid Films 99: 53; European Patent Application No. 83204845.9
222. Hann RA, Gupta SK, Fryer JR, Eyres BL (1985) Thin Solid Films 134: 35
223. Kovacs GJ, Vincett PS, Sharp JH (1985) Can J Phys 63: 346
224. Hua YL, Roberts GG, Ahmad MM, Petty MC, Hanack M, Rein M (1986) Philos Mag B 53: 105
225. Hua YL, Petty MC, Roberts GG, Ahmad MM, Hanack M, Rein M (1987) Thin Solid Films 149: 163
226. Cook MJ, Daniel MF, Dunn AJ, Gold AA, Thomson AJ (1986) J Chem Soc Chem Commun 863

227. Barger WR, Snow AW, Wohltjen H, Jarvis NL (1985) Thin Solid Films 133: 197
228. Baker S, Roberts GG, Petty MC (1983) IEE Proceedings, Part 1, 130: 260
229. Snow AW, Barger WR, Klusty M, Wohltjen H, Jarvis NL (1986) Langmuir 2: 513
230. Fujiki M, Tabei H (1988) Langmuir 4: 320
231. Kalina DW, Crane SW (1985) Thin Solid Films 134: 109
232. Fujiki M, Kurihara T, Tabei H: submitted to Langmuir
233. Fujiki M, Tabei H, Imamura S (1987) Jpn J Appl Phys, Part 1, 26: 1224
234. Roberts GG (1983) Sens Act 4: 131
235. Roberts GG, Pitt CW (1983) Thin Solid Films 99: No (1–3), First international conference on LB films, Durham, Great Britain, Sept. 20–22 (1982) (Proceedings); Chem Abstr 98: B 96087 f
236. Peterson IR, Girling IR (1985) Sci Prog 69: 533
237. Roberts GG (1985) Adv Phys 34: 475
238. Sugi M (1985) J Molec Electron 1: 3
239a. Orthmann E, Wegner G (1986) Angew Chem 98: 1114
239b. Orthmann E (1986) Doctoral Thesis, University of Mainz
240a. Fryer JR, Hann RA, Eyres BL (1985) Nature 313: 382
240b. Fryer JR (1986) Mol Cryst Liq Cryst 137: 49
241a. Loutfy RO, Sharp JW, Hsiao CK, Ho R (1981) J Appl Phys 52: 5218
241b. Loutfy RO, Hsiao CK, Ho R (1983) Can J Phys 61: 1416
242. Batey J, Petty MC, Roberts GG (1984) Electronics Lett 20: 838
243. Hua YL, Petty MC, Roberts GG, Ahmad MH, Yates HM, Mauny N, Williams JO (1988) J Lumin 40&41: 861
244. Honeybourne CL, Ewen RJ (1983) J Phys Chem Solids 44: 833
245. Mockert H (1987) Doctoral Thesis, University Tübingen
246. Matsushita (1984) Electric Industrial Co, Zpn Tokyo Koho: JP 58 23, 585 [83 23, 535]: Chem Abstr 100: 29068
247. Snow A, Barger W, Jarvis NL, Wohltjen H (1984) National SAMPE Technique Conf 16: 388
248. Snow A, Jarvis NL, Barger W, Wohltjen H (1985) IEEE Trans Elec Dev 32: 1170

Author Index Volumes 1–74